JOSEPH MOXON

Mechanick Exercises or the Doctrine of Handy-Works

Introduction by John S. Kebabian

Reprinted from the 1703 edition

THE ASTRAGAL PRESS
Morristown, New Jersey
1989

This edition reprinted with the cooperation
of The Early American Industries Association.

Introduction Copyright © 1975 by
The Early American Industries Association.

Library of Congress Cataloging in Publication Data

Moxon, Joseph, 1627-1700.
  Mechanick exercises, or, The doctrine of handy-
works/Joseph Moxon: Introduction by
John S. Kebabian.
    p. cm.
    Reprint, with a new introd. Originally published:
3rd ed. London. Printed for D. Midwinter, 1703.
    ISBN 0-9618088-1-0: $25.00
    1. Industrial arts—Early works to 1800.
2. Sundials—Early works to 1800. I. Title.
II. Title: Mechanick exercises. III. Title: Doctrine of
handy-works.
TT144.M93 1989   89-71
670—dc19

Published by
THE ASTRAGAL PRESS
One South Street, Box 338
Morristown, New Jersey 07963-0338

Manufactured in the United States of America

INTRODUCTION

"For History of Nature Wrought, or Mechanicall, I find some Collections Made of Agriculture, and likewise of Manuall Arts, but commonly with a rejection of experiments familiar and vulgar. For it is esteemed a kinde of dishonour unto Learning, to descend to enquirie or Meditation uppon Matters Mechanicall...But if my judgement bee of any waight, the use of Historie Mechanical, is of all others the most radicall, and fundamentall towards Naturall Philosophie, such Naturall Philosophie, as shall not vanish in the fume of subtile, sublime or delectable speculation, but such as shall bee operative to the endowment, and benefit of Mans life...Many ingenious practizes in all trades, by a connexion and transferring of the observations of one Arte, to the use of another, when the experiences of severall misteries shall fall under the consideration of one man's mind".

These passages are from Francis Bacon's work, *The Twoo Bookes...Of the proficience and advancement of Learning, divine and humane,* published in 1605.[1] It is interesting to note that Moxon himself refers to Bacon's example in the preface to the present work. Bacon is certainly correct in noting the disparagement of "Manuall Arts" in works before his own time. Even in his own century, few works of this nature were produced. It was only in the eighteenth century that there appeared the *Descriptions des Arts et métiers,* the great Encyclopédie of Diderot and treatises in depth on the separate branches of the trades and crafts.

Joseph Moxon's *Mechanick Exercises: or the*

Doctrine of Handy-Works was one of those pioneering books which were inspired, directly or indirectly, by Bacon's advocacy. Moxon (1627-1691) was the son of James Moxon, a nonconformist (Puritan) printer, who went into exile in Holland from 1637 to 1643. This experience was invaluable for his son, who retained his knowledge of the Dutch language throughout his life, and whose writings on the "Handy-Work" of printing reflect his knowledge of Dutch printing practices. In Holland, James Moxon printed Bibles in the Genevan version favored by the Puritans, as well as polemical works which the British authorities found very offensive, and which led to his being prosecuted and fined by the Dutch authorities. Soon after the return of the Moxons to England, Joseph became a partner of his father in the printing business. He soon abandoned that trade for that of cartographer, globemaker, and dealer in mathematical instruments. Later still, he re-entered printing to publish many works in connection with his cartographic firm — manuals of astronomy and geography, books on navigation, architecture, and an important pioneering work on hydraulics by Isaac de Caus.

The year 1678 was an important one in Moxon's career - he was then elected a Fellow (member) of the Royal Society of London for Improving Natural Knowledge, and he began the publication of his *Mechanick Exercises*. While there was no direct connection between Francis Bacon and the Royal Society, his writings on experimental science were an important element in the intellectual movement which led to its foun-

dation. Bacon's advocacy of the "Manuall Arts"
had found in Moxon a most vigorous proponent.
John Evelyn, the diarist, one the founders of the
Royal Society, and a leader of English science and
culture of his era, introduced Moxon and his
work to Sir Joseph Williamson, President of the
Society. Another outstanding scientist of the
period, Robert Hooke, also assisted in the
publication of the *Exercises*. This first volume
contained descriptions and pictures of the trades
of smithing, joinery, carpentry, and turning.

In 1684 the second volume of the *Exercises* appeared, describing the trade of printing.[2] The
first volume, the *Doctrine of Handy-Works* appeared originally in periodical form, i. e., in
pamphlet parts, one to be issued each month at 6
pence per part.[3] Publication was completed in
1680, and the part-publication of the second
volume, the *Whole Art of Printing,* extended
from 1683 to 1684.

The present reprint is of Volume I only
-smithing, joinery, carpentry, turning,
bricklayery, followed by *Mechanick Dyalling,
Teaching Any Man. . . To Draw a True Sun-Dyal.*
This is the third edition of the "Arts" and the
fourth of the "Dyalling", published together in
1703. It is the first complete edition - earlier editions and issues did not include the "Bricklayery"
section (pages 237-287).[4]

An essential element in Moxon's work is the
series of twenty-six engraved plates, containing illustrations of about 170 tools, besides such things
as single- and multiple-curved mouldings and
cornices,[5] plans and elevations of buildings,

wood-work, etc. These probably were engraved by Moxon himself. The engravings are clear, straightforward, and well adapted to the author's purpose, that of teaching by text and picture.[6]

Illustrations of sets of tools for particular trades had begun to appear in the 16th and earlier 17th centuries. One such is to be found in Agostino Gallo's *Vinti Giornate della Agricoltura,* 1569; of the woodcut plates of that work, several are of tools. A set of "Instruments for Graffing" (grafting) by Leonard Mascall, published in London, 1572, is reproduced in *The Chronicle* of the Early American Industries Association, December, 1975. Mr. Joseph E. Sanford has traced the derivation of Moxon's set of joiner's tools (see engraving at page 69 of the present work) to Andre Felibien's *Des Principes de l'Architecture,* Paris, 1676.[7] And finally, Benno Forman has traced the source of Moxon's figure of the swash-work lathe to Jacques Besson's *Theatrum Instrumentorum,,* Lyons, 1569 (see engraving at p. 227, fig. B).[8] It is, however, very probable that the great majority of Moxon's figures of tools were drawn by him from actual examples rather than from books, as he certainly saw them all in use when he was writing his text.

While Moxon's direct influence has not as yet been traced in the works of his successors such as Diderot and the authors of the *Arts et Métiers,* it is very probable that is was an important source, directly or indirectly. English examples in the field of politics, culture and technology were closely examined and imitated in 18th century France - the great Diderot *Encyclopedie* began as

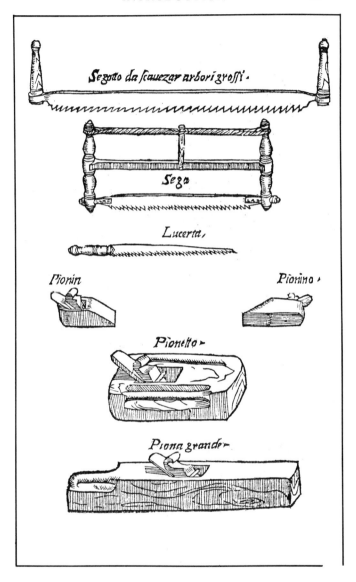

Figures of tools, from Gallo, *Vinti Giornate*.

a mere translation of the *Cyclopedia* of Ephraim Chambers, 1728. And Moxon's modern descendants are numerous indeed; *Books in Print* lists no less than two thousand five hundred books whose title begins with "How To...". Moxon can rightly claim every one of these as his progeny.

FOOTNOTES

1. Pages 6, 10.

2. The two volumes of this work are seldom found together. They were issued together apparently only in the edition of 1684. Modern editions and reprints similarly are of only one or the other of the volumes.

3. Moxon's book was the first to be issued in this manner. Hundreds of works were later so issued, to as late as the 1920's - Defoe's *Robinson Crusoe*, the novels of Dickens and Thackeray, Wells's *Outline of History*, etc. The purpose of periodical publication was to promote a larger sale by this form of "installment" purchase.

4. Benno Forman, editor of the 1970 reprint of Moxon (vol. 1) considered that the bricklayery section was not written by Joseph Moxon, but by his son James

5. These terms are not copyright.

6. See Moxon, *Mechanick Exercises...Art of Printing*, 1962, ed. Herbert Davis and Harry Carter, pp. xlv, xxvi. Moxon was not a professional engraver, and these examples have the same amateurish quality that is found in his one signed engraving. The engravings of the *Mechanick Dyalling* are better, and are probably the work of his son James.

7. *The Chronicle* of the EAIA, Sept., 1941, page 150.

8. Introduction to the 1970 edition of *Mechanick Exercises* (Vol. 1), ed. Forman, p. xxiii.

The best account of the life and works of Joseph Moxon is the Oxford edition of the *Mechanick Exercises. . . Art of Printing,* ed. Davis and Carter. Mr. Forman's introduction, noted above, is a detailed account of the background of the *Exercises,* Vol. 1.

Mechanick Exercifes.

OR THE
DOCTRINE
OF
HANDY-WORKS.

Applied to the Arts of $\left\{\begin{array}{l}\text{Smithing}\\ \text{Joinery}\\ \text{Carpentry}\\ \text{Turning}\\ \text{Bricklayery.}\end{array}\right.$

To which is added

Mechanick Dyalling : Shewing how to draw a true Sun-Dyal on any given Plane, however Scituated ; only with the help of a ftraight *Ruler* and a pair of *Compaffes*, and without any *Arithmetical Calculation.*

The Third Edition.

By - JOSEPH MOXON, *Fellow of the Royal Society, and Hydrographer to the late King* Charles.

LONDON:
Printed for *Dan. Midwinter* and *Tho. Leigh*, at the *Rofe and Crown* in St. Paul's-Church-Yard. 1703.

PREFACE.

I See no more *Reason*, *why the Sordidness of some Workmen, should be the cause of contempt upon* Manual Operations, *than that the excellent Invention of a* Mill *should be dispis'd, because a blind Horse draws in it. And tho' the* Mechanicks *be, by some, accounted Ignoble and Scandalous? yet it is very well known, that many Gentlemen in this Nation, of good Rank and high Quality, are conversant in* Handy-Works : *And other Nations exceed us in numbers of such. How pleasant and healthey this their Diversion is, their Minds and Bodies find ; and how Harmless and Honest, all sober men may judge?*

That Geometry, Astronomy, Perspective, Musick, Navigation, Architecture, *&c. are excellent Sciences, all that know but their very Names will confess : Yet to what purpose would* Geometry *serve, were it not to contrive Rules for* Handy-Works? *Or how could* Astronomy *be known to any perfection, but by Instruments made by Hand?*

A 2 *What*

PREFACE.

What Perspective *should we have to delight our Sight? What* Musick *to ravish our Ears? What* Navigation *to Guard and Enrich our Country? Or what* Architecture *to defend us from the Inconveniencies of different Weather, without* Manual Operations? *Or how waste and useless would many of the* Productions *of this and other* Counties *be, were it not for* Manufactures.

To dive into the Original of the Mechanicks *is impossible, therefore I shall not offer at it; only I shall say, it is* Rational *to think, that the* Mechanicks *began with* Man, *he being the only Creature that Nature has imposed most Necessity upon to use it, endow'd with greatest* Reason *to contrive it, and adapted with properest Members (as Instruments) to perform it.*

Nor is it easie to find by any Authority, what part of the Mechanicks *was first Practised by* Man; *therefore I shall wave that too, and only consider, that if we our selves were the first* Men, *what Branch of the* Mechanicks *we should first Need, and have recourse to.*

I have considered, and Answer, That without the Invention of Smithing *primarily, most other* Mechanick *Invention would*

PREFACE.

would be at a stand: The Instruments, or Tools, that are used in them, being either made of Iron, or some other matter, form'd by the help of Iron. But pray take Notice, that by Iron, I also mean Steel, it being originally Iron.

Nor would I have you understand, that when I name the Mechanicks, *I mean that rough and Barbarous sort of working which is used by the Natives of* America, *and some other such Places; for, though they did indeed make Houses, Canoes, Earthen Pots, Bows, Arrows, &c. without the help of Iron, because they had then none amongst them: Yet since Iron is now known to them, they leave of their old way of working without it, and betake themselves to the use of it. Nor are, at this day, (though now they have in part the use of Iron) their* Machines *made by good and ready Rules of* Art; *for they know neither of* Rule, Square, *or* Compass; *and what they do, is done by Tedious Working, and he that has the best Eye at Guessing, works best upon the* Straight, Square *or* Circle, *&c.*

The Lord Bacon, *in his Natural History, reckons that* Philosophy *would be improv'd,*

PREFACE.

improv'd, by having the Secrets of all Trades lye open; not only because much Experimental Philosophy, is Coucht amongst them; but also that the Trades themselves might, by a Philosopher, be improv'd. Besides, I find, that one Trade may borrow many Eminent Helps in Work of another Trade.

Hitherto I cannot learn that any hath undertaken this Task, though I could have wisht it had been performed by an abler hand then mine; yet, since it is not, I have vetured upon it.

I thought to have given these Exercises, the Title of The Doctrine of Handy-Crafts; but when I better considered the true meaning of the Word Handy-Crafts, I found the Doctrine would not bear it; because Hand-Craft signifies Cunning, or Sleight, or Craft of the Hand, which cannot be taught by Words, but is only gained by Practise and Exercise; therefore I shall not undertake, that with the bare reading of these Exercises, any shall be able to perform these Handy-Works; but I may safely tell you, that these are the Rules that every one that will endeavour to perform
them

PREFACE.

them *muſt* follow; *and that by the true ob-ſerving them, he may, according to his ſtock of Ingenuity and Diligence, ſooner or later, inure his hand to the* Cunning *or* Craft *of working like a* Handy-Craft, *and conſequently be able to perform them in time.*

For the Reaſon *aforeſaid I intend to begin with* Smithing, *which comprehends not only the* Black-Smith's Trade, *but takes in all* Trades *which uſe either* Forge *or* File, *from the* Anchor-Smith, *to the* Watch-Maker; *they all working by the ſame* Rules, *tho' not with equal exactneſs, and all uſing the ſame* Tools, *tho' of ſeveral Sizes from thoſe the common* Black-Smith *uſes, and that according to the various purpoſes they are applied to: And in order to it, I ſhall firſt ſhew you how to ſet up a* Forge, *and what* Tools *you muſt uſe in the* Black-Smith's *work; then the* Rules, *and ſeveral* Circumſtances *of* Forging, *till your Work come to the* File: *Then of the ſeveral Sorts of* Iron *that are commonly uſed; and what ſort is fitteſt for each purpoſe. Afterwards of* Filing *in general, and the* Rules *to be obſerved in it, in the making of* Jacks,

PREFACE.

Jacks, Hinges, Screws, Clocks, Watch-es, &c. *In which Examples, you will find all other Sorts of* Forging *or* Filing *work whatſoever comprehended. And laſtly, as a cloſe to* Smithing, *I ſhall Exerciſe upon* Steel, *and its ſeveral Sorts, and how to Order and Temper it for its ſeveral Uſes; and what Sort is fitteſt for each particular purpoſe; as which is fitteſt for* Edge-Tools, *which for* Springs, *which for* Punches, *&c.*

Some perhaps would have thought it more Proper, *to have introduced theſe* Exerciſes *with a more* Curious, *and leſs Vulgar Art, than that of* Smithing; *but I am not of their Opinion; for* Smithing *is in all parts, as curious a* Handy-Craft, *as any is:* Beſides, *it is a great Introduction to moſt other* Handy-Works, *as* Joynery, Turning, *&c. they (with the* Smith*) working upon the* Sraight, Square, *or* Circle, *though with different* Tools, *upon different* Matter; *and they all having dependance upon the* Smith's Trade, *and not the* Smith *upon them.*

Joſeph Moxon.

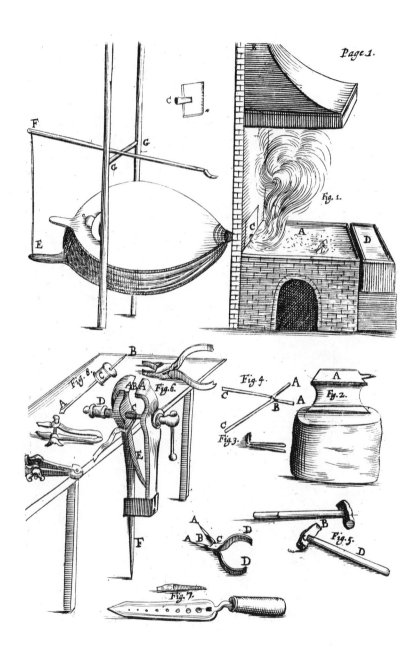

Fig. 1.

Fig. 8.

Fig. 6.

Fig. 4.

Fig. 3.

Fig. 2.

Fig. 5.

Fig. 7.

MECHANICK EXERCISES:

OR,

The Doctrine of *Handy-Works*.

Of SMITHING *in General*.

Definition.

SMITHING *is an Art-Manual, by which an irregular Lump (or several Lumps) of Iron, is wrought into an intended Shape.*

This Definition, needs no Explanation; therefore I shall proceed to give you an Account of the Tools a Smith uses; not but that (they being so common) I suppose you do already know them; but partly because they may require some precaution in setting them up fittest to your use; and partly because it behoves you to know the Names, Smiths call the several parts of them by; that when I name them in Smith's Language (as I shall oft have occasion to do in these *Exercises*) you may the easier understand them, as you read them.

Of setting up a Smith's Forge.

THE *Hearth*, or Fire-place of the *Forge* marked A. (in Plate 1.) is to be built up from your floor with Brick about two foot and an half; or sometimes two foot nine Inches high, according to the purpose you design your *Forge* for; for if your *Forge* be intended for heavy work, your *Hearth* must lie lower than it need be for light

A   work,

work, for eafinefs of management, and fo broad
as you think convenient: It may be built with
hollow Arches underneath, to fet feveral things
out of the way. The Back of the *Forge* is built upright to the top of the Ceiling, and inclofed o-
ver the Fire-place with a *Hovel,* which ends in
a *Chimney* to carry away the Smoak, as B. In the
back of the *Forge* againft the Fire-place, is fixed a
thick Iron Plate, and a taper Pipe in it about five
Inches long, called a *Tewel,* or (as fome call it)
a *Tewel-Iron* marked *, which Pipe comes through
the Back of the *Forge,* as at C. Into this taper
Pipe or *Tewel* is placed the Nofe, or Pipe of the
Bellows. The Office of this *Tewel,* is only to preferve the Pipe of the Bellows, and the back of
the *Forge* about the Fire-place from burning.
Right againft the Back is placed at about twenty
Inches, or two foot diftance, the *Trough,* and
reaches commonly through the whole breadth of
the *Forge,* and is as broad and deep as you think
good, as at D. The *Bellows* is placed behind the
Back of the *Forge,* and hath as aforefaid, its Pipe
fitted into the Pipe of the *Tewel,* and hath one of
its Boards fixed fo that it move not upwards or
downwards. At the Ear of the upper Bellows
board is faftened a *Rope,* or fometimes a *Thong* of
Leather, or an Iron *Chain* or *Rod,* as E; which
reaches up to the *Rocker,* and is faftened there to
the farther end of the Handle, as at F. This *Handle* is faftened a crofs a *Rock-ftaff,* which moves
between two Cheeks upon the *Center-pins,* in
two Sockets, as at G. So that by drawing down
this Handle, the moving Board of the *Bellows* rifes, and by a confiderable weight fet on the top
of its upper Board finks down again, and by this
Agitation performs the Office of a pair of *Bellows.*

Of

Of the Anvil.

THE fhape of a Black Smith's *Anvil* I have
inferted in this Figure, though it is fometimes made with a *Pike*, or *Bickern*, or *Beak-iron*,
at one end of it, whofe ufe I fhall fhew you when
I come to round hollow work. Its *Face* muft be
very flat and fmooth, without Flaws, and fo hard
that *a File will not touch it* (as Smiths fay, when a
File will not cut, or race it.) The upper Plain
A. is called the *Face* ; it is commonly fet upon a
wooden *Block*, that it may ftand very fteady and
folid, and about two foot high from the floor, or
fometimes higher, according to the ftature of
the Perfon that is to work at it.

Of the Tongs.

THere are two forts of *Tongs* ufed by Smiths ;
the one the *Straight-nofed Tongs*, ufed when
the work is fhort, and fomewhat flat, and generally for all Plate Iron. The other *Crooked-nos'd*
Tongs, to be ufed for the forging fmall Bars, or
fuch thicker work, as will be held within the
Returns of their *Chaps*. The *Chaps* are placed near
the Joint, becaufe, that confidering the length
of the *Handles*, they hold the Iron fafter than
they would do, were they placed farther from
the Joint, as in the Fig. 3. 4. A the *Chaps*, B the
Joint, CC the *Handles*.

Of the Hammer, and the Sledge.

THere are feveral forts of *Hammers* ufed by
Black-Smiths ; as firft the *Hand-hammer,*
which is fometimes bigger, or lefs, according to
the Strength of the Work-man ; but it is a *Ham-*
mer of fuch weight, that it may be weilded, or
governed, with one hand at the *Anvil.* Secondly, the *Up-hand Sledge,* ufed by under-Workmen,
when the Work is not of the largeft, yet requires
help

help to batter, or *draw it out*; they ufe it with
both their hands before them, and feldom lift
their *Hammer* higher than their head. Thirdly,
the *About Sledge* is the biggeft *Hammer* of all, and
is alfo ufed by under-Workmen, for the battering, or *drawing out* of the largeft Work; and
then they hold the farther end of the *Handle* in
both their Hands, and fwinging the *Sledge* above
their Heads, they at Arms end let fall as heavy a
Blow as they can upon the Work. There is alfo
another *Hammer* ufed by them, which they call
a *Rivetting-hammer*. This is the fmalleft *Hammer*
of all, and very rarely ufed at the *Forge*, unlefs
your Work prove very fmall; but upon cold I-
ron it is ufed for rivetting, or fetting ftraight,
or crooking fmall work. In Fig. 5. A the *Face*,
B the *Pen*, C the *Eye*, D the *Handle*.

Of the Vice.

THE *Vice* muft be fet up very firmly that it
fhake not, and ftand upright with its *Chaps*,
parallel or range with your *Work-bench*; becaufe
fquare filing, is a great piece of good Work-
manfhip in a Smith; and fhould the Vice not
ftand upright, and range with the Work-bench,
the *Chaps* pinching upon two fquare fides, would
make the top fide of your work either lean towards you, or from you; and confequently you
filing (as a good Workman ought to do) upon
the flat, or Horizontal Plain of your work, would
take off more of that Angle, or Edge, which rifes higher than the Plain, and lefs off that Edge,
that lies lower than the Plain; fo that one Angle
being higher, or lower, than the other, your work
inftead of being filed *Square*, would be filed *Squa-
re-wife*, when you fhall have filed all its flat fides,
and that more or lefs, according to the leaning
of the *Chaps* of your *Vice.* AA the *Face*, hath its
two

two ends in a ftraight Line with the middle of its *Face*, or *Plain*. B the *Chaps* muft be cut with a Baftard Cut, and very well tempered; C the *Screw Pin*, cut with a fquare ftrong Worm. D the *Nut*, or *Screw Box*, hath alfo a fquare *Worm*, and is brazed into the round *Box*. E the *Spring* muft be made of good Steel, and very well temper'd: Where note that the wider the two ends of the *Spring* ftand afunder, the wider it throws the *Chaps* of the *Vice* open. F the *Foot* muft be ftraight, and therefore will be the ftronger to bear good heavy blows upon the work fcrewed in the *Chaps* of the *Vice*, that it neither bow, or tremble.

Of the Hand-Vice.

OF the *Hand-Vice* are two Sorts, one is called the *Broad Chapt Hand-Vice*, the other the *Square Nos'd Hand-Vice*. The Office of the *Hand-Vice*, is to hold fmall work in, that may require often turning about; it is held in the left hand, and each part of your work turned upwards fucceffively, that you have occafion to file with your right. The *Square-nos'd Hand-Vice* is feldom ufed, but for filing fmall Globulous Work, as the Heads of Pins that round off towards the Edges, &c. And that becaufe the *Chaps* do not ftand fhouldering in the way, but that the flat of the *File* may the better come at the Edges. Their *Chaps* muft be cut as the *Vice* aforefaid, and well tempered.

Of the Plyers.

PLyers are of two Sorts, *Flat Nos'd*, and *Round Nos'd*. Their Office is to hold, and faften upon all fmall work, and to fit it in its place. The *Round Nos'd Plyers* are ufed for turning, or bowing Wyer, or fmall Plate, into a circular Form. The *Chaps* of the *Flat Nos'd Plyers*, muft

A 3 alfo

alfo be cut and temper'd , as the *Chaps* of the *Vice.* A the *Nofe,* B the *Chaps,* C the *Joint,* DD the *Handles.*

Of *the* Drill, *and* Drill-Bow.

DRills are 'ufed for the making fuch Holes as *Punches* will not conveniently ferve for; as a piece of work that hath already its Shape, and muft have an hole , or more , made in it. Here the force of a *Punch,* will fet your work out of order and fhape, becaufe it will both batter the Surface of the Iron, and ftretch its Sides out : The fhank of a Key alfo, or fome fuch long Hole, the *Punch* cannot ftrike, becaufe the Shank is not forged with fubftance fufficient; but the *Drill,* tho' your work be filed and polifh'd, never batters or ftretches it, but cuts a true round Hole, juft in the point you firft place it. You muft have feveral Sizes of *Drills,* according as your work may require. The fhape in Fig. 8. is enough to fhew the Fafhion of it; but it muft be made of good Steel, and well temper'd. A the *Point,* A B the *Shank,* C the *Drill-barrel* : Where note, that the bigger the *Drill-barrel* is, the eafier it runs about, but lefs fwift.

And as you muft be provided with feveral *Drills,* fo you may fometimes require more than one *Drill-bow,* or at leaft, feveral *Drill-ftrings;* the ftrongeft Strings for the largeft *Drills,* and the fmalleft *Strings* for the fmalleft *Drills* : But you muft remember, that whether you ufe a fmall or ftrong *String,* you keep your *Drill-Bow* ftraining your String pretty ftiff, or elfe your String will not carry your Barrel briskly about. But your String and Bow, muft both be accommodated to the Size of your *Drill;* and if both, or either, be too ftrong, they will break, or bend your *Drill;* or if too weak, they will not carry about the Barrel, as aforefaid. The

The *Drill-Plate*, or *Breaſt-Plate*, is only a piece of flat Iron, fixt upon a flat Board, which Iron hath an hole punched a little way into it, to ſet the blunt end of the Shank of the *Drill* in, when you drill a hole : Workmen inſtead of it, many times uſe the *Hammer*, into which they prick a hole a little way on the ſide of it, and ſo ſet the *Hammer* againſt their Breaſt.

Of the Screw-Plate, and its Taps.

THE *Screw-Plate* is a Plate of Steel well temper'd, with ſeveral holes in it, each leſs than other, and in thoſe *Holes* are *Threds* grooved inwards; into which *Grooves*, fit the reſpective *Taps* that belong to them. The *Taps* that belong to them, are commonly made tapering towards the Point, as Fig. 7. ſhews. But theſe tapering *Taps*, will not ſerve for ſome ſorts of works, as I ſhall ſhew in its proper place.

Theſe are the moſt Eſſential Tools uſed in the Black-Smith's Trade ; but ſome accidental work , may require ſome accidental Tools, which, as they may fall in, I ſhall give you an account of in convenient place.

Of Forging in general.

I Think it needleſs to tell you how to make your Fire, or blow it, becauſe they are both but Labourers work ; nor how little, or big, it need to be, for your own reaſon will, by the Size of your work, teach you that ; only let me tell you the Phraſe Smiths uſe for [make the Fire] is, *Blow up the Fire*, or ſometimes, *Blow up the Coals.*

When it is burning with the Iron in it, you muſt, with the *Slice*, clap the Coals upon the out-ſide cloſe together, to keep the heat in the body of the Fire ; and as oft as you find the Fire begin to break out, clap them cloſe again, and

    with

with the *Wafher* dipt in Water, wet the out-fide of the Fire to damp the out-fide, as well to fave Coals, as to ftrike the force of the Fire into the in-fide, that your work may heat the fooner. But you ought oft to draw your work a little way out of the Fire, to fee how it *takes its Heat*, and quickly thruft it in again, if it be not hot enough : For each purpofe your work is defigned to, ought to have a proper *Heat* fuitable to that purpofe, as I fhall fhew you in the feveral *Heats* of Iron : For if it be too cold, it will not *feel the weight of the Hammer* (as Smiths fay, when it will not batter under the *Hammer*) and if it be too hot, it will *Red-fear*, that is, break, or crack under the *Hammer*, while it is working between hot and cold.

Of the feveral Heats *Smiths take of their Iron.*

THere are feveral degrees of *Heats* Smiths take of their Iron, each according to the purpofe of their work. As firft, a *Blood-red Heat.* Secondly, a *White Flame Heat.* Thirdly, a *Sparkling*, or *Welding Heat.*

The *Blood-red Heat* is ufed when Iron hath already its form and fize, as fometimes fquare Bars, and Iron Plates, *&c.* have, but may want a little Hammering to fmooth it. Ufe then the Face of your *Hand-hammer*, and with light flat Blows, hammer down the irregular Rifings into the Body of your Iron, till it be fmooth enough for the File. And note,that it behoves a good Workman,to hammer his Work as true as he can; for one quarter of an hour fpent at the *Forge*, may fave him an hours work at the *Vice.*

The *Flame*, or *White Heat*, is ufed when your Iron hath not its Form or Size, but muft be forged into both ; and then you muft take a piece of Iron thick enough, and with the *Pen* of your

Ham-

Hammer, (or fometimes, according to the fize of your work, ufe two or three pair of hands with *Sledges* to) batter it out ; or, as Workmen call it, to *draw it out*, till it comes to its breadth, and pretty near its fhape ; and fo by feveral *Heats*, if your work require them, frame it into Form and Size ; then with the Face of your *Hand-hammer*, fmooth your work from the Dents the *Pen* made, as you did with a *Blood-red Heat*.

A *Sparkling*, or *Welding-heat*, is only ufed when you *double up* your Iron (as Smiths call it) to make it thick enough for your purpofe, and fo *weld*, or work in the *doubling* into one another, and make it become one entire lump; or it is ufed when you join feveral Bars of Iron together to make them thick enough for your pur-pofe, and work them into one Bar ; or elfe it is ufed when you are to join, or *weld* two pie-ces of Iron together end to end, to make them long enough; but, in this cafe, you muft be very quick at the *Forge* ; for when your two ends are throughout of a good *Heat*, and that the infide of the Iron be almoft ready to Run, as well as the outfide , you muft very haftily fnatch them both out of the Fire together, and (after you have with the Edge of your *Hammer* fcraped off fuch Scales or Dirt as may hinder their incorporating) with your utmoft diligence clap your left hand-piece, upon your right hand-piece, and with all fpeed (left you lofe fome part of your good Heat) fall to Hammering them together, and work them foundly into one another : and this, if your Bars be large , will require another, or fomtimes two or three pair of Hands befides your own to do : but if it be not throughly *welded* at the firft *Heat*, you muft reiterate your *Heats* fo oft, till they be throughly *welded* ; then with a *Flame-heat* (as before

before) fhape it, and afterwards fmooth it with
a *Blood-red Heat*. To make your Iron come the
fooner to a *Welding-heat*, you muft now and then
with your *Hearth-ftaff* ftir up the Fire, and throw
up thofe Cinders the Iron may have run upon;
for they will never burn well, but fpoil the reft
of the Coals; and take a little white Sand between your Finger and your Thumb, and throw
upon the heating Iron, then with your Slice,
quickly clap the outfide of your Fire down a-
gain; and with your *Wafher* dipt in Water, damp
the outfide of the Fire to keep the Heat in.

But you muft take fpecial Care that your I-
ron *burn* not in the Fire, that is, that it do not
run or melt; for then your Iron will be fo brittle, that it will not endure Forging without
breaking, and fo hard, that a *File* will not
touch it.

Some Smiths ufe to ftrew a little white Sand
upon the *Face* of the *Anvil* alfo, when they
are to hammer upon a *Welding-heat*; for they fay
it makes the Iron *weld*, or incorporate the better.

If through Miftake, or ill management, your
Iron be too thin, or too narrow towards one of
the ends; then if you have fubftance enough
(and yet not too long) you may *up-fet* it, that is,
take a *Flame-heat*, and fet the heated end upright upon the *Anvil*, and hammer upon the cold
end, till the heated end be beat, or *up-fet*, into
the Body of your Work. But if it be a long
piece of Work, aud you fear its length may
wrong the middle, you muft hold it in your left
hand, and lay it flat on the *Anvil*; but fo as the
heated end intended to be *up-fet*, may lie a little over the further fide of the *Anvil*, aud then
with your *Hand-hammer* in your right hand, beat
upon the heated end of your work, minding
that every ftroak you take, you hold your work
ftiff

ftiff againft the *Face* of the *Hammer*. Afterwards
fmooth it again with a *Blood-red Heat*.

If you are to Forge a *Shoulder* on one, or each
fide of your work, lay the Shank of your Iron
at the place where your *Shoulder* muft be on the
edge of your *Anvil* (that edge which is moft convenient to your hand) that if more *Shoulders* be
to be made, turn them all fucceffively, and hammer your Iron fo, as that the Shank of the Iron
that lies on the flat of the *Anvil*, feel as well the
weight of your Blows, as the *Shoulder* at the
edge of the *Anvil*; for fhould you lay your
blows on the edge of the *Anvil* only, it would
inftead of flatting the Shank to make the *Shoulder*, cut your work through.

Your Work will fometimes require to have
holes punched in it at the Forge, you muft then
make a Steel *Punch* to the fize and fhape of the
hole you are to ftrike, and harden the point of
it without tempering, becaufe the heat of the
Iron will foften it faft enough, and fometimes
too faft, but then you muft re-harden it; then
taking a *Blood-heat* of your Iron, or if it be very
large, almoft a *Flame-heat*; lay it upon your
Anvil, and with your left hand, place the point
of the *Punch* where the hole muft be, and with
the *Hand-hammer* in your right hand punch the
hole; or if your work be heavy, you may hold
it in your left hand, and with your Punch fixed
at the end of a *Hoop-ftick*, or fome fuch Wood,
hold the ftick in your right hand, and place the
point of your *Punch* on the work where the hole
muft be, and let another Man ftrike, till your
Punch come pretty near the bottom of your
work; which when it does, the fides of your
work round about the hole, will rife from the
Face of the *Anvil*, and your Punch will print a
bunching mark upon the hole of a *Bolfter*, that is,
a thick

a thick Iron with a hole in it, and placing your
Punch, as before, ſtrike it through. But you muſt
note, that as oft as you ſee your Punch heat, or
change Colour, you take it out of the hole, and
pop it into Water to re-harden it, or elſe it will
batter in the hole you intend to ſtrike, and not
only ſpoil it ſelf, but the Work too, by running
aſide in the Work. Having punched it through
on the one ſide, turn the other ſide of your work,
and with your Hammer ſet it flat and ſtraight,
and with a *Blood-heat* punch it through on the
other ſide alſo ; ſo ſhall that hole be fit for the
File, or ſquare bore, if the curioſity of your
purpoſed Work cannot allow it to paſs without
filing. When your Work is Forged, do not quench
it in water to cool it, but throw it down upon
the *Floor*, or *Hearth*, to cool of it ſelf ; for the
quenching it in water will harden it ; as I ſhall
ſhortly ſhew you, when I come to the Tempering
of Steel.

Of Brazing *and* Soldering.

YOU may have occaſion ſometimes to *Braze*
or *Solder* a piece of work ; but it is uſed by
Smiths only, when their work is ſo thin, or
ſmall, that it will not endure *Welding*. To do
this, take ſmall pieces of Braſs, and lay them on
the place that muſt be brazed, and ſtrew a little
Glaſs beaten to powder on it to make it run the
ſooner, and give it a *Heat* in the *Forge*, till (by
ſometimes drawing it a little way out of the Fire)
you ſee the Braſs run. But if your work be ſo
ſmall, or thin, that you may fear the Iron will
run as ſoon as the Braſs, and ſo you loſe your
work in the Fire, then you muſt make a *Loam*
of three parts Clay, and one part Horſe-dung,
and after they are wrought and mingled very
well together in your hands, wrap your work
with the Braſs, and a little beaten Glaſs upon
                                              the

the place to be brazed clofe in the *Loam,* and laying it a while upon the *Hearth* of the *Forge* to dry, put the lump into the Fire, and blow the *Bellows* to it, till you perceive it have a full *Heat,* that is, till the Lump look like a well burnt Coal of Fire ; then take it out of the Fire, and let it cool : Afterwards break it up, and take out your Work.

Thus much of Forging in general. It remains now, that you know what forts of Iron are fitteft for the feveral Ufes, you may have occafion to apply them.

Of feveral Sorts of Iron, *and their proper Ufes.*

IT is not my purpofe, in this place, to tell you how Iron is made, I fhall defer that till I come to treat of Mettals, and their Refinings. Let it at prefent fatisfie thofe that know it not, that Iron is, by a violent Fire, melted out of hard Stones, called *Iron-Stones* ; of thefe *Iron-Stones,* many Countries have great plenty. But becaufe it waftes fuch great quantities of Wood to draw the Iron from them, it will not, in many Places, quit coft to ufe them. In moft parts of *England,* we have abundance of thefe *Iron-Stones;* but our *Englifh* Iron, is generally a courfe fort of Iron, hard and brittle, fit for Fire-bars, and other fuch courfe Ufes; unlefs it be about the Forreft of *Dean,* and fome few places more, where the Iron proves very good.

Swedifh Iron is of all Sorts, the beft we ufe in *England.* It is a fine tough fort of Iron, will beft endure the Hammer, and is fofteft to file; and therefore moft coveted by Workmen, to work upon.

Spanifh Iron, would be as good as *Swedifh* Iron, were it not fubject to *Red-fear,* (as Workmen phrafe it) that is to crack betwixt hot and cold. Therefore when it falls under your hands, you
muft

muſt tend it more earneſtly at the Forge.But tho'
it be good, tough, ſoft Iron,yet for many Uſes,
Workmen will refuſe it, becauſe it is ſo ill, and
un-evenly wrought in the Bars,that it coſts them
a great deal of labour to ſmooth it ; but it is
good for all great works that require *welding*, as
the bodies of Anvils,Sledges, large Bell-clappers,
large Peſtles for Mortars, & all thick ſtrong Bars,
*&c.*But it is particularly choſen by *Anchor-Smiths,*
becauſe it abides the Heat better than other Iron,
and when it is well wrought, is tougheſt.

There is ſome Iron comes from *Holland* (tho'
in no great quantity) but is made in *Germany.*
This Iron is called *Dort Squares*, only becauſe it
comes to us from thence, and is wrought into
ſquare Bars three quarters of an Inch ſquare. It
is a bad,courſe Iron,and only fit for ſlight Uſes,
as Window-Bars, Brewers-Bars, Fire-Bars, *&c.*

There is another ſort of Iron uſed for making
of *Wyer*, which of all Sorts is the ſofteſt and
tougheſt : But this Sort is not peculiar to any
Country, but is indifferently made where any
Iron is made, though of the worſt ſort ; for it
is the firſt Iron that runs from the *Stone* when it
is melting, and is only preſerved or the making of *Wyer.*

By what hath been ſaid, you may ſee that the
ſofteſt and tougheſt Iron is the beſt : Therefore
when you chuſe Iron,chuſe ſuch as bows ofteneſt
before it break, which is an Argument of tough-
neſs; and ſee it break ſound within, be grey of
Colour like broken Lead, and free from ſuch
gliſtering Specks you ſee in broken *Antimony,*
no flaws or diviſions in it; for theſe are Arguments that it is ſound, and well wrought at
the Mill.

Of

Of Filing *in General.*

THE feveral forts of Files that are in common ufe are the *Square,* the *Flat,* the *three Square,* the *half Round,* the *Round,* the *Thin File, &c.* All thefe fhapes you muft have of feveral *Sizes,* and of feveral *Cuts.* You muft have them of feveral fizes, as well becaufe you may have feveral fizes of work, as for that it fometimes falls out that one piece of work may have many parts in it joined and fitted to one another, fome of them great, and others fmall ; And you muft have them of feveral *Cuts,* becaufe the *Rough-tooth'd File* cuts fafter than the *Baftard-tooth'd File,* the *Fine-tooth'd File* fafter than the *Smooth-tooth'd File.*

The *Rough* or *Courfe-tooth'd File* (which if it be large, is called a *Rubber*) is to take off the unevennefs of your work which the *Hammer* made in the Forging; the *Baftard-tooth'd file* is to take out of your work, the deep cuts, or file-ftrokes, the *Rough-file* made ; the *Fine-tooth'd file* is to take out the cuts, or file-ftrokes, the *Baftard-file* made; and the *Smooth-file* is to take out thofe cuts, or file-ftrokes, that the *Fine file* made.

Thus you fee how the *Files* of feveral *Cuts* fucceed one another, till your Work is fo fmooth as it can be filed. You may make it yet fmoother with *Emerick, Tripoli, &c.* But of that in its proper place, becaufe it fuits not with this Section of *Filing.*

You muft take care when you ufe the *Rough File,* that you go very lightly over thofe dents the *Hammer* made in your work, unlefs your work be forged fomewhat of the ftrongeft, for the dents being irregularities in your work, if you fhould file away as much in them, as you do off the Eminencies or Rifings, your work (whether it be ftraight or circular) would be as irregular , as it was before you filed it : And
when

when you file upon the Prominent, or rifing
Parts of your Work, with your *courfe cut File,*
you muſt alſo take care that you file them not
more away than you need, for you may eaſily
be deceived; becauſe the *courfe File* cuts deep,
and makes deep ſcratches in the Work ; and before you can take out thoſe deep ſcratches with
your finer cut Files, thoſe places where the Rifings were when your work was forged, may
become dents to your Hammer dents ; therefore
file not thoſe Riſings quite ſo low, as the dents
the Hammer made, but only ſo low as that the
ſcratches the *Rough-file* makes may lie as low, or
deep in your work, as your Hammer dents do;
for then, when you come with your ſmoother
Cut Files, after your *Rough-file,* the ſcratches of
your *Rough-file,* and your Hammer-ſtrokes, or
dents, may both come out together. But to do
this with greater certainty, hold your File ſo,
that you may keep ſo much of the length of your
File as you can to rub, range, (or, as near
range as you can) upon the length of your
work ; for ſo ſhall the File enter upon the ſecond Riſing on your work, before it goes off
the firſt, and will ſlip over, and not touch the
dent or hollow between the two Riſings, till
your Riſings are brought into a ſtraight line
with your hollow dent. But of this more ſhall
be ſaid when I come to the Practice of Filing,
upon ſeveral particular ſorts of work.

If it be a ſquare Bar, (or ſuch like) you are
to file upon, all its Angles, or Edges, muſt be
left very ſharp and ſtraight. Therefore your *Vice*
being well ſet up, according to foregoing Directions, you muſt in your filing athwart over
the *Chaps* of the *Vice,* be ſure to carry both your
hands you hold the *file* in, truly Horizontal, or
flat over the Work; for ſhould you let either of
your

your hands mount, the other would dip, and the edge of that Square it dips upon would be taken off; and fhould you let your hand move never fo little circularly, both the Edges you file upon would be taken off, and the Middle of your intended Flat would be left with a Rifing on it. But this Hand-craft, you muft attain to by Practice; for it is the great Curiofity in Filing.

If it be a round Piece, or Rod of Iron, you are to file upon, what you were forbid upon Square Work, you muft perform on the Round for you muft dip your Handle-hand, and mount your end-hand a little, and laying pritting near the end of your File to the Work, file circularly upon the Work, by mounting your Handle-hand by degrees, and dipping your End-hand, in fuch manner, as when the Middle of your File comes about the top of your Work, your File may be flat upon it, and as you continue your ftroaks forwards, ftill keep your hands moving circularly till you have finifhed your full Stroak, that is, a Stroak the whole length of the File. By this manner of Circular filing, you keep your Piece, or Rod round; but fhould you file flat upon the top of your work, fo many times as you fhall remove, or turn your work in the *Vice*, fo many Flats, or Squares, you would have in your work; which is contrary to your purpofe.

When you thruft your *File* forwards, lean heavy upon it, becaufe the *Teeth* of the *File* are made to cut forwards; but when you draw your *File* back, to recover another thruft, lift, or bear the File lightly juft above the work; for it cuts not coming back.

Thus much of FILING in General.

B *Of*

*Of the making of Hinges, Locks, Keys, Screws,
and Nuts, Small and Great.*

Of Hinges.

IN *Fig.*1. A the *Tail*, B the *Cross*, C D D D D E
the *Joint*, D D D D the *Pin-hole.* When the
Joint at **C** on the *Tail*, is pind in the
Joint at E in the *Cross*, the whole *Hinge* is
called a *Cross-Garnet.*

    Hinges, if they be small (as for Cup-board
doors; *Boxes, &c.*) are cut out of cold Plate I-
ron with the (*a*) *Cold-Chiffel,* but you mark the
out-lines of your intended *Hinge,* as *Fig.* 1. the
Cross-Garnet, either with Chalk, or elſe raſe
upon the Plate with the corner of the *Cold-
Chiffel,* or any other hardned Steel that will
ſcratch a bright ſtroke upon the Plate ; and
then laying the Plate flat upon the *Anvil,* if the
Plate be large, or upon the (*b*) *Stake,* if the Plate
be ſmall, take the *Cold-Chiffel* in your left hand,
and ſet the edge of it upon that Mark, or Raſe,
and with the *Hand-hammer* in your right hand,
ſtrike upon the head of the *Cold-Chiffel,* till you
cut, or rather punch the edge of the *Cold-Chiffel,* almoſt thro' the Plate in that Place, I ſay,
almoſt through, becauſe, ſhould you ſtrike it
quite through, the edge of the *Cold-Chiffel* would
be in danger of battering, or elſe breaking; for
the *Face* of the *Anvil* is hardned Steel, and a
light blow upon its *Face* would wrong the edge
of the *Cold-Chiffel* ; beſides, it ſometimes happens, that the *Anvil,* or *Stake,* is not all over
ſo hard as it ſhould be, and then the *Cold-Chiffel* would cut the *Face* of the *Anvil,* or *Stake,*
and conſequently ſpoil it: Therefore when the
edge of the *Cold-Chiffel* comes pretty near the
bot-

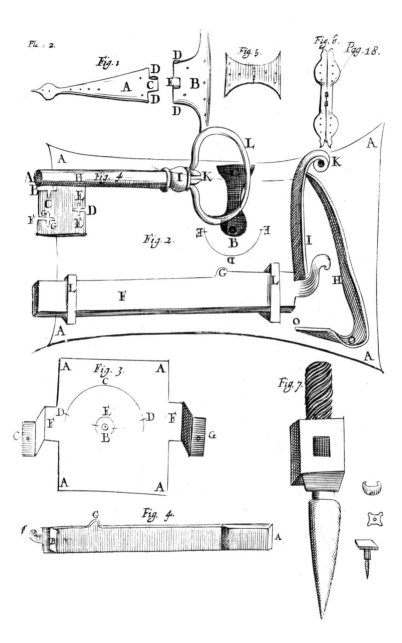

Pl. 2.

Fig. 1.

Fig. 5.

Fig. 6.   Pag. 18.

Fig. 4.

Fig. 2.

Fig. 3.

Fig. 7.

bottom of the Plate, you muſt lay but light blows upon the *Cold-Chiſſel ;* and yet you muſt ſtrike the edge of the *Cold-Chiſſel* ſo near through the bottom of the Plate, that you may break the remaining ſubſtance aſunder with your Fingers, or with a pair of *Plyers,* or ſometimes by pinching the Plate in the *Vice,* with the Cut place cloſe to the Superficies of the *Chaps* of the *Vice ;* and then with your Fingers and Thumb, or your whole hand, wriggle it quite aſunder. But having cut one breadth of the *Cold-Chiſſel,* remove the edge of it forward in the Raſe, and cut another breadth, and ſo move it ſucceſſively, till your whole intended ſhape be cut out of the Plate.

When you cut out an *Hinge,* you muſt leave on the length of the Plate A B in this Figure, Plate enough to lap over for the *Joints,* I mean, to *Turn,* or *Double* about a round Pin, ſo big as you intend the Pin of your *Hinge* ſhall be, and alſo Plate enough to *Weld* upon the inſide of the *Hinge* below the *Pin-hole* of the *Joint,* that the *Joint* may be ſtrong.

The ſize, or diameter of the *Pin-hole,* ought to be about twice the thickneſs of the Plate you make the *Hinge* of, therefore lay a wyre of ſuch a diameter towards the end B, in this Figure on

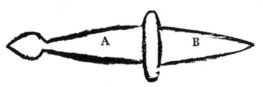

the *Tail piece,* a-thwart the Plate as CD, and *Double* the end of the Plate B, over the wyre to lap over it, and reach as far as it can upon the end A ; then *hammer* the Plate that is lap'd over the wyre cloſe to the wyre, to make the *Pin-hole* round ; but if your Plate be thick, it will require the taking of an *Heat* to make the

ham-

hammer the clofer to the wyre, and confequently make the *Pin-hole* the rounder : Your work
may alfo fometimes require to be Screwed into
the *Vice,* with the doubled end upwards, and the
bottom fide of the wyre clofe againft the *Chaps*
of the *Vice,* and then to *hammer* upon the very
top of the *Pin-hole* to round it at the end alfo.
When you have made the *Pin-hole* round in the
infide, take the *Pin* CD out of the *Pin-hole,* and
put the *Joint-end* of the *Hinge* into the Fire to
make a *Welding-heat;* which when it hath, fnatch
it quickly out of the Fire, and *hammer,* or *weld,*
the end B upon the *Tail-piece* A till they be incorporate together.   But you muft have a care
that you *hammer* not upon the Plate of the *Pin-
hole,* left you ftop it up, or batter it ; when it
is well Welded, you muft again put in the *Pin*
CD, and if it will not well go into the *Pin-
hole,* (becaufe you may perhaps have *hammer'd*
either upon it, or too near it, and fo have fomewhat clofed it) you muft force it in with your
hammer ; and if it require, take a *Blood-heat,* or
a *Flame-heat,* of the *Joint* end) and then force
the *Pin* into the *Pin-hole,* till you find the *Pin-
hole* is again round within, and that the *Pin,* or
Wyre, turn evenly about within it.

　　Afterwards with a *Punch* of hardned Steel
(as you were taught *Page* 11. 12.) *Punch* the
Nail-holes in the Plate; or if your Plate be
very thin, you may *punch* them with a *(c)* cold
Punch.   After all, *fmooth* it as well as you can
with your *Hand-hammer ;* take a *Blood-red-heat,*
if your work require it, if not, *fmooth* it cold ;
fo will the *Tail-piece* be fit for the *File. Double,*
and *Weld* the *Crofs-piece,* as you did the *Tail-piece.*

　　Having *forg'd* your *Hinge* fit for the *File,* you
muft proceed to make the *Joint,* by cutting a
Notch in the Middle of the *Pin-hole* between
D D in Plate 2. on the *Crofs,* as at E, and you
muft cut down the Ends of the *Pin-hole* on the
Tail-

Tail-piece, as at D D, till the *Joint* at C fit exactly into the Notch in the *Crofs,* and that when the *Pin* is put into the *Pin-hole* D D on the *Crofs,* the *Pin-hole* in the *Tail-piece* may alfo receive the *Pin ;* then by holding the *Tail-piece* in one Hand, and the *Crofs* in the other, double the *Tail* and *Crofs* towards one another, to try if they move evenly and fmoothly without fhaking on the *Pin;* which if they do, the *Joint* is made ; if they do not, you muft examine where the Fault is, and taking the *Pin* out, mend the Fault in the *Joint.*

Then *File* down all the Irregularities the *Cold-Chiffel* made on the Edges of your Work, and (if the Curiofity of Work require it) *file* alfo the outer Flat of your Work.But tho'*Smiths* that make Quantities of *Hinges,* do *brighten* them, (as they call it) yet they feldom *file* them, but *Grinde* them on a Grindftone till they become *bright,*&c.

Having finifhed the *Joint,*put the *Pin* in again; but take care it be a little longer than the Depth of the *Joint,* becaufe you muft batter the Ends of the *Pin* over the outer Edges of the *Pin-hole,* that the *Pin* may not drop out when either Edge of the *Crofs* is turned upwards.

The chiefeft Curiofity in the making thefe, and, indeed, all other *Hinges* is, 1. That the *Pin-hole* be exactly round, and not too wide for the *Pin.* 2. That the *Joints* are let exactly into one another, that they have no play between them, left they fhake upwards or downwards, nor yet are forced too hard into one another,left when they are nailed on the Door, the *Joint* be in Danger of Breaking. 3. That the *Crofs,* and the *Tail* lie on the Under-fide exactly flat, for fhould they warp out of flat when they are nailed on, the Nails would draw the *Joint* a-wry, and not only make it move hard, and unevenly, but by oft Opening and Shutting break the *Joint.* 4. If your Work be intended to be curious, the

true

true *Square-filing* the Upper-fide, as you were
taught *Page* 15, 16, 17. is a great Ornament.

(*a*) Smiths call all *Chiffels* they ufe upon cold
Iron, *Cold-Chiffels.*

(*b*) The *Stake* is a fmall *Anvil*, which either
ftands upon a broad Iron Foot, or Bafis, on
the *Work-Bench*, to remove as Occafion offers;
or elfe it hath a ftrong Iron *Spike* at the Bottom, which Iron *Spike* is let into fome certain
Place of the *Work-Bench* not to be removed.
Its Office is to fet fmall cold Work ftraight
upon, or to Cut or Punch upon with the *Cold-
Chiffel*, or *Cold-Punch.*

(*c*) *Smiths* call all *Punches* they ufe upon cold
Iron, *Cold-Punches.*

If the *Hinge* you are to make be large, and Plate-
Iron is not ftrong enough for it, you muft
Forge it out of Flat Bar-Iron, as you were taught
from *Page* 7 to *Page* 12.

The manner of working *Duftails*, *Fig.* 5. and
Side-hinges, *Fig.* 6. &c. is (the fhape confidered)
in all refpects the fame I have here fhewed you
in *Crofs-Garnets*; but in thefe (or others) you
may (if your Work require Curiofity) inftead
of *Doubling* for the *Joint*, *Forge* the *Round* for the
Joint of full Iron, and afterwards *Drill* a Hole
through it, for the *Pin-hole*; and by curious *Filing*, work them fo true into one another, that
both fides of the *Hinge* fhall feem but one Piece;
as I fhall fhew more at large, when I come to
the making of Compaffes, and other Joints for
Mathematical Inftruments.

Of Locks *and* Keys.

AS there are *Locks* for feveral Purpofes, as
Street-door Locks, called *Stock-Locks*; *Cham-
ber-door Locks*, called *Spring-Locks*; *Cupboard-Locks*,
Cheft-Locks, *Trunk-Locks*, *Pad-Locks*, &c. So
are there feveral Inventions in *Locks*, I mean, in
the

the Making and Contriving their *Wards,* or *Guards.* But the Contrivances being almoſt innumerable, according to the various Fancies of Men, ſhall be referred to another Time to diſcourſe ; and I ſhall now ſhew you the Working of a *Spring-Lock,* which when you know how to do, your Fancy may play with Inventions, as you beſt like.

In *Fig.* 2. A A A A the *Main-plate,* B C the *Keyhole.* E D E the *Top-hook,* E E *Croſs-wards,* F the *Bolt,* G the *Bolt-Toe,* or *Bolt-Nab.* H the *Draw-back Spring,* I the *Tumbler,* K the *Pin* of the *Tumbler,* L L the *Staples.*

In *Fig.* 3. A A A A the *Cover-Plate,* B the *Pin,* B C D the *Main-ward,* D D *Croſs-wards,* E the *Step-ward* or *Dap-ward.*

In *Fig.* 4. A the *Pin-hole,* B the *Step,* or *Dapward,* C the *Hook-ward,* D the *Middle,* or *Main Croſs-ward,* E E the *Croſs-ward,* F the *Main-ward,* G G *Croſs-ward,* H the *Shank,* I the *Pot,* or *Bread,* K the *Bow-ward,* L the *Bow,* B C D E E F G G the *Bit.*

Firſt, Cut out of an Iron Plate with a *Cold-Chiſſel,* the Size and Shape of the *Main-Plate,* as you were taught to cut the *Croſs* and *Tail-piece* of the *Croſs-Garnet ;* then conſider what Depth you intend the *Bit* of the *Key* ſhall have, and ſet that Depth off on the *Main-Plate,* by leaving about half an Inch of Plate between the Bottom of the *Key-hole,* and the Lower Edge of the *Main-Plate,* as at C (or more or leſs, according to the Size of the *Lock.*) Then meaſure with a Pair of *Compaſſes* between the Bottom of the *Bit,* and the *Centre* of your *Key* (or your intended *Key)* and ſet that diſtance off from C to B, near the Middle between the two Ends of the *Main-Plate,*and with the (*a*) *Prick-punch,* make there a Mark to ſet one *Foot* of your *Compaſſes* in, then opening your *Compaſſes* to the Middle of the *Bit* of your intended *Key,* as

to

to D, defcribe the Arch E D E for the true Place
the *Top-hoop* muft ftand on.

Then cut one other Piece of Plate as A A A A
in *Fig.* 3. for a *Cover-plate*, with two Pieces one
on each fide, long enough to make *Studs* of to
turn downwards, and then outward again as F F,
G G, that the *Cover-plate* may ftand off the *Main-
plate*, the Breadth of the *Bit* of the *Key* ; and at
the two End of thefe *Studs* Punch holes, as G G,
to *Rivet* the *Cover-plate* into the *Main-plate*. In
the Middle of this Plate make the *Centre*, as at B,
then open your *Compaffes* to three Quarters the
Length of the *Bit*, and half the Diameter of the
Shank of the *Key*, and placing one *Foot* in the
Point B, defcribe with the other *Foot* the Arch
D C D for the true Place of the *Main-ward*, then
fet your *Compaffes* to a little more than half the
Diameter of the *Shank*, and place one *Foot* (as
before) in the *Centre* B, and with the other *Foot*
defcribe the fmall Arch E, for the true Place the
Step-ward, or (as fome call it) the *Dap-ward* muft
ftand : So have you the true Places of the *Wards*,
for ano rdinary *Spring-Lock* ; you may (if the
Depth of your *Bit* will bear it) put more *Wards* in
your Plates. But you muft note, that the more
Wards you put in, the weaker you make your *Key*;
becaufe that to every *Ward* on the Plates, you
muft make a Slit, or *Ward* in the *Bit* of the *Key*;
and the more *Wards* you make, the weaker the
Iron of the *Bit* will be ; and then if the *Bolt*
fhoot not eafily backwards, or forwards, the *Bit*
may be in Danger of Breaking.

Having marked on your Plates the Places of
all your *Wards*, you muft take thin Plate, and
with *Hammering* and *Filing* make them both (*b*)
Hammer-hard, and of equal Thicknefs all the way.
Then *file* one Edge very ftraight , by laying a
ftraight Ruler juft within the Edge of it, and drawing, or racing with a Point of hardned Steel, a
bright Line by the fide of the *Ruler*; *File* away
the

the Edge of the Plate to that Line, then draw (as before) another ſtraight Line Parallel to the firſt ſtraight Line, or which is all one, Parallel to the filed Edge, juſt of the Breadth you intend the *Wards* ſhall be, and file as before, only, you muſt leave two, or ſometimes three *Studs* upon this Plate, one near each End, and the other in the Middle, to *Rivet* into the *Main-plate,* to keep the *Ward* fixt in its Place. Therefore you muſt take care when you elect this thin Piece of Plate, that it be broad enough for the *Ward,* and theſe Studs too. Then laying the Plate a-thwart the *Pike* of the *Bickern,* hold your Hand even with the *Face* of the *Bickern,* and *hammer* this Plate down ſomewhat by the ſide of the *Pike,* and by Degrees you may (with care taken) bring it unto a circular Form, juſt of the Size of that Circle you deſcribed on the *Main-plate ;* which when you have done, you muſt apply this *Ward* to the Circle you deſcribed on the *Main-plate ;* ſetting it in the Poſition you intend it ſhall be fixed, and marking with a Steel Point where the *Studs* ſtand upon that Circle, in thoſe marks *Punch* holes to *Rivet* the *Studs* to. Work ſo by all the other *Wards.*

If you have a *Pin* to the *Lock, Punch* a Hole through the *Centre* on the *Cover-plate,* ſomewhat ſmaller than the Wyre you are to make your *Pin* of, becauſe you may then *file* one End of the *Pin* away to a *Shank,* which muſt fit the ſmaller Hole on the Plate, and the whole Thickneſs of the *Pin* will be a *Sholder,* which will keep the *Pin* ſteddy in the *Centre-hole* of the Plate, when the *Pin* is *rivetted* into the Plate. But becauſe there is ſome Skill to be uſed in *Rivetting,* I ſhall, before I proceed any farther, teach you

The manner of Rivetting.

RIvetting is to batter the Edges of a *Shank* o-ver a Plate, or other Iron, the *Shank* is let into, fo as the Plate, or other Iron, may be clinched clofe, and fixed between the Battering at the End of the *Shank* and the *Sholder*. So that

When you *Rivet* a *Pin* into a Hole, your *Pin* muft have a *Sholder* to it thicker than the Hole is wide, that the *Sholder* flip not through the Hole, as well as the *Shank;* but the *Shank* of the *Pin* muft be exactly of the Size of the Hole the *Shank* muft be *Rivetted* into, and fomewhat longer than the Plate is thick ; *file* the End of the *Shank* flat, fo fhall the Edges of the End, the ea-filier batter over the Plate ; then put your *Shank* into the Hole, wherein it is to be *Rivetted,* but be fure you force the *Shank* clofe up to the *Sholder ;* then turn the Top of this *Sholder* down-wards (Plate and all) upon your *Stake,* but lay it fo, as that the *Sholder* lie folid, and the *Shank,* at the fame time, ftand directly upright, and with your left Hand, keep your Work bearing hard upon the Flat, or *Face* of the *Stake.* Then holding your *Hammer* in your Right-hand, hold the Edge of the *Face* of it Dripping a-flope from the Right-hand outwards, and lay pretty light Blows upon the Edge of the End of the *Shank,* turning with your Left-hand your Work round, to the *Face* of the *Hammer,* till you have battered the Edges of the *Shank* quite round about ; but this is feldom done, with once turning your Work about; therefore you may thus work it round again and again, till you find it is pretty well *Rivetted ;* then lay heavier Blows upon it, fometimes with the *Face,* fometimes with the *Pen* of the *Hammer,* till the End of the *Shank* is bat-tered effectually over the Plate.

One main Confideration in *Rivetting* is, that the *Pin* you *rivet* in, ftand upright to the Plate,

or other Iron you *rivet* it upon; for if it do not
ſtand upright, you will be forced to ſet it upright, after it is *rivetted*, either in the *Vice*, or
with your *Plyers*, or with your *Hammer*, and that
may, if your Plate be thin, bow it, or if it be
thick, break the Shank, or elſe the *Sholder* of your
Rivet, and ſo you loſe your Labour, and ſometimes ſpoil your Work.

Another Conſideration is, that when you *rivet*
a *Pin* to any Plate, and you fear it may afterwards twiſt about by ſome force that may be
offered it, you muſt, to provide againſt this
Danger, *file* the *Shank* you intend to *Rivet*, either Square, or Triangular, and make the Hole
in the Plate you *rivet* it into, of the ſame Size
and Form, and then *rivet* in the *Shank*, as before. There are two ways to make your Hole,
Square or Triangular, one is by *filing* it into
theſe Forms, when it is firſt Punched round;
the other by making a *Punch* of Steel, of the Size
and Shape of the *Shank* you are to *rivet*, and
punching that *Punch* into the Plate, make the
ſame Form.

Now to return where I left off. The *Pins* and
Shanks of theſe *Wards* muſt be made of a long
Square Form, becauſe, (the Plates of the *Wards*
being thin) ſhould you make them no broader
than the Plate is thick, the *Studs*, or *Shanks*
would be too weak to hold the *Wards*, therefore
you muſt make the *Rivetting-ſhank* three or four
times, or ſometimes more, as broad as the Plate
is thick, and then *rivet* them in, as you were
taught juſt now.

Then place the *Cover-plate* upon the *Main-
plate*, ſo as the *Centre* of the *Cover-plate*, may ſtand
directly over and againſt the *Centre* of the *Main-
plate*, and make marks through the Hole G G,
of the *Studs* of the *Cover-Plate* upon the *Main-
plate*, and on thoſe Marks Punch holes, and fit
two *Pins* into them, to faſten the *Cover-plate* on to
the

the *Main-plate*, but you muft not yet *rivet* them down, till the *Key-hole* be made, becaufe this *Cover-plate* would then ftop the Progrefs of the *File* through the *Main-plate*, when you *file* the *Key-hole*. When you have placed the *Cover-plate* upon the *Main-plate*, and fitted it on with *Pins*, fo, as you may take it off, and put it on again, as your Work may require, you muft *Punch* the *Key-hole*, or rather drill two Holes clofe by one another, if the *Key-hole* falls near the *Wards*, becaufe *Punching* may be apt to fet the *Wards* out of Form, and with fmall *Files*, file the two Holes into one another, to make the Hole big enough to come at it with bigger *Files*, and then file your *Key-hole* to your intended Size and Shape.

The *Key-hole* being finifhed, forge your *Key*, as you were taught, *Page* 7. and if your *Key* is to have a *Pin-hole*, drill the Hole in the Middle of the End of the *Shank*, then file the *Wards*, or Slits in the *Bit* with thin *Files*; yet fometimes Smiths *Punch*, or cut them with a *Cold-Chiffel*, at the fame Diftances from the Middle of the *Pin-hole* in the End of the *Shank* (which is the fame *Centre*, which was made before, in the *Main-plate* on the *Cover-plate*) which you placed the *Wards* at, from the *Centre* of the *Main* and *Cover-plate*. But before you file thefe *Wards* too deep into the *Bit* of the *Key*, make Trials, by putting the *Bit* into the *Key-hole*, whether the *Wards* in the *Bit*, will agree with the *Wards* on the Plates, which if they do, you may boldly cut them to the Depth of the *Wards* on the Plate ; if not, you muft alter your Courfe till they do; but you muft take great Care in Cutting the *Wards* down ftraight, and fquare to the Sides of the *Bit* ; for if they be not cut down ftraight, the *Wards* on the Plates, will not fall in with the *Wards* in the *Bit* of the *Key*; and if they be not Square to the Sides of the *Bit*, the *Bit* will not only be weaker than it need be, but it will

fhew

ſhew unhandſomely, and like a Botch to the Eye.

The *Croß* and *Hock-wards* is made, or, at leaſt, entred at the *Forge*, when the Iron hath a *Blood*, or almoſt a *Flame Heat*, yet ſometimes Smiths do it on cold Iron, with a thin *Chiſſel*, as you was taught *Page* 11. 12. But you muſt take care that your *Chiſſel* be neither too thick, or too broad, for this Punching of *Wards* is only to give the thin *Files* Entrance to the Work; which Entrance when you have, you may eaſily file your *Croß*, or *Hook-wards*, wider or deeper, as your Work may require; but if your *Chiſſel* be too broad, or too thick, it will make the *Wards* in the *Bit* too long, or too wide, and then (as I ſaid before) the *Bit* of your *Key* will prove weaker than it needs to be.

Having made the *Wards* on the Plate, and in the *Bit* of the *Key*, you muſt *Forge* the *Bolt* of a conſiderable Subſtance, Thick and Square at the End that ſhoots into the *Staple* in the Frame of the Door, that it may be ſtrong enough to guard the whole Door; but the reſt of the *Bolt* that lies between the two *Staples* on the *Main-plate*, may be made very thin inwards, that is, the Side that lies towards the *Main-plate*, which becauſe it cannot be ſeen when the *Bolt* is fixed upon the Plate, I have made a Figure of it, and turned the Inſide to View, as in *Fig.* 4. where you may ſee, that the End A, hath a conſiderable Subſtance of Iron to guard the whole Door, as aforeſaid, and B is a Square *Stud*, which doth as well keep the Outſide flat of the *Bolt* on the Range, as ſerve for a *Stud* for the *Spring* H in *Fig.* 2. to preſs hard againſt, and ſhoot the *Bolt* forwards: This *Bolt* muſt be wrought ſtraight on all its Sides, except the Topſide, which muſt be wrought ſtraight only as far as the *Sholder* G, called the *Toe*, or *Nab* of the *Bolt*, which riſes, as you ſee in the Figure, conſiderably high, above the Straight on the Top of the *Bolt*: The Office of this *Nab*,

is

is to receive the Bottom of the *Bit* of the *Key*, when in turning it about, it shoots the *Bolt* backwards or forwards.

Having *forged* and *filed* the *Bolt*, you must fit the Hollow-side of it towards the *Main-plate*, at that Distance from the *Key-hole*, that when the *Key* is put into the *Key-hole*, and turned towards the *Bolt*, the Bottom of the *Bit* may fall almost to the Bottom of the *Nab*, and shoot the *Bolt* back so much, as it needs to enter the *Staple* in the *Door-frame*. And having found this true Place for the *Bolt*, you must with square *Staples*, just fit to contain the *Bolt* with an easie Play, fasten these *Staples*, by *Rivetting* them with the *Bolt* within them, one near the *Bolt* end, the other near the *Nab* end, as at L L to the *Main-plate*.

Then *Punch* a pretty wide Hole in the *Main-plate*, as at K, to receive a strong *Pin*, and *file* a *Sholder* to the *Shank* of the *Pin* that goes into the Plate. This *Pin* is called the *Pin of the Tumbler*; the *Tumbler* is marked I, which is a long Piece of *Iron*, with a round Hole at the Top to fit the *Pin* of the *Tumbler* into, that it may move upon it, as on a *Joint*, and it hath an *Hook* returning at the Lower End of it, to fall into the Breech of the *Bolt*, and by the *Spring* H forces the *Bolt* forwards, when it is shot back with the *Key*. This *Spring* is made of Steel, and afterwards temper'd (as I shall shew you in proper Place.) It is fixed at the Bottom of the *Main-plate*, by two small Shanks proceeding from that Edge of the *Spring* that lies against the *Main-plate*, as at O O : These Shanks are to be *rivetted* (as you were taught even now) on the other Side of the *Main-plate*.

All things being thus fitted, *punch* an Hole on each Corner of the *Main-plate* for *Nails* to enter, that must nail the *Lock* to the *Door*. Or if you intend to screw your *Lock* on the *Door*, you must make wide Holes, big enough to receive the
Shank

Shank of the *Screw.* Laſt of all, *rivet* down your
Cover-plate to the *Main-plate*, and *file* your *Key*,
and *poliſh* it too, if you will; ſo ſhall the *Lock*
and *Key* be finiſhed.

(*a*) A *Prick-punch*,is a Piece of temper'd Steel,
with a round Point at one End, to prick a round
Mark in cold Iron.

(*b*) *Hammer-hard*,is when you harden Iron, or
Steel, with much hammering on it.

The making of Screws *and* Nuts.

THE *Shank* of the *Screw* for Doors,and many
other Purpoſes, muſt be *forged* ſquare near
the *Head*,becauſe it muſt be let into a Square-hole,
that it may not twiſt about when the *Nut* is
turned about hard upon the *Screw-pin.* Therefore
take a Square-bar, or Rod of Iron, as near the
Size of the *Head* of the *Screw-pin* as you can, and
taking a *Flame-heat* of it, lay ſo much of this Bar
as you intend for the Length of the *Shank*, with
one Square-ſide flat, upon the Hither-ſide of the
Anvil, and *hammer* it down to your intended
Thickneſs: But have a care you do not ſtrike
your Iron on this Side the Edge of the *Anvil*,
leſt you cut the Iron,as I told you *Page* 11. Thus,
at once, you will have two Sides of your *Shank*
forged; the Under-ſide made by the *Anvil*, and
the Upper-ſide beaten flat with the *Hammer*:
The *Head* will be in the main Rod of Iron; then
if your Iron grows cold, give it another *Heat*,
and lay one of the unwrought Sides upon the
Hither-ſide of the *Anvil*, juſt to the *Head*, and
hammer that down, as before, ſo ſhall the two
other Square-ſides be made; then *hammer* down
the Corners of ſo much of this *Shank*, as you intend for the *Screw-pin*, and round it, as near as
you can, with the *Hammer*; ſet then the *Chiſſel*
to the Thickneſs you intend the *Head* ſhall have,
and ſtrike it about half through, then turn the
Sides ſucceſſively, and cut each Side alſo half
through, till it be quite cut off. If the *Sholder* be
not ſquare enough, hold it in your *Square-nos'd*
                                              Tungs.

Tongs, and take another *Heat*, and with speed
(left your Work cool) screw the *Shank* into the
Vice, so as the *Sholder* may fall flat upon the *Chaps*
of the *Vice;* then *hammer* upon the *Head,* and
square the *Sholder* on two Sides, do the like for
squaring the other two Sides.   This was, in part,
taught you before, in *Page* 11. but because
the cutting this Iron Rod, or Bar, just above the
Sholder makes the *Head,* and for that I did not
mention it there, I thought fit (since the Purpose
required it) to do it here : The *Forging* of the
Nuts are taught before, *Page* 11. 12.

   Having *forged* and *filed* your *Shank* square, and
the *Head* either Square or Round, as you intend
it shall be, *file* also the *Screw-pin,* from the Ri-
sings and dents left at the *Forge ;* and *file* it a little
Tapering towards the End, that it may enter the
Screw-plate ; the Rule how much it must be Tapering is this, consider how deep the Inner *Grooves* of the *Screw-plate* lie in the outer *Threds,* and
file the End of the *Screw-pin* so much smaller than
the rest of the *Screw-pin,* for the outer *Threds* of
the *Screw-plate* must make the *Grooves* on the *Screw-
pin,* and the *Grooves* in the *Screw-plate,* will make
the *Threds* on the *Screw-pin.*   Having fitted your
self with a Hole in your *Screw-plate* (that is,
such a Hole whose Diameter of the hollow *Groc-
ves,* shall be equal to the Diameter of the *Screw-
pin,* but not such a Hole, whose Diameter of
the outer *Threds,* shall be equal to the Diameter
of the *Screw-pin,* for then the *Screw-plate* will
indeed turn about the *Screw-pin,* but not cut any
Grooves, or *Threds* in it) *screw* the *Shank* with the
Head downwards in the *Vice,* so as that the *Screw-
pin* may stand directly upright, and take the
Handle of the *Screw-plate* in your Right-hand, and
lay that Hole flat upon the *Screw-pin,* and press it
very hard down over it, and turn the *Screw-plate*
evenly about with its *Handle* towards you, from the
Right towards the Left-hand, so shall the outer
                                                    Threds

Threds of the *Screw-plate* cut *Grooves* into the *Screw-pin*, and the fubftance of the Iron on the *Screw-pin*, will fill up the *Grooves* of the *Screw-plate*, and be a *Thred* upon the *Screw-pin*. But take this for Caution, that, as I told you, you muft not make your *Screw-pin* too fmall, becaufe the *Screw-plate* will not cut it, fo if you make it too big (if it do enter the *Screw-plate* where it is Taper) it will endanger the breaking it, or, if it do not break it, yet the *Screw-plate* will, after it gets a little below the Tapering, go no farther, but work and wear off the *Thred* it made about the Tapering.

To fit the *Pin* therefore to a true fize, I, in my Practife, ufe to try into what *hole* of the *Screw-plate*, the *Tap* or place of the *Tap*, (if it be a tapering *Tap*,) I make the *Nut* with, will juft flide through ; (*Threads* and all ;) (which generally in moft *Screw-plates* is the *hole* next above that to be ufed) for then turning my *Pin* about in that *hole*, if the *Pin* be irregularly *filed*, or but a little too big on any part of it, the *Threds* of that *Hole* will cut fmall marks upon the *Pin*, on the irregular places, or where it is too big ; fo that afterwards *filing* thofe Marks juft off, I do at once *file* my *Pin* truly round, and fmall enough to fit the *Hole* I make my *Screw-pin* with.

As the *Hole* of the *Screw plate* muft be fitted to the *Screw-pin*, fo muft the *Screw-tap* that makes the *Screw* in the *Nut*, be fitted to to the round *hole* of the *Nut* ; but that *Tap* muft be of the fame fize of your *Screw-pin* too, which you may try by the fame *hole* of the *Screw-plate* you made the *Screw-pin* with. *Screw* the *Nut* in the *Vice* directly flat, that the *hole* may ftand upright, and put the *Screw-tap* upright in the *hole* ; then if your *Screw-tap* have an *handle*, turn it by the *handle* hard round in the *Hole*, fo will the *Screw-tap* work it felf into the *Hole*, and make *Grooves* in it to fit the *Threds* of

C　　　　　　　　the

the *Screw-pin*. But if the *Screw-tap* have no *han-dle*, then it hath its upper end filed to a long fquare, to fit into an hollow fquare, made near the *handle* of the *Screw-plate* ; but that long fquare hole, o-ver the long fquare on the top of the *Tap*, and then by turning about the *Screw-plate*, you will al-fo turn about the *Tap* in the *hole*, and make *Grooves* and *Threds* in the *Nut*.

But though fmall *Screws* are made with *Screw-plates*, yet great *Screws*, fuch as are for *Vices*, *Hot-Preffes*, *Printing-Preffes*, &c. are not made with *Screw-plates*, but muft be cut out of the main Iron, with heavy blows upon a *Cold-Chiffel*. The man-ner of making them, is as follows.

The Rules and manner of Cutting Worms *upon great* Screws.

THE *Threds* of *Screws*, when they are bigger than can be made in *Screw-plates*, are call'd *Worms*. They confift in length, breadth and depth ; the length of a *Worm* begins at the one end of the *Spindle*, and ends at the other ; the breadth of the *Worm*, is contain'd between any two *Grooves* on the *Spindle*, viz. The upper and un-der *Groove* of the *Worm*, in every part of the *Spindle* ; the depth of the *Worm*, is cut into the Diameter of the *Spindle*, viz. The depth, between the outfide of the *Worm*, and the bottom of the *Groove*.

The depth ought to be about the one feventh part of the Diameter, on each fide the *Spindle:*

You ought to make the *Groove* wider than the *Worm* is broad, becaufe the *Worm* being cut out of the fame intire piece with the *Spindle*, will be as ftrong as the *Worm* in the *Nut*, tho' the *Worm* on the *Spindle* be fmaller ; for you cannot come at the *Worm* in the *Nut*, to cut it with *Files*, as you may the *Spindle*, and therefore you muft either

Turn

Turn up a Rod of Iron, to twift round about the *Grooves* on the *Spindle*, and then take it off, and *Braze* it into the *Nut*, or elfe you muft *Caft* a *Nut* of *Brafs* upon the *Spindle*, which will neither way be fo ftrong as the *Worm* cut out of the whole Iron, by fo much as *Brafs* is a weaker Mettal than Iron, and therefore it is that you ought to allow the *Worm* in the *Nut*, a greater breadth than the *Worm* on the *Spindle*, that the ftrength of both may, as near as you can, be equaliz'd; for both being put to equal force, ought to have equal ftrength. The *Worm* may very well be the one feventh part fmaller than the *Groove* is wide, as aforefaid.

Having confider'd what breadth the *Worm* on the *Spindle* fhall have, take a fmall thin Plate of Brafs, or Iron, and *file* a fquare notch at the end of it, juft fo wide, and fo deep, as your *Worm* is to be broad and deep, and *file* the fides of the Plate that this notch ftands between, juft to the width of the *Groove*. This Plate, muft be a *Gage* to *file* your *Worm* and *Groove* to equal breadth by; then draw a ftraight and upright Line the whole length of the *Spindle*; divide from this line the Circumference of the whole *Spindle* into eight equal Parts, and through thofe Divifions, draw feven Lines more parallel to the firft Line; then open your *Compaffes* juft to the breadth of one *Worm*, and one *Groove*, and fet off that diftance as oft as you can, from the one end of the Spindle to the other, (but I fhould firft have told you, that the end of your Spindle muft be fquare to the outfide) and with a *Prick-Punch*, make a mark to every fetting off on that line : Do the like to all the other ftraight upright Lines. Note, that you may chufe one of thefe eight upright Lines for the firft, and make the next towards your left Hand, the fecond (but then the firft muft ftand towards you) and the

next

next that, the third, and fo on. And the top
mark of every one of thefe upright ftraight
Lines, fhall be call'd the firft Mark, the next under that the fecond Mark, the third, the third
Mark, and fo downwards in Order and Number.

Having marked one of thefe eight Lines at the
top of the *Spindle*, to begin the winding of the
Worm at, with a Black-lead Pencil, draw a line
from that Mark to the fecond Mark, on the next
upright Line towards the left hand, from thence
continue drawing on with your Pencil to the third
Mark, on the third upright Line, draw on ftill to
the fourth Mark, on the fourth upright Line,
and fo onwards, till you have drawn over the
eight ftraight Lines, which when you have done,
you muft ftill continue on, drawing downwards
to each lower Mark on each fucceffive upright
Line, till you have drawn your *Worm* from end
to end: Then examine, as well as you can, by
your Eye, whether the *Worm* you have carried on
from Mark to Mark with the Black-led Pencil,
do not break into Angles, which if it do any
where, you muft mend it in that place: Then
with the edge of an *half-round File*, file a fmall
Line in the Black-lead Line, and be fure that the
Line you are *filing*, run exactly through all the
Marks that the Black-lead Pencil fhould have run
through (if it did not, for want of good guidance of the Hand.) This fmall Line is only for a
guide to cut the *Groove* down by; for the making
of a *Screw* is, indeed nothing elfe, but the cutting the *Groove* down, for then the *Worm* remains:
But you muft not *file* in this fmall line, but leave
it as a guide to lie on the middle of the *Worm*
(as I faid before): Therefore to cut down the
Groove, take a *Cold-Chiffel*, fomewhat thinner than
you intend the *Groove* fhall be wide, *viz.* about
the

the thickneſs of the breadth of the *Worm,* and, with heavy blows, cut out the *Groove* pretty near. The reaſon why you ſhould not offer to cut the *Grooves* to their full wedth at the firſt, is, becauſe your Hand may carry the *Cold-Chiſſel* ſomewhat awry, and ſhould yonr *Cold-Chiſſel* be as thick as the *Groove* is wide, you could not ſmooth the Irregularities out, without making the *Worm* narrower than you intended it : Then with a *Flat-file* open and ſmooth the *Groove,* *filing* in the middle between the two next fine Lines cut by the *half-round File,* till you have wrought the *Spindle* from end to end, ſo ſhall the *Worm* remain. But you muſt not expect, that though the *Groove* be cut, it is therefore finiſhed, for now you muſt begin to uſe the thin *Plate-Gage,* and try firſt, whether the *Worm* have equal breadth all the way. Secondly, whether the *Grove* have equal breadth all the way. And Thirdly, whether the *Groove* have equal depth all the way ; and where ever you find the *Worm* too broad, you muſt *file* it thinner, and where the *Groove* is not deep enough, *file* it deeper ; therefore in cutting down the *Groove* you may obſerve, that if, at firſt, you *file* the *Worm* never ſo little too narrow or the *Groove* never ſo little too deep, you ſhall have all the reſt of the *Worm* or *Groove* to *file* over again ; becauſe the whole *Worm* muſt be brought to the breadth of the ſmalleſt part of it, and the whole *Groove* to the depth of the deepeſt place all the way, eſpecially if the *Nut* be to be *Caſt* in *Braſs* upon the *Spindle* ; becauſe the Mettal running cloſe to the *Spindle* will bind on that place, and not come off it ; but if the *Nut* be not to be *Caſt* in *Braſs,* but only hath a *Worm* brazed into it, this niceneſs is not ſo abſolutely neceſſary, becauſe that *Worm* is firſt *Turned up,* and bowed into the *Grooves* of the *Spindle,* and you may try that before it is

Brazed

Braz'd in the *Nut*, and if it go not well about, you may mend, or botch it, either by *Hammering* or *Filing*, or both.

The manner of *Casting* the *Nut* upon the *Spindle*, I shall shew when I come to the *Casting* of *Mettals*; and the manner of *Brazing* hath been Taught already. *Num.* I. *fol.* 12, 13.

If your *Spindle* is to have three or four *Worms* winding about it, as *Coining-Presses* and *Printing-Presses* have, that they may not wear out too fast, you must divide the Circumference into three or four equal Parts, and having straight upright Lines, drawn as before, begin a *Worm* at each of those three, or four Divisions, on the Circumference, and considering the breadth of your *Worm* and width of your *Groove*, measure that width as oft as you can on all the upright Lines, and making Marks on those at each Setting off, draw as before, a Line from the end of the *Spindle*, on the first upright Line to the Mark below it, which is the second Mark on the second upright Line, from thence to the third Mark, on the third upright Line, and so on to the other end of the *Spindle*. Having drawn the first *Worm*, work the other *Worm* as this.

Thus much may at present suffice for *great Screws.*

MECHA-

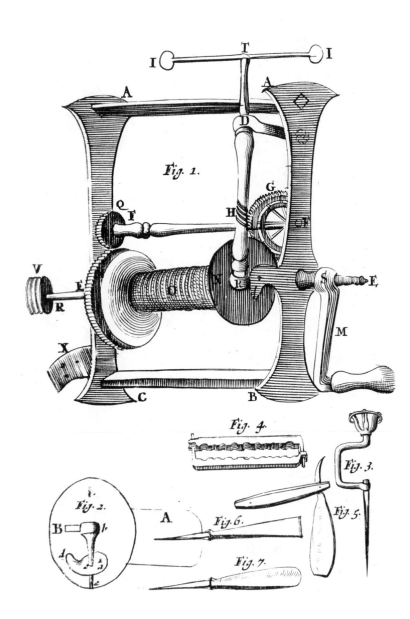

MECHANICK EXERCISES;

O R,

The Doctrine of *Handy-Works*

Viz. *The making of Jacks and Bullet-Molds, the twisting of Iron, and Case-hardning it, with the use of some Tools not treated of before : Also of the several sorts of Steel, the manner of Softning, Hardning and Tempering them.*

Of Jacks.

FIG. 1. is call'd a *Worm-Jack.* A B the *Fore-side,* AC the *Back-side,* A A the *Top-piece,* BC the *Bottom-piece,* altogether the *Jack-frame,* E EK the *Main-Spindle,* N O N the *Main-Wheel* and *Barrel,* O the *Barrel,* D the *Wind-up-piece,* fastned into the *Barrel,* F F the *Worm-wheel Spindle,* G the *Worm-wheel,* Q the *Worm-Nut,* H the *Worm,* R the *Stud* of the *Worm-Spindle,* D the *Worm-Loop,* L the *Wind-up-piece,* M the *Winch* or *Winder* or *Handle,* the Iron part is the *Winder,* the Wood the *Handle,* S the *Eye of the Winder,* I I the *Fly,* T the *Socket* of the *Fly,* V the *Struck-Wheel,* X the *Stayes* or *Back fastnings.*

First you are to Forge the *Jack-frame,* and on the left side of the *Foreside,* a Shank for the *Stud* of the *Worm-spindle,* as you are taught *Numb* I. *fol.* 8, 9, 10, 11, 12. and then file it as you were taught *Numb.* I. *fol.* 14, 15, 16.

The

The *top* and *bottom Pieces* are let into fquare
holes at the ends of the *Fore* and *Backfide.* But
you muft Forge the *top* and *bottom Pieces* with two
fmall Squares towards the ends of them, and two
round ends for *Screw-pins,* beyond thofe fquares.
The fmall fquares are to be fitted into fquare holes
into the *Fore* and *Backfides,* and the round *Screw-
pins* are to make *Screws* of, to which a fquare *Nut*
is to be fitted to draw the *top* and *bottom Pieces*
clofe and right up to the infides of the *Fore* and
Backfides. The manner of Filing of thefe Ends
you were, in part, taught *Numb.* II. *fol.* 15, 16.
and *Numb.* I. *fol.* 29. but another way is by trying your Work with an Inftrument, call'd by
Workmen, a *Square,* as you fee defcrib'd in this
Figure.

Of the Square *and its Ufe.*

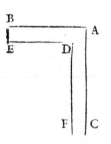

THE fides A B C are call'd the *Outer-fquare*;
the fides D E F the *Inner-fquare.* Its Ufe is
thus. If your Work, as in this
Cafe, be an *Outer-fquare,* you
muft ufe the *Inner-fquare,* D E F
to try it by; applying either
the fide E D or D F (but fuppofe the fide E D) to one of
the fides of your Work, chufe
the flatteft and trueft wrought;
if neither of the fides be flat,
make of them flat, as you were
taught *Numb.* I. *fol.* 15, 16. if then you find the
fide D F of your *Square* lie all the way even upon
the adjoining fide of your Work, you may conclude thofe fides are Square; but if the adjoining
fide of your Work comply not all the way with
the adjoining fide of the *Square,* you muft file a-
way your Work where the *Square* rides upon it,
till the whole fide be wrought to comply with
                                                the

the adjoining fide of the *Square*, that is, till both the fides of your Work agree with both the fides of the *Squares*, when they are appli'd to one another. Having tried two fides Square, make a third fide of your Work Square, by applying one of the fides of the *Square* to one of thofe fides of your Work, that are already made fquare, and as before, try the third untry'd fide, and make that Square ; and by the fame Rule make the fourth fide fquare.

If the Work you are to file be an hollow fquare, you muft apply the outer Square A B C to it, and try how, when one fide of the *Square*, is applied to one fide of your Work, the other fide of your Work agrees with the other fide of the *Square* ; which if it do, all is well : But if the *Square* and the Work comply not with one another, you muft file the Work where it bears the *Square* off. But to return where I left.

Having made thefe two ends fquare, you muft fit the length of them to the thicknefs of the *Fore* and *Backfides* into which they are to enter, but fo as the Squares be not full fo long as to come quite thro' the *Fore* and *Backfides*, left when the *Nuts* are fcrew'd on the *Screw-pins* that are at the ends of thefe Squares, they fcrew full up to the Squares, and bear againft the corners of them ; which if they do, the *Nuts* will not draw the *Fore* and *Backfides* clofe againft the fhoulder of the Squares, on the *top* and *bottom Pieces*, and then the whole *Jack Frame* will not ftand faft and firm together.

But before you fit this *Frame* thus together, you muft confider the Diameter of the *Main-wheel*, that you may Pnuch round Holes in the *Fore* and *Backfides* to enter the *Main-fpindle*. Therefore open your Compafs to half the intended Diameter of the *Main-wheel*, and half a quarter, or an whole quarter of an Inch more for play, between the

the Semi-diameter of the *main Wheel*, and the upper flat of the *bottom Piece*, and set that distance
off from the upper flat of the *bottom Piece*, on the
Fore and *Backsides*, and with a round Punch, somewhat smaller than the intended size of the *main
Spindle*, Punch Holes at that setting off. Your
Punch must be smaller than the *main Spindle*, because the holes may perhaps not be so exactly
round, or Punch'd so truly upright, or perfectly
smooth as they ought to be ; and should you make
the holes so wide at first as they need to be, you
could not mend them , without making them
wider. These holes must be Punch'd at the *Fire*
or *Forge* (as Smiths say, when they take an *Heat*
of their Work to Punch it) because the *Fore* and
the *Backsides* are *too strong* (as Smiths say) that is,
too thick to Punch with the *Cold Punch*. The
way of Punching them you were taught *Numb*. I.
fol. 11, 12. Besides a *Cold Punch* is commonly
made flat at the bottom, and therefore does not
prick an Hole, but cut an Hole (if the Iron be
not too strong) for that flat bottom, and the upright side about it, met in an Angle or Edge at
the bottom, which Edge, by the force of the
Hammer, cuts the Iron (if it be not too strong)
when it is laid upon a *Bolster*, as it is describ'd
Numb. I. *fol*. 12. and should you cut out so much
Iron in the *Fore* and *Backsides*, as would entertain
the *main Spindle* (it being thick) you will make
the *Fore* and *Backsides* too wide ; therefore as I
said, the Holes must be prickt in the *Fore* and
Backsides at the *Fire* or *Forge*, which with a sharp
pointed *Punch* is sooner done ; nor does pricking
diminish the substance or strength of the Iron, but
makes it swell out at the sides, and retain both
substance and strength. The irregularity or swel-
ling out that this Punching makes on the flats of
the *Fore* and *Backsides*, you must Hammer down
again

again with almoſt a *Blood-red-heat,* I ſay, almoſt a *Blood-red-heat*; becauſe, ſhould you take too great an *Heat,* you may make the *Fore* and *Backſides* ſtretch, and ſo put the whole *Jack-frame* out of order.

Having punch'd the Holes for the *main Spindle,* you muſt Punch the Holes in the *Fore* and *Backſides* for the *Worm-wheel Spindle,* as you Punch the Holes for the *main Spindle*; but theſe muſt be ſmall Holes, to entertain the ſmall Ends or Pins of the *Worm-wheel Spindle.*

Theſe Holes thus Punch'd, may perhaps not be exactly round or fit your ſize, nor will they be ſmooth enough within; therefore, with a ª *Square-bore,* you muſt ᵇ open them wider to your ſize, and that opening them in the inſide, will both round and ſmooth them.

You muſt alſo Punch a ſquare hole towards the top of the *Foreſide,* for the *Shank* of the *Worm-Loop.*

Then Forge and fit in your *Main-wheel Spindle,* and your *Worm-wheel Spindle,* which Spindles muſt both be exactly ſtraight between the corners of their two ends (unleſs you like to have Moldings for Ornaments on them) and Forge a Square towards the ends of both the Spindles, to fit into a ſquare hole in the middle of the *Croſs* of their *Wheels,* and leave ſubſtance enough for a ſhoulder beyond the ſquare, to ſtop the ſquare hole in the *Croſs* of the *Wheels* from ſliding farther on the *Spindle,* and you muſt leave ſubſtance of Iron enough to Forge the *Nut* of the *Worm-wheel* near the other end. But in this, and indeed in all other Forging remember (as I told you *Numb.* I. *fol. 9.*) that it behoves you to *Hammer* or *Forge* your Work as true as you can, leaſt it coſt you great pains at the *Vice.*

Then

Then Forge the *Worm-spindle*, which is all the way round and ftraight, unlefs you will have Moldings for Ornaments (as aforefaid) upon the *Shank* of it: But you muft be fure to Forge fubftance enough for the *Worm* to be cut out of it.

The *Main* and *Worm-wheels* are Forg'd round and flat.

The manner of Forging thefe Wheels (which in Smith's Language is, *Turning up the Wheels*) is, firft, to draw out a fquare Rod (as you were taught *Numb. I. fol. 9.* among the feveral *Heats of Iron*) fomewhat thicker than you intend your *Wheel* fhall be; but it muft be almoft as thin on one fide, as you intend the inner edge of the *Wheel* fhall be, and the oppofite to it above twice that thicknefs for the outer edge of the *Wheel*: the reafon you will find by and by. Having drawn from your fquare Rod a convenient length, *viz.* almoft three times the Diameter of your intended Wheel, you muft take almoft a *Flame-heat,* and Hammer all along the whole length upon the thick edge, fo will you find the long Rod by this Hammering, turn by degrees rounder and rounder in, upon the thin edge, which you Hammer'd not upon, till it become a Circle, or pretty near a Circle. But you muft make it fomewhat more than a Circle, for the ends muft lap over one another, that they may be *welded* upon one another.

Thus you may fee the Reafon for making the outer edge of the Rod thick, and the oppofite Edge thin; for your Hammering upon the outer edge only, and not on the inner, makes the outer edge a great deal thinner, and at the fame time makes the Wheel broader.

The

The Reafon why I told you, you fhould draw fourth the Rod to almoft three times the Diameter of the Wheel, and not to the Geometrical proportion ; is, becaufe that in Hammering upon it to make it round, the Rod will ftretch fo confiderably, that it will be long enough to make a *Wheel* of your intended Diameter, and moft commonly fomewhat to fpare. But to return.

Before you take a *welding Heat*, as by *Numb.* I. *fol. 9*, 10. you muft flatten the two ends that are to be *welded* together, to a little more than half their thicknefs, that when they are lapt over one another, and *welded* together, they may be no thicker than the other part of the *Wheel*.

If the *Wheel* be not *turned up* fo round, that with a little labour you may mend them at the *Vice* ; you muft with *Blood red Heats* Hammer them round upon the *Pike* or *Bickern* of the *Anvel*, holding with your *Tongs* the inner edge of the *Wheel* upon it, and Hammering upon the outer edge of the *Wheel*, till the *Wheel* be fit for the *Vice* : Their infides muft be divided into four equal Parts or four ᶜ *Dufftail* notches to be fild into them. The *Dufftail* notches are cut in the inner edge of the *Wheel*, fomewhat more than a quarter of an Inch deep, and fpreading fomewhat wider towards the outer edge. The notches are to receive the four ends of a *Crofs* Forg d fomewhat thicker towards the ends than the thicknefs of the *Wheel*, and muft be filed outer *Dufftails*, to let exactly into the inner *Dufftail* notches made in the infide of the *Wheel*. They muft be Forg d thicker than the *Wheel*, becaufe they muft batter over both the flat fides of the *Wheel*, to keep the *Wheel* ftrong and fteady upon the *Crofs* ; and fometimes (for more fecurity) they are *brazed* into the *Wheel* (yet that is but feldom) the middle of this *Crofs*
is

is made broad, that when the fquare of the *Spin-dle*, it may have ftrength enough to bear the vio-lence offered at, as well in winding up the great weight, that keeps the *Wheels* in motion, as in the checking and turning the *Jack-winder* back, to fet the *Jack* a going, when by the winding up, it may be fubject to ftand ftill, or fometimes, for want of weight, or elfe for want of Oiling or fome other accident.

These *Wheels* thus Forg'd and Filed flat, muft be divided, the *main Wheel* commonly into 64 equal parts, and the *worm Wheel* into 32 equal parts; but thefe Numbers are not exactly obferv d by Smiths, for fometimes they make them more and fometimes lefs, either according to the fize of their *Wheels*, or according as they intend their *Wheels* fhall go, fwifter or flower about (for the fewer the *Teeth* on a *Wheel* are, the fooner a *Wheel* goes about and the more *Teeth* on a *Wheel*, the flower the *Wheel* goes about) or fometimes as they have open'd their Compaffes to divide them: For if by luck, they at firft open their Compaffes to fuch a width, as will juft meafure out on a Circle, (which they defcribe on the Center of the *Wheel* for that purpofe) their intended number, than the *Wheel* fhall have the intended Number of *Teeth*; if not, let it fomewhat fall fhort, or exceed that Number, they matter not, but make that Num-ber of *Teeth* on the *Wheel*. And having thus di-vided the *Wheel*, they by the fide of a ftraight Ru-ler laid to the Center, and every divifion markt on the *Wheel*, draw or fcratch a ftraight line from the outer limb of the *Wheels*, to the Circle, which Circle (I fhould have told you before) is defcrib'd at that diftance from the outer Verge, they in-tend the *Teeth* fhall be cut down to. This is in-deed a rough way of working, but the Office of a *Jack* is well enough performed by this rough

Work;

Work; and the usual prizes such, as will scarce
pay Workmen for better, as they say.

These *Wheels* thus divided, must be cut down
into these Divisions with a ᵈ *Jack-file*, the *Main-
wheel* straight thwart the outer Verge, (which to
speak Mathematically, makes an Angle of 90 degrees with the flat sides of the *Wheel*,) and the
Worm-wheel aslope, making an Angle of about
115 degrees with its sides, that is, an Angle of
25 degrees, with a line drawn straight athwart
the outer Edge of the *Wheel*, and that *Teeth* of the
Worm-wheel may gather themselves into the *Grooves*
of the *Worm* in the *Worm-spindle*; the *Worm* on the
Worm-spindle running about 65 degrees aslope from
this Axis, or Perpendicular of the *Worm-spindle*;
the notches you make with the File must be so
wide, as to contain about twice the thickness of
of each *Tooth*: Therefore you may observe, that
the Number of *Teeth* cannot be assign'd, because
the Sizes of all *Jack wheels* are not of equal Diameters, and the Sizes of the *Teeth* must be filed
very square and smooth, as the corners taken off,
and rounded on both sides towards the middle of
the top or end of the *Tooth*, which much helps
the *Teeth* to gather in upon the *Teeth* of the *Nut*,
and the *Worm* on the *Worm-spindle*.

The *Teeth* of the *Wheels* being cut down, and
the whole *Wheel* finish'd, they must be forc'd stiff
and hard upon the square of the *Spindle*, close up
to the Shoulder; which Square being made somewhat longer than the *Cross* of the *Wheel* is thick,
must with a *Cold-Chissel* be cut on the top of that
Square, to make the Iron that comes through the
Square hole of the *Wheel*, spread over the *Cross*
of the *Wheel*, and then that spreading must be
battered with the *Pen* of the Hammer; that it
may stand up stiff against the shoulder of the
Square, on the other side of the *Wheel*; but in
doing

doing this, you muſt be very careful that the
Spindle ſtand exactly Perpendicular to the flat ſides
of your *Wheels*; for ſhould the *Spindle* lean never
ſo little to one, or the other ſide of the *Wheel*, the
the *Wheel* when it is moving in the *Jack-frame*
would not move perpendicular, but wabble towards the *Fore* or *Backſides* of the *Jack-frame,* and
perhaps by this irregular motion, before a revolution of the *Wheel* be perform'd , it would go off
from the length of the *Teeth* of the *Nut.*

Then file the *Spindle-pins* (which are the ends of
the *Spindle,* that go into the Center-holes of the
Fore and *Backſides* of the *Jack-frame*) exactly
round and fit to their Center-holes, and place
them into their proper Center holes. Then try
if the *Wheels* are exactly round on their outer
edges, and that in turning about, their flat ſides
wabble not, but in a revolution keep Parallel to
the *Fore* and *Backſides.* The way Smiths uſe to
try them by is, to turn them about by the *Spindle,*
and holding a piece of Chalk ſteddy to the outer
Limb of the *Wheel,* not letting the Point of the
Chalk ſlip forwards or backwards, or towards the
right or left Hand, for then if the Chalk make a
white ſtroke round the whole *Wheel,* and that
white ſtroke lie exactly Parallel to the two outer
Edges of the *Wheel,* the *Wheel* is not only round,
but ſtands alſo true upon its *Spindle,* that is, Perpendicular to the *Spindle,* and the *Spindle* Perpendicular to the flat of it: But if the Chalk does
not touch round the *Wheel,* you muſt file down ſo
much of the outer Verge of the *Wheel,* where the
Chalk does touch, as will bring down or equalize
the Diameter of the *Wheel* in that place, to the
Diameter of the *Wheel* in the place where it
does not touch; ſo you may conclude the *Wheel*
is round. If the Mark of the Chalk lie not exactly in the middle between the two edges of
the

the *Wheel*, then it is not Perpendicular to the *Spindle*, and you muſt with the Hammer ſet it right, that is Perpendicular, by forcing the *Wheel* over from the ſide it leans too much to, or elſe by forcing the *Spindle*, which is all one; yet this is an help you ought not to rely upon but in caſe of neceſſity; rather be ſure your *Wheel* and *Spindle* ſtand Perpendicular to one another, before you faſten the *Wheel* upon the ſquare of the *Spindle*, for by this help the ſquare on the *Spindle* will be apt to looſen in the ſquare of the *Wheel*, and you will have your *Wheel* to new faſten upon the Square of the *Spindle* again.

As you try'd the *Wheels* with Chalk, ſo you muſt try the *Nut*, the *Worm* and the *Spindle*.

The upper part of the *Worm-ſpindle*, muſt be Fil'd truly round to fit into the *Worm-loop*, that it ſhake not in it, and yet go very eaſily about, without the leaſt ſtopping. At the upper end of this round on the *Worm Spindle*, you muſt file a ſquare to fit the ſquare hole of the *Fly* upon.

The *Shank* of the *Worm-loop* and the *Stud* of the *Worm-ſpindle*, muſt ſtand ſo far off the left ſide of the fore ſide, that the *Teeth* of the *Worm-wheel*, may fall full into the *Grooves* of the *Worm*; for ſo both being cut with the ſame ſlope, the ſlope *Teeth* of the *Worm-wheel* will gather into the ſlope *Grooves* of the *Spindle*, and preſſing upon the *Worm*, drive about the *Worm-ſpindle* and the *Fly*.

The *Fly* is made ſometimes with two, ſometimes with four Arms from the Center, and ſometimes the Arms are made longer, ſometimes ſhorter: The more Arms, and alſo the longer Arms, are to make the *Jack* go ſlower.

There is yet a ſmall matter more of Iron-work about the *Jack*, which is the *Tumbler*; but it lies in the farther end of the *Barrel*, and cannot well

D   be

be defcrib'd without a particular Figure, which therefore I have inferted. As in *Fig.* 2. A the *Barrel*, B the *Main fpindle* coming through the *Barrel*, ^a the Center of the *Tumbler* moving upon the *Center-pin*, which is faften'd into an Ironplate behind the *Barrel.* ^b The *Coller* upon the *Main-fpindle*, from which proceeds a *Tongue*, which paffes through a pretty wide hole at ^c in the *Tumbler*, as far as ^{e d} the *Catch of the Tumbler.* The *Tumbler* moves as aforefaid, upon the Center hole ^a, but receives the *Tongue* through it at ^c, and paffes as far as ^e. This *Tongue* ferves as a *Check* to the *Tumbler*, that it cannot tumble above an Angle of 20 degrees, from the Iron-plate it is faften'd to ; and that the width of its Centerhole, and the width of the *Tongue* paffes through, and the motion of the *Coller* about the *Mainfpindle* allows it ; but were the Center-hole ^a, and its *Center-pin* fit, and the Hole ^c, and the *Tongue* that alfo paffes through it alfo fit, and the *Coller* fixt, it could not move at all. But this play is enough for it, to do the purpofe it is defign'd for. The *Tumbler* is fo plac'd behind the *Barrel*, that while the *Jack line* is winding up upon the *Barrel*, its round britch paffes forwards by all the *Croffes* of the *Main-wheel*, and the *Point* or *Catch* ^d, as then claps it felf fnug or clofe to the Ironplate of the *Barrel*: But when the *Barrel* is turn'd to the contrary way, the weight of the *Catch* in half a revolution of the *Barrel* (let the *Tumbler* be pofited where it will) makes it open and fall from the Iron-plate, and butt againft one or other of the *Croffes* on the *Main-wheel*, and fo thrufts the *Main wheel* about with the *Barrel*.

The *Eye* of the *Winch* or *Winder*, is forg'd as you were taught to forge the *Pin-hole* in the *Crofsgarnet*, *Numb.* II. *fol.* 18. But that was to be a fmall round hole, and therefore you were directly

ly to lay a fmall round piece of Iron or Wyre,
where you intended the Pin hole fhould be, and
lap the other end of your Work over it ; but
this is to be a wide fquare hole, therefore you
muft lay a fquare piece of Iron of your fize,
where the *Eye* of the *Jack-winch* fhall be and lap
or double the other end over it, and Weld and
Work as you were directed. The reft of the *Winch*
is but common *Forging* and *Filing* Work, which
hath been fufficiently taught already.

The Wood-work belonging to the *Jack,* is a
Barrel, a *Spit-wheel* and a *Handing of the Winch* ;
which being *Turners* Work, I fhall fay nothing
to, till I come to the Art of *Turning.* Only
thofe *Wheels* that have more than one *Groove* in
them, are call d Two, Three, *&c. Struck-wheels,*
in Workmens corrupting Language ; but I fuppofe, originally two *Stroak,* three *Stroak-wheels,*
&c. from the number of *Grooves* that are in
them.

The Excellencies of a good *Jack* are, 1. That
the *Jack-frame* be Forg'd and Fil d Square, and
conveniently Strong, well fet together, and will
Screw clofe and tight up. 2. That the *Wheels* be
Perpendicularly, and ftrongly fix'd on the Squares
of the *Spindles.* 3. That the *Teeth* be evenly cut
and well fmooth'd, and that the *Teeth* of the *Worm-
wheel* fall evenly into the *Groove* of the *Worm.*
4. That the *Spindle Pins* fhake not between
the *Fore* and *Backfides,* nor are too big, or too
little for their Center holes.

[a] The *fquare Bore,* is a fquare Steel Point or
Shank well Temper'd, fitted into a fquare
Socket in an Iron *Wimble* : It is defcrib'd,
Fig. 3. Its ufe is to open a Hole and make it
truly round and fmooth within ; when you
ufe it, you muft fet the Head againft your

Breaft

Breaſt, and put the Point of the *ſquare Bore*
into the Hole you punch'd or would open,
and turning the Handle about, you with it
turn about the Shank of the *ſquare Bore*,
whoſe Edges cut away the Irregularities
of the Iron made in the Punching.   But you
muſt thruſt or lean hard with your Breaſt
againſt the Head of the *ſquare Bore*, that it
may cut the faſter : And you muſt be ſure to
guide the *ſquare Bore* truly ſtraight forwards
in the Hole, leſt the Hole be wrought aſlope
in the Iron.

ᵇ To *open an Hole*, is in Smith's Language, to
make the Hole wider.

ᶜ A *Dufftail*, is a Figure made in the form of a
Doves-tail, and is us'd by many other Handy-
crafts, as well as Smiths, but moſt eſpecially
by Joyners, as I ſhall ſhew, when I come to
Joynery.

ᵈ A *Jack-file*, is a broad File ſomewhat thin on
both Edges, and ſtronger in the Middle.

The manner of making Molds *to Caſt* Leaden-
Bullets *in.*

I Inſert the making of *Bullet molds*, becauſe
there is ſome ſort of Work in them different
from what hath yet been taught.   The Handles,
and the Heads are Forg'd as other Work, but
the two concave Hemiſphers, are firſt Punch'd
with a round ended *Punch*, of the ſhape and almoſt of the ſize you intend the Bullet ſhall
be.   They muſt be Punch'd deep enough at the
Forge with a *blood red heat* ;   then are the Edges
of the Chaps Filed flat, firſt with a common File
the common way, but afterwards with an uſing
File as Workmen call it.   The uſing File, is a
long and broad File, exactly flat on both its cut
ſides, having a ſquare Iron handle down out at
one

one end with an hole in it; but the Handle is
not to hold it by when you ufe it, but the hole
in it to go over a pin you hang it upon, when
you do not ufe it. When you ufe it, you muſt
lay it flat upon the Work bench, with its Handle,
from you, and you muſt take care that it lies folid and fteady, left when you Work upon it, it
flip from you; therefore you may ftrike a Nail
in at the hole in the Handle, a little way into
the Work bench, that you may draw it again,
when you have done with the *ufing File,* you may
drive in a fmall Tack on each fide the *ufing File,* to
keep it fteddy or you may Tack down two fmall
thin boards on either fide and rip them off again
when you have done. Your *ufing File* lying thus
ftraight and fteddy before you, lay the Chaps of
one half of the *Mold* flat upon the hither end of
the *ufing File,* and holding your two Thumbs, and
your two Fore-fingers upon the Head of the
Mold, thruſt your Work hard down from you
the whole length of the *Ufing-file,* then draw
your Work lightly back, and thruſt it again hard
from you; retire thefe thruſts thus, till upon the
Chaps of the *Mold,* you can fee no irregularities,
or the File-ftroaks of the common File left, fo
may you be fure that the Chaps of the *Mold* is
truly flat. Do the like by the other half of the
Mold.

Now you muſt try whether each of thefe concaves be an exact half-round; thus you may defcribe an Arch a little more than a Semi-circle,
juſt of the Diameter of the *Bullet,* upon the end
of a thin piece of Brafs-latin, draw a ftraight
Line through the Center, and the Arch on both
fides it, for the limits of the Semi-circle; File
very curioufly all the Brafs away on the end, juſt
to this Semi-circle, and juſt to the Diametral-

line,

line, on either fide of the Semi-circle, fo have
you a convex Semi-circle: Put this convex Semi-
circle into the Concave *Molds*, if it fits them fo
as the Convex reaches juſt the bottom of the
Molds, when its Shoulder touches juſt the Chaps
of the *Mold*, they are each a true concave He-
mifphere. But if the Shoulder of the Convex
(that is, a Diametral-line prolong'd) rides upon
the Chaps of the Concave, and the bottom of
the Convex touch not the bottom of the Concave, the Concave is Punch'd too deep, and muſt
have its Chaps rubb'd upon the *Uſing-file* again,
till it comply with the Convex. Then put into
the two Concaves a round *Bullet*, that will juſt
fill them both, and pinching the Heads of the
Mold cloſe together in a *Vice*, with the *Bullet* in
it, drill an hole through both the handles of the
Joint. The reaſon why the *Bullet* is put into the
Mold is, becauſe the Chaps of the two Halves
ſhould lie exactly upon one another, whilſt the
hole for the *Joint* is drilling. Then fit a Rivet-
rin for this hole, and Rivet them together, but
not ſo hard, but that the *Mold* may open and ſhut
pretty eaſie, and yet go true. Then take the
Bullet out, and File in each half of the Head,
half a round hole directly againſt one another for
the ᵃ *Gear*, which two half holes, when the *Mold*
is ſhut, will make one round hole.

You may now try with Clay, or by caſting a
leaden *Bullet* in it, whether it be exactly round
or no; for making a true round hole in a thin
piece of Braſs, juſt of the Circumference of the
Chaps, you may try if the *Caſt-bullet* will juſt paſs
thro', and alſo fill that hole when the *Bullet* is
turn'd every way; which if it do, you may
conclude the *Mold* is true. This thin piece of
Braſs, with a round hold in it, is call'd a *Sizer*.

But

But the infide wants cleanfing, for hitherto it is only Punch'd. Therefore you muft provide a ᵇ *Bullet-bore*, with which you may bore the infide of each half to clear it. Or if they be not quite deep enough Punch d, you may bore them deeper. You may bore them feverally, or together, by putting the *Bullet-bore* into the *Mold*, fo as the *Shank* may come through the *Geat*.

In this Section you fee, firft the ufe of a *Ufing-file*, an Inftrument of great ufe for a flat Filing ; for by it you may make two pieces of Iron of fomewhat confiderable breadth, fo true, that by laying the two flat fides upon each other, they fhall draw up one another. It is much ufed by *Clock-makers*, *Watch-makers*, *Letter-mold-makers*, and indeed all others that frame Square-work on Iron, Steel or Brafs. Secondly, the ufe of a *Bullet-bore*, which though it be feldom us'd, yet it may ferve not only for *Bullet-molds*, but for other purpofes ; and by altering its fhape into an Oblong, a Cone or Cilinder, you may bore thefe hollow Figures either for *Molds*, or fome other accidental Ufes.

ᵃ A *Geat*, is the hole through which the Mettal runs into the *mold*. The Word is us'd by moft *Founders*.

ᵇ The *Bullet-bore*, is a *Shank* of Steel, having a Steel *Globe* or *Bullet* at one end, juft of your intended *Bullet* fize. This Globular end muft be Hatch'd with a fine cut, by a *File-cutter*, and Harden'd and Temper'd. The end of the *Shank*, this Globular Bore is faftned to, muft be round and fo fmall, that when the *Bullet-bore* is in the *mold*, the *Geat* will eafily receive it. The other end of the *Shank* muft be fitted into the fquare Socket of the *Wimble*, and have a Shoulder to it,

to

to ſtop the Socket from ſliding too far upon
the *Shank*. From this Shoulder, the reſt of
the *Shank* muſt run Tapering down, to the
ſmall end the *Bullet-bore* is faſtned to. You
muſt Work with it, as you were taught to
Work with the *Square-bore*.

Of *Twiſting of the Iron*.

SQuare and flat Bars, ſometimes are by Smiths,
Twiſted for Ornament. It is very eaſily done;
for after the Bar is Square or flat Forg'd (and if
the curioſity of your Work require it truly Fil'd)
you muſt take a *Flame-heat*, or if your Work be
ſmall, but *Blood-red heat*, and you may twiſt it
about, as much or as little as you pleaſe, either
with the *Tongs*, *Vice* or *Hand-vice*, &c.

Of *Caſe-hardning*.

CAſe-hardning is ſometimes us'd by *File-cutters*,
when they make courſe *Files* for Cheapneſs,
and generally moſt *Raſps* have formerly been made
of Iron and *Caſe-hardned*, becauſe it makes the
outſide of them hard. It is us'd alſo by *Gun-
ſmiths*, for Hardning their Barrels; and it is
us'd for *Tobacco-boxes*, *Cod-piece-buttons*, *Heads* for
Walking-ſtaves, &c. And in theſe Caſes, Workmen to ſet a greater value on them in the Buyers
eſteem, call them *Steel-barrels*, *Steel-tobacco-boxes*,
Steel-buttons, *Steel-heads*, &c. But Iron thus
hardned takes a better Poliſh and keeps the Poliſh much longer and better, than if the Iron
were not *Caſe hardned*. The manner of *Caſe-
hardning* is thus, Take *Cow-horn* or *Hoof*, dry it
thoroughly in an Oven, and then beat it to Powder, put about the ſame quantity of Bay-Salt to it,
and mingle them together with ſtale Chamberly,
or elſe White-wine-vinegar. Lay ſome of this
mixture upon the Loam, made as you were
                                                    taught

taught *Numb.* I. *fol.* 13. And cover your Iron all
over with it; then wrap the Loam about all, and
lay it upon the Hearth of the Forge to dry and
harden : When it is dry and hard, put it into
the Fire and blow up the Coals to it, till the
whole Lump have juſt a *Blood-red-heat*, but no
higher, left the quality of your mixture burn
away and leave the Iron as ſoft as at firſt. Then
take it out and quench it : Or, inſtead of Loam,
you may wrap it up in Plate Iron, ſo as the mixture may touch every part of your Work, and
blow the Coals to it, as aforeſaid.

Of ſeveral ſorts of Steel in common uſe among
Smiths.

THE difficulty of getting good Steel makes
many Workmen (when by good hap they
light on it) commend that Country-Steel for
beſt, from whence that Steel came. Thus I
have found ſome cry up *Flemiſh-ſteel,* others *Swediſh, Engliſh, Spaniſh, Venice,* &c. But according
to my Obſervation and common Conſent of the
moſt ingenious Workmen, each Country pro-
duces almoſt indifferently good and bad ; yet
each Country doth not equally produce ſuch Steel,
as is fit for every particular purpoſe, as I ſhall
ſhew you by and by. But the ſeveral ſorts of
Steel, that are in general uſe here in *England,*
are the *Engliſh,* the *Flemiſh,* the *Swediſh,* the
Spaniſh and the *Venice-ſteel.*

The *Engliſh-ſteel* is made in ſeveral places in
England, as in *Yorkſhire, Glouceſterſhire, Suſſex,* the
Wild of Kent, &c. But the beſt is made about
the *Forreſt of Dean,* it breaks Fiery, with ſomewhat a courſe Grain But if it be well wrought
and proves ſound, it makes good Edge-tools,
Files and Punches. It will work well at the Forge,
and take a good Heat.

The

The *Flemiſh-ſteel* is made in *Germany,* in the Country of *Stiermark* and in the *Land of Luyck* : From thence brought to *Colen,* and is brought down the River *Rhine* to *Dort,* and other parts of *Holland* and *Flanders,* ſome in *Bars* and ſome in *Gads,* and is therefore by us call'd *Flemiſh-ſteel,* and ſometimes *Gad-ſteel.* It is a tough ſort of Steel, and the only Steel us'd for Watch-ſprings. It is alſo good for Punches ; File-cutters alſo uſe it to make their Chiſſels of, with which they cut their Files. It breaks with a fine Grain, works well at the Forge, and will take a weld-ing Heat.

I cannot learn that any Steel comes from *Swe-den*, but from *Dantzick* comes ſome which is call'd *Swediſh-ſteel*: It is much of the ſame Qua-lity and Fineſs with *Flemiſh-ſteel.*

The *Spaniſh-ſteel* is made about *Biſcay.* It is a fine ſort of Steel, but ſome of it is very dif-ficult to work at the Forge, becauſe it will not take a good Heat ; and it ſometimes proves very unſound, as not being well *curried,* that is well wrought. It is too quick (as Workmen call it) that is, too brittle for Springs or Punches, but makes good fine Edg'd-tools.

Venice-ſteel is much like *Spaniſh ſteel,* but much finer, and Works ſomewhat better at the Forge. It is us'd for Razors, Chirurgion's In-ſtruments, Gravers, *&c.* Becauſe it will come to a fine and thin Edge. Razor makers gene-rally clap a ſmall Bar of *Venice-ſteel* between two ſmall Bars of *Flemiſh-ſteel*, and ſo Work or Weld them together, to ſtrengthen the back of the Razor, and keep it from crack-ing.

There

There is another fort of Steel, of higher commendations than any of the forgoing forts. It is call'd *Damafcus-fteel*; 'tis very rare that any comes into *England* unwrought, but the *Turkifh-Cymeters* are generally made of it. It is moft difficult of any Steel to Work at the Forge, for you fhall fcarce be able to ftrike upon a Blood-heat, but it will *Red-fear*; infomuch that thefe *Cymeters* are, by many Workmen, thought to be caft Steel. But when it is wrought, it takes the fineft and keeps the ftrongeft Edge of any other Steel. Workmen fet almoft an ineftimable value upon it to make Punches, Cold-punches, &c. of. We cannot learn where it is made, and yet as I am inform'd, the Honourable Mr. *Boyl* hath been very careful and induftrious in that enquiry; giving it in particular charge to fome Travellers to *Damafcus*, to bring home an Account of it: But when they came thither they heard of none made there, but were fent about 50 Miles into the Country and then they were told about 50 Miles farther than that : So that no certain Account could be gain'd where it is made. *Kirman* towards the Ocean affords very fine Steel, of which they make Weapons highly priz'd ; for a *Cymeter* of that Steel, will cut through an Helmet with an eafie blow. *Geog. Rect. fol.* 279.

The Rule to know good Steel by.

BReak a little piece of the end of the Rod, and obferve how it breaks ; for good Steel breaks fhort of all Gray, like froft work Silver. But in the breaking of the bad you will find fome veins of Iron fhining and doubling in the Steel.

Of

Of *Nealing of Steel.*

HAving chofe your Steel and forg'd it to your
intended fhape, if you are either to File
Engrave or to Punch upon it, you ought to
Neal it firft, becaufe it will make it fofter and
confequently work eafier. The common way
is to give it a *Blood-red-heat* in the Fire, then
take it out, and let it cool of it felf.

There are fome pretenders to know how to
make Steel as foft as Lead; but fo oft as my
Curiofity has prompted me to try their preten-
ded Proceffes, fo oft have they fail'd me ; and
not only me, but fome others, careful Obfer-
vers. But the way they moft boaft of, is the
often heating the Iron or Steel in red-hot Lead,
and letting it cool of it felf with the Lead. I
have many times try'd this without any other
fuccefs, than that it does make Iron or Steel as
foft as if it were well Neal'd the common way,
but no fofter : And could it be otherwife, the
fmall Iron Ladles, that Letter-founders ufe to
the cafting of Printing Letters, would be very
foft indeed ; for their Iron Ladles are kept con-
ftantly Month after Month in melting Mettal,
whereof the main Body is Lead, and when they
caft fmall Letters, they keep their Mettal red-
hot ; and I have known them many times left in
the Mettal and cool with it, as the Fire has gone
out of it felf ; but yet the Iron Ladles have
been no fofter , than if they had been well
Neal'd the common way. But perhaps thefe
Pretenders mean the Iron or Steel fhall be as foft
as Lead, when the Iron or Steel is red-hot ; if
fo, we may thank them for nothing.

But

But that which makes Steel a very ſmall matter ſofter than the common way of Nealing is, by covering Steel with a courſe Powder of Cow-Horns, or Hoofs, or Rams-Horns , and ſo in-cloſing it in a Loam: Then put the whole Lump into a Wooden Fire to heat red-hot and let it lie in the Fire till the Fire go out of it ſelf, and the Steel cool with the Fire.

Of *Hardning and Tempering Steel.*

ENngliſh, *Flemiſh* and *Swediſh-ſteel*, muſt have a pretty high heat given them, and then ſuddenly quench in Water to make them very hard ; but *Spaniſh* and *Venice-ſteel* will need but a Blood-red-heat, and then when they are quench'd in Water, will be very hard. If your Steel be too hard, that is to brittle, and it be an edg'd or pointed Inſtrument you make, the edge or point will be very ſubject to break ; or if it be a Spring, it will not bow, but with the leaſt bend-ing it will ſnap aſſunder : Therefore you muſt *let it down* (as Smiths ſay) that is, make it ſofter, by *tempering* it: The manner is thus, take a piece of Grin-ſtone or Whet-ſtone and rub hard upon your Work to take the black Scurf off it, and brighten it ; then let it heat in the Fire, and as it grows hotter you will ſee the Colour change by degrees, coming to a light goldiſh Colour, then to a dark goldiſh Colour, and at laſt to a blew Colour ; chooſe which of theſe Colours your Work requires, and then quench it ſuddenly in Water. The light goldiſh Colour is for Files, Cold-chiſſels and Punches, that Punch into Iron and Steel: The dark goldiſh Colour for Punches to uſe on Braſs, and generally for moſt Edge-tools: The blew Colour gives the Temper to Springs in general, and is alſo us'd to Beautifie both Iron and Steel ; but then Workmen ſome-times

times grind *Indico* and *Sallad-oyl* together, and rub that mixture upon it, with a woollen Rag, while it is heating, and let it cool of it felf.

There is another fort of *Hardning,* call'd *Hammer-hardning,* It is moft us'd on Iron or Steel Plates, for *Dripping pans, Saws, Straight-Rulers,* &c. It is perform'd only, with well Hammering of the Plates, which both fmooths them, and beats the Mettal firmer into its own Body, and fomewhat hardens it.

The manner of Forging Steel, either for Edge-tools, Punches, Springs, *&c.* Is (the feveral fhapes confider'd) the fame with forging Iron: Only this general Rule obferve, from an old *Englifh* Verfe us'd among Smiths, when they Forge Edge-tools,

> *He that will a good Edge win,*
> *Muft Forge thick and Grind thin.*

The End of Smithing.

MECHA-

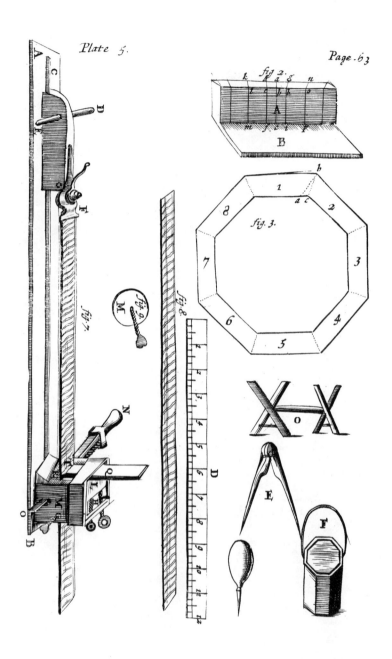

Plate 5.

Page. 63

fig. 2.

A

B

fig. 3.

b

1

a c

8

2

7

3

6

4

5

M

fig. 9.

fig. 8.

D

O

E

F

fig. 7.

MECHANICK EXERCISES;

OR,

The Doctrine of *Handy-Works*

The Art of JOINERY.

Definition.

JOINERY, *is an Art Manual, whereby several Pieces of Wood are so fitted and join'd together by* Straight-line, Squares, Miters *or any* Bevel, *that they shall seem one intire Piece.*

Explanation.

By *Straight-Lines* I mean that which in Joyner's Language is call'd a Joint, That is, two Pieces of Wood are Shot (that is Plained,) or else they are Pared, that is, the irregularities that hinder the closing of the two Pieces are cut off with a Pairing-chissel. They are Shot or Pared (as I said) so exactly straight, that when they are set upon one another, light shall not be discern'd betwixt them. This they call Shooting of a Joint, or Paring to a Joint, because these two Pieces are with Glew commonly join'd together, either to make a Board broad enough for their purpose, or to ª Clamp one piece of Wood to the end of another piece of Wood to keep it from Casting or Warping.

By

By *Squares*, I mean the making of Frames, either for Door-cafes or fuch like, which is the Framing of two pieces of Wood athwart two other pieces of Wood, fo as the four Angles of the Frame may comply with the *Square* marked D.

By *Miters* are meant the joining of two pieces of Wood, fo as the Joint makes half a Square, and does comply with the *Miter-fquare* marked E.

By a *Bevel* is meant any other Angle: As Frames that may be made of *Pentagon, Hexagon, Octagon,* &c. Figures.

§ 1. *The Names of Joyners Tools defcrib'd, in Plate IV.*

A A Work-bench. *b* The Hook in it, to lay Boards or other *b* Stuff flat againft, whilft they are *c* Trying or Plaining. *c* The Bench-Screw (on its hither fide) to Screw Boards in, whilft the Edges of them are Plaining or *d* Shooting; and then the other edge of the Board is fet upon a Pin or Pins (if the Board be fo long as to reach the other Leg) put into the Holes marked *a a a a a* down the Legs of the Bench; which Pin or Pins may be removed into the higher or lower holes, as the breadth of the Board fhall require: So then, the Bench-fcrew keeps the Board clofe to the edge of the Bench, and the Pins in the Legs keep it to its height, that it may ftand fteddy whilft the other edge is working upon: For in the Shooting of a Joint, if the Board keeps not its exact pofition, but fhakes or trembles under the Plain, your Joint will very hardly be truly ftraight. *d* The Hold-faft, let pretty loofe into round holes marked *b b b b b b,* in the Bench: Its Office is to keep the Work faft upon the Bench, whilft you either Saw, Tennant,

Mor-

Mortefs, or fometimes *Plain* upon it, *&c.* It performs this Office with the knock of an *Hammer*,
or *Mallet*, upon the *head* of it ; for the *Beak* of it
being made crooked downwards, the end of the
Beak falling upon the flat of the *Bench*, keeps the
head of the *Hold-faft* above the flat of the *Bench*,
and the *hole* in the *Bench* the *Shank* is let into being
bored ftraight down, and wide enough to let the
Hold-faft play a little, the *head* of the *Hold-faft* being
knockt, the point of the *Beak* throws the *Shank*
a-flope in the *hole* in the *Bench*, and preffes its
back-fide hard againft the edge of the *hole* on the
upper Superficies of the *Bench*, and its fore-fide
hard againft the opperfite fide of the under Superficies of the *Bench*, and fo by the point of the *Beak*,
the *Shank* of the *Hold-faft* is wedged between the
upper edge, and its opperfite edge of the round
hole in the *Bench*. Sometimes a double *Screw* is
fixed to the fide of the *Bench*, as at ᵍ ; or fometimes its farther *Cheek* is laid an edge upon the
flat of the *Bench*, and faftned with an *Hold-faft*,
or, fometimes, two on the *Bench*. *e* A *Mallet*.

§. 2. BBBBBBBB *Plains* of feveral Sorts: as,

B 1. A Fore *Plain*. *a* The *Tote*. *b* The *Mouth*.
c The *Wedge*. *d* The *Iron*. *e* The *Sole*.
f The *Fore-end*. *g* The *Britch*. *f g h* The *Stock*.
All together *A Plane*. It is called the *Fore Plane*
becaufe it is ufed before you come to work either
with the *Smooth Plane*, or with the *Joynter*. The
edge of its *Iron* is not ground upon the ftraight, as
the *Smooth Plane*, and the *Joynter* are, but rifes
with a Convex-Arch in the middle of it ; for its
Office being to prepare the Stuff for either the
Smoothing Plane, or the *Joynter*, Workmen fet the
edge of it *ᶜ Ranker* than the edge either of the
Smoothing Plane, or the *Joynter* ; and fhould the
Iron of the *Plane* be ground to a ftraight edge,

and it be fet never fo little Ranker on one end of
the edge than on the other, the *Ranker* end would
(bearing as then upon a point) in working, dig
Gutters on the Surface of the *Stuff* ; but this *Iron*
(being ground to a Convex-Arch) though it
fhould be fet a little *Ranker* on one end of its edge
than on the other, would not make Gutters on
the Surface of the *Stuff*, but (at the moft)
little hollow dawks on the *Stuff*, and that more
or lefs, according as the *Plane* is ground more or
lefs Arching. Nor is it the Office of this *Plane* to
fmooth the *Stuff*, but only (as I faid) to prepare
it, that is, to take off the irregular Rifings, whether on the fides, or in the middle, and therefore
it is fet fomewhat *Ranker*, that it may take the
Irregularities the fooner off the *Stuff*, that the
Smoothing Plane, or the *Joynter*, may afterwards
the eafier work it *Try*. The manner of *Trying*
fhall be taught, when I come to Treat of the ufe
of the *Rule*.

You muft note, that as I told yon in *Smithing*,
Num. I. *fol.* 14, 15, 16. it was the Office of the
courfe tooth'd File to take off the prominent Irregularities the *Hammer* made in the *Forging*, &c. and
that you were not to *file* them more away than
you need, fo the fame Caution is to be given you
in the ufing of this *fore Plane* in *Joynery*, for the
reafon there alledged in *Smithing*, whether, to a-
void Repetition, I refer you ; only with this Confideration, that there *Iron*, or *Steel*, was the matter wrought upon, and there a *courfe File* the *Tool* ;
but now *Wood* is the matter, and a *Courfe*, or *Fore-*
Plane, the *Tool*.

§. 3 Of *fetting* the *Iron*.

WHen you *fet* the *Iron* of the *Fore-Plane*, confider the *Stuff* you are to work upon, *viz.*
Whether it be *hard* or *foft*, or *Curling*, as *Joyners*
call

O

call *Crofs grain'd Stuff* : If it be *hard* or *curling*, you muſt not *ſet* the *Iron* veay *rank*, becauſe a Man's ſtrength will not cut deep into hard *Wood* ; and if it be not hard *Wood*, but *curling*, or *knotty*, and the *Iron Rank-ſet*, you may indeed work with it till you come to ſome *Knot*, or *Curl*, but then you may either tear your *Stuff*, or break the edge of your *Iron* ; therefore you may perceive a reaſon to *ſet* the *Iron fine* for *curling*, and *knotty Stuff*.

But if you ask me how *rank* your *Iron* ought to be ſet ? I anſwer, If your Wood be *ſoft*, and your *Stuff free*, and *frowy*, that is, evenly temper'd all the way, you may *ſet* the *Iron* to take a ſhaving off the thickneſs of an old coined Shilling, but ſcarce thicker ; whereas, if your *Stuff* be *hard*, o *curling*, or *knotty*, you ſhall ſcarce be able to take a ſhaving off the thickneſs of an old Groat. Therefore you muſt examine the Temper of your *Stuff*, by eaſy Trials, how the *Plane* will work upon it, and *ſet* your *Iron* accordingly. And obſerve this as a General Rule, that the *Iron* of the *Fore-Plane* is, for the firſt working with it, to be *ſet* as *rank* as you can make good work with ; and that for ſpeed ſake.

If your *Iron* be *ſet* too *rank*, knock with an *Hammer* upon the *Britch* of the *Stock*, and afterwards upon the *Wedge* ; for this knocking upon the *Britch*, if you knock hard enough, 'twill raiſe the *Iron* a little, and *ſet* it *fine* ; if you knock not hard enough, you muſt knock again, till the *Iron* do riſe ; but if you knock too hard, it will raiſe the *Iron* ſo much, that its edge will riſe above the *Sole* into the *Mouth* of the *Stock*, and conſequently not touch the *Stuff* : Therefore you muſt knock ſoftly at firſt, till, by trials, you find the *Iron* riſes to a convenient *fineneſs*. But as this knocking on the *Britch* raiſes the *Iron*, ſo it alſo raiſes and looſens the *Wedge* ; therefore (as aforeſaid) whenever

you knock upon the *Britch*, you muſt alſo knock
upon the *Wedge*, to ſoften the *Iron* again.

If you have raiſed the edge of the *Iron* too *fine*,
you muſt knock ſoftly upon the head of the *Iron*,
and then again upon the *Wedge*, and this you may
ſometimes do ſeveral times, till you fit your *Iron*
to a convenient *fineneſs*.

When you have occaſion to take your *Iron* out
of the *Stock* to *rub* it, that is, to *whet* it, you may
knock pretty ſmart Blows upon the *Stock*, between the *Mouth* and the *Fore-end*, to looſen the
Wedge, and conſequently the *Iron*.

Theſe ways of *ſetting*, are uſed to all other
Planes, as well as *Fore-planes*.

In the uſing of this, and indeed, all other
Planes, you muſt begin at the hinder end of the
Stuff, the Grain of the Wood lying along the
length of the *Bench*, and Plane forward, till you
come to the fore-end, unleſs the *Stuff* proves
Croſs-grain'd, in any part of its length ; for then
you muſt turn your *Stuff* to Plane it the contrary
way, ſo far as it runs *Croſs-grain'd*, and in Planeing, you muſt, at once, lean pretty hard upon the
Plane, and alſo thruſt it very hard forwards, not
letting the *Plane* totter to, or from you-wards,
till you have made a Stroak the whole length of
the *Stuff*. And this ſometimes, if your *Stuff* be
long, will require your making two or three ſteps
forwards, e er you come to the fore-end of the
Stuff : But if it do, you muſt come back, and begin again at the farther end, by the ſide of the
laſt plan'd Stroak, and ſo continue your ſeveral
lays of Planeing, till the whole upſide of the *Stuff*
be planed.

And if the *Stuff* be broad you are to Plane upon, and it *warp* a little with the *Grain*, or be any
ways crooked in the breadth, you muſt then turn
the *Grain* athwart the *Work-bench*, and Plane upon
the

Plate (4)

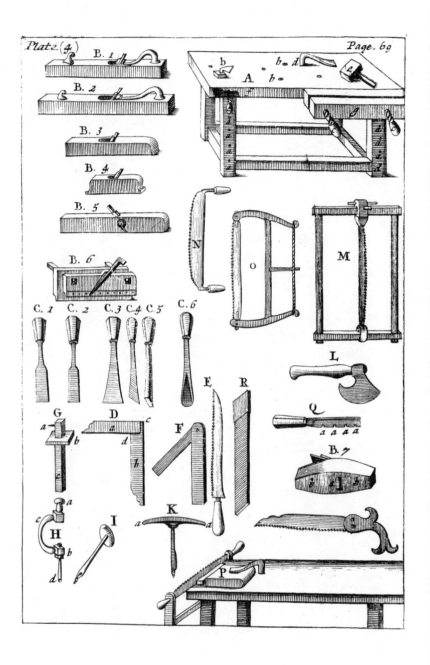

the *Crofs-grain.* For, if your work be hollow in the middle, you muſt Plane both the Bearing ſides thinner, till they come to a *Try* with the middle. Then turn the other ſide of your work, and working ſtill *Crofs-grain'd,* work away the middle, till it come *Try* with the two ſides.

This way of *Crofs-grain'd* working, is, by Work-men, called *Traverfing.*

Thus have you, in general, the uſe of all the other *Planes* : But the uſe of thoſe Planes, that are deſigned for other particular purpoſes, I ſhall ſhew, as they come in Order.

§. 4. Of the *Joynter.* B. 2.

THE *Joynter* is made ſomewhat longer than the *Fore-plane,* and hath its *Sole* perfectly ſtraight from end to end. Its Office is to follow the *Fore-plane*, and to *ſhoot* an edge perfectly ſtraight, and not only an edge, but alſo a Board of any thickneſs; eſpecially when a *Joynt* is to be *ſhot.* Therefore the Hand muſt be carried along the whole length, with an equal bearing weight, and ſo exactly even, and upright to the edges of the Board, that neither ſide of the *Plane* encline either inward or outwards, but that the whole breadth be exactly ſquare on both its ſides; ſuppoſing its ſides ſtraight : ſo will two edges of two Boards, when thus *ſhot*, lie ſo ex-actly flat and ſquare upon one another, that light will not be difcerned betwixt them. But yet it is counted a piece of good Workmanſhip in a *Joyner,* to have the Craft of bearing his Hand ſo curiouſly even, the whole length of a long Board; and yet it is but a ſleight to thoſe, Practice hath inur'd the Hand to. The *Joynter* is alſo uſed to *Try* Tables with, (large or ſmall) or other ſuch broad Work; and then *Joyners* work, as well up-on the *Traverſe* with it, as with the Grain of the

E 3 Wood,

Wood, and also Angularly, or Corner-wise, that they may be the more assur'd of the flatness of their Work.

Its *Iron* must be *set* very *fine*, so fine, that when you wink with one Eye, and set that end the straight side of the *Iron* is next to the other Eye, there appears a little above an hairs breadth of the edge above the Superficies of the *sole* of the *Plane*, and the length of the edge must lie perfectly straight with the flat breadth of the *sole* of the *Plane*: For the *Iron* being then well wedg'd up, and you working with the *Plane* thus *set*, have the greater assurance that the *Iron* cannot run too deep into the *Stuff*, and consequently you have the less danger that the *Joynt* is wrought out of straight.

§. 5. The Use of the *Strike-block*.

THe *Strike-block* marked B 3. is a *Plane* shorter than the *Joynter*, having its *sole* made exactly flat, and straight, and is used for the *shooting* of a short *Joynt*; because it is more handy than the long *Joynter*. It is also used for the framing, and fitting the Joynts of *Miters* and *Bevels*; but then it is used in a different manner from other *Planes*: For if the *Miter* and *Bevel* you are to fit be small, you must hold it very steddy in your left hand, with the *sole* of it upwards, and its fore-end towards your right hand: and you must hold your work in your right hand very steddy: Then apply the sawn *Miter*, or sawn *Bevel* at the end of your *Stuff*, to the fore-end of the *Strike-block*, and so thrust it hard and upright forwards, till it pass over the edge of the *Iron*, so shall the edge of the *Iron*, with several of these thrusts continued, cut, or plane off your *stuff* the roughness that the *Teeth* of your Saw made: But if your work be so big that you cannot well weild

it

it in your right hand, you muſt ſet the end of
your work in the *Bench-ſcrew*, and Plane upon it
with a *ſmoothing Plane.*

§. 6. *The Uſe of the* Smoothing-Plane.

THe *Smoothing-plane* marked B 4. muſt have its
Iron ſet very *fine*, becauſe its Office is to
ſmoothen the work from thoſe Irregularities the
Fore-plane made.

§. 7. *The Uſe of the* Rabbet-Plane.

THe *Rabbet-plane* marked B 5. is to cut part of
the upper edge of a Board, or other *Stuff*,
ſtraight, that is, ſquare down into the Board,
that the edge of another Board alſo cut down in
the ſame manner, may fit and join into the Square
of the firſt Board thus cut away : And when two
Boards are thus *lapped* on the edges over one another ; this *lapping* over is called *Rabbetting.*

The *Rabbet-plane* is alſo ſometimes uſed to ſtrike
a *Facia* in a piece of *Molding* ; as ſhall be ſhewed
in its proper place.

The ſides of the *Iron* are not incloſed in the
Stock of this *Plane*, as the fore-going *Planes* are,
but the *Iron* is full as broad as the *ſtock* is thick,
that the very Angles of the edge of the *Iron* may
not be born off the *Stuff*, to hinder the ſtraight
and ſquare cutting it down : Nor doth it deliver its ſhaving at a *Mouth* on the top of the
Stock as the other *Planes* do : But it hath its
Mouth on the ſides of the *Plane*, and delivers its
ſhavings there. Its *Iron* is commonly about an
Inch broad.

§. 8. *The Uſe of the* Plow.

THe *Plow* marked B 6. is a narrow *Rabbet-
plane*, with ſome Additions to it : *viz.* two
ſquare *Staves*, marked *a a* (yet ſome of them
E 4   have

have the upper edges of them rounded off for the better compliance with the Hand.) Thefe *Staves* are let ftiff through two fquare Morteffes in the *Stock*, marked *b b*. They are about feven or eight Inches long, and ftand ftraight and fquare on the farther fide of the *Stock*; and thefe two *Staves* have fhoulders on the hither fide of the *Stock*, reaching down to the wooden *fole* of the *Plane*, (for there is alfo an *Iron fole* belonging to the *Plow*.) To the bottom of thefe two Shoulders is, Rivitted with Iron Rivets, a *Fence* (as Workmen call it) which comes clofe under the *Wooden fole*, and its depth reaches below the *Iron fole* about half an Inch: Becaufe the *Iron* of the Plow is very narrow, and the fides of it towards the bottom are not to be inclofed in the *Stock*, for the fame reafon that was given in the *Rabbet-plane*; therefore upon the *Stock* is let in, and ftrongly nailed, an Iron Plate of the thicknefs of the Plow-Iron, for Wood of that breadth will not be ftrong enough to endure the force the lower end of the Plow-Iron is put to: This Iron-Plate is almoft of the fame thicknefs that the breadth of a Plow-Iron is. Joyners have feveral *Plows*, for feveral widths of *Grooves*.

The Office of the *Plow* is, to plow a narrow fquare *Groove* on the edge of a Board; which is thus perform'd. The Board is fet an edge with one end in the *Bench-fcrew*, and its other edge upon a Pin, or Pins, put into a Hole, or Holes in the Leg, or Legs of the Bench, fuch an Hole, or Holes, as will, moft conveniently for height, fit the breadth of the Board: Then the *Fence* of the *Plow* is fet to that Diftance off the Iron-Plate of the Plow, that you intend the *Groove* fhall lie off the edge of the Board: As if you would have the *Groove* lie half an Inch off the Board, then the two *ftaves* muft, with the *Mallet*, be knocked

through

through the Morteſſes in the *Stock*, till the *Fence* ſtands half an Inch off the Iron-Plate ; and if the *Staves* are fitted ſtiff enough in the Morteſs of the *Stock*, it will keep at that Diſtance whilſt you Plow the *Groove* : For the *Fence* (lying lower than the *Iron* of the *Plane*) when you ſet the *Iron* of the *Plow* upon the edge of the Board, will lie flat againſt the farther edge of the Board, and ſo keep the *Iron* of the *Plow* all the length of the Board at the ſame Diſtance, from the edge of the Board that the *Iron* of the *Plow* hath from the *Fence.* Therefore your *Plow* being thus fitted, plow the *Groove* as you work with other *Planes*, only as you laid hold on the *Stock* of other *Planes* when you uſe them, now you muſt lay hold of the two *ſtaves* and their *ſhoulders*, and ſo thruſt your Plow forwards, till your *Groove* be made to yonr depth.

If the *Staves* go not ſtiff enough in the Mortefs of the Stock, you muſt ſtiffen them, by knocking a little wooden Wedge between the Staves and their Morteſſes.

§. 9. *Of* Molding-Planes.

THere are ſeveral other *Planes* in uſe amongſt Joyners, called *Molding-planes*; as, the *Round*, the *Hollow*, the *Ogee*, the *Snipes-bill*, the *Rabbet-plane*, the *Grooving-plane*, &c. And of theſe they have ſeveral ſorts, *viz.* from half a quarter of an Inch, to an Inch and a half. They are uſed as other *Planes* are. In the Planeing of Stuff, you muſt uſe *Planes* whoſe *Irons* have different Mountings ; and that according to the hardneſs, or ſoftneſs of the Wood, you are to work upon : For if the Wood be hard, the *Iron* muſt ſtand more upright than it need do, if the Wood be ſoft : For ſoft Wood, as *Deal*, *Pear-tree*, *Maple*, &c. The *Iron* is ſet to make an Angle of 45 Degrees,

grees, with the *Sole* of the *Plane*: But if it be very hard Wood you are to Plane upon, as *Box, Ebony, Lignum Vitæ,* &c. It is set to 80 Degrees, and sometimes quite upright: So that these hard Woods, are, indeed, more properly said to be Scraped, than Planed.

But before you come to use your *Planes,* you must know how to grind, and whet them, for they are not so fitted when they are bought, but every Workman accomodates them to this purpose, as if it be an hard Wood he is to work on, he grinds his *Basil* to a more obtuse Angle, than he would do for soft Wood.

The *Basil,* or Angle, an Iron is ground to, to work on soft Wood is about 12 Degrees, and for hard Wood about 18, or 20 Degrees. Where note, That the more acute, or thinner the *Basil* is, the better and smoother the *Iron* cuts; and the more obtuse and thicker, the stronger the Edge is to work upon hard Work.

§. 10. *Of Grinding and Whetting the Iron, and other* Edge-Tools.

WHen you grind your *Iron,* place your two Thumbs under the *Iron,* and your Fingers of both Hauds upon the *Iron,* and so clap down your *Iron* to the Stone, holding it to that Angle with the Stone you intend the *Basil* shall have: Keep the *Iron* in this Posture, without either mounting, or sinking its ends all the while the *Stone* is turning about; and when you lift the *Iron* off the *Stone,* to see if it be ground to your Mind; if it be not, you must be sure you place the *Iron* again in the same Position on the *Stone* it had before; for else you will make a double *Basil* on your *Iron*: But if it be true set on the *Stone,* and steddily kept to that Position, your *Basil* will be *Hollow,* and the smaller your *Grind-*

stone

ſtone is, the hollower it will be. You may know when it is well Ground, by the evenneſs, and entireneſs of the Edge all the way.

Having ground your *Iron*, you muſt ſmoothen the edge finer with a good *Whet-ſtone*. Thus, hold the edge of your *Iron* upwards in your left Hand, and your *Whet-ſtone* in your right, and having firſt ſpit upon your Stone to wet it, apply it to the *Baſil* of your *Iron*, in ſuch a Poſition, that it may bear upon the whole breadth of the *Baſil*; and ſo working the *Stone* over the *Baſil*, you will quickly wear the courſer grating of the *Grind-ſtone* off the edge on that ſide: Then turn the flat ſide of the *Iron*, and apply the *Stone* flat to it, till you have worn off the courſe gratings of the *Grind-ſtone*, on that ſide too.

Joiners often grind their *Irons* upon a flat *Grind-ſtone* alſo: And then they hold the *Iron* alſo in their Hands, in the ſame Poſture as if it were to be ground on the *Round Grind-ſtone*: Yet then inſtead of keeping the *Iron* on one place of the *Stone*, they thruſt it hard ſtraight forwards, almoſt the length of the *Stone*, and draw it lightlier ſtraight back again, keeping it all the while at the ſame Angle with the Superficies of the *Stone*; and then ſmoothen its edge with the *Whet-ſtone*, as if it had been ground upon the round *Grind-ſtone*. And this they do ſo often, till they have rubbed the hollowneſs of the *Baſil* to a flat, and then they grind it again upon the round *Grind-ſtone*.

This Order and Manner of *Setting*, *Grinding* and *Smoothing* a *Baſil* and *Edge*, is alſo uſed in all other *Edge-tools Joiners* uſe.

§. 10.

§. 10. *Of* Chiſſels *of ſeveral Sorts.* *And firſt of* Formers.

FOrmers marked C 1. C 3. are of ſeveral ſizes. They are called *Formers,* becauſe they are uſed before the *paring Chiſſel,* even as the *fore Plane* is uſed before the *ſmoothing Plane.* The *Stuff* you are to work upon being firſt ſcribed, (as I ſhall ſhew in its proper place) you muſt ſet the edge of the *Former,* a little without the ſcribed Stroak. with its *Baſil* outwards, that it may break, and ſhoulder off the Chips from your Work, as the Edge cuts it. And you muſt bear the *Helve* of the *Former* a little inwards over the *Stuff,* that the *Former* do not at firſt cut ſtraight down, but a little outwards : For, ſhould you venture to cut ſtraight down at the firſt, you might with a negligent, or unluckly knock with the *Mallet,* drive the edge of the *Former* under the work. and ſo cut, before you are a- ware, more off the under ſide than the upper ſide of your Work, and ſo (perchance) ſpoil it. Therefore you may make ſeveral Cuttings, to cut it ſtraight down by little and little, till your Work is made ready for the *paring Chiſ- ſel.* When it is uſed, the *Helve* of it is knockt upon with a *Mallet,* to drive the edge into the *Stuff.*

§. 11. *Of the* Paring-Chiſſel.

THe *Paring-Chiſſel* marked C 2. muſt have a very fine and ſmooth edge : Its Office is to follow the *Former,* and to *pare* off, and *ſmoothen,* the Irregularities the *Former* made.

It is not knockt upon with the *Mallet,* but the Blade is claſped upon the out-ſide of the hin- dermoſt Joints of the fore and little Fingers, by the clutched inſide of the middle and third
Fingers

Fingers of the right Hand, and fo its edge being fet upon the *fcribed line*, and the top of the *Helve* placed againft the hollow of the infide of the right fhoulder, with preffing the fhoulder hard upon the *Helve*, the edge cuts and pares away the Irregularities.

This way of handling, may feem a Prepofterous Pofture to manage an Iron Tool in, and yet the reafon of the Original Contriver of this Pofture is to be approved; For, fhould Workmen hold the *Blade* of the *Paring-Chiffel* in their whole Hand, they muft either hold their Hand pretty near the *Helve*, where they cannot well manage the *Tool*, or they muft hold it pretty near the edge, where the outfide of the Fingers will hide the *fcribed line* they are to *pare* in. But this Pofture, all Workmen are at firft taught, and Practice doth fo inure them to it, that if they would, they could not well leave it.

§. 12. *Of the* Skew-Former.

THe *Skew-Former* marked C 4. is feldom ufed by Joiners, but for cleanfing acute Angles, with its acute Angle on its edge, where the Angles of other *Chiffels* will not fo well come.

§. 13. *Of the* Mortefs-Chiffel.

THe *Mortefs-Chiffel* marked C 5. is a narrow *Chiffel*, but hath its *Blade* much thicker, and confequently ftronger (that it may endure the heavier blows with the *Mallet*) than other *Chiffels* have, fo that in grinding it to an edge, it is ground to a very broad *Bafil* as you may fee in the Figure. Its Office is to cut deep fquare holes, called *Morteffes*, in a piece of Wood. Joiners ufe them of feveral Breadths according as the Breadths of their *Morteffes* may require.

§. 14.

§. 14.   *Of the* Gouge.

THe *Gouge* marked C 6. Is a *Chiſſel* having a round edge, for the cutting ſuch Wood as is to be Rounded, or Hollowed.

Theſe ſeveral ſorts of *Chiſſels* Joiners have of ſeveral Sizes, that they may be accommodated to do ſeveral Sizes of Work.

MECHA.

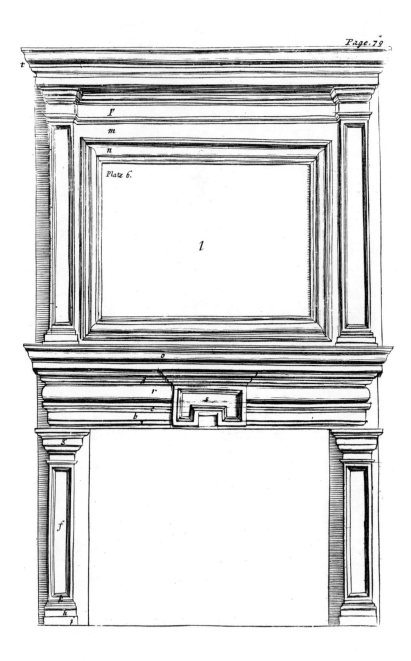

MECHANICK EXERCISES;

O R,

The Doctrine of *Handy-Works*

Continued in the Art of JOINERY.

§. 15: *Of the* Square, *and its Ufe.*

THE *Square*, marked D, is two adjunct Sides of a Geometrical Square. *a* The *Handle.* *b* The *Tongue.* *c* The *Outer Square.* *d* The *Inner Square.* For Joiner's ufe, it is made of two pieces of Wood, the one about an Inch thick, and the other about a quarter of an Inch thick : Thefe two pieces are feverally fhot exactly ftraight, and have each of their Sides parallel to each of their own Sides. The thick Piece (called the Handle) hath a Mortefs in it, as long within a quarter of an Inch, as the thin piece (called the Tongue) is broad, and ftifly fo wide, as to contain the thicknefs of the Tongue. The Tongue is faftned into the Mortefs of the Handle with Glew and wooden Pins, fo as the two outer fides (and then confequently the two inner fides) may ftand at right Angles with one another.

The Reafon why the Handle is fo much thicker than the Tongue, is, becaufe the Handle fhould on either fide become a Fence to the Tongue.

And

And the reason why the Tongue hath not its whole breadth let into the end of the Handle is, because they may with less care strike a line by the side of a thin than a thick piece: For if inftead of holding the Hand upright when they strike a Line, they should hold it never so little inwards, the shank of a Pricker falling against the top edge of the Handle, would throw the Point of a Pricker farther out than a thin Piece would : To avoid which Inconvenience, the Tongue is left about half an Inch out of the end of the Handle.

Another Reason is, That if with often striking the Pricker against the Tongue it becomes ragged, or uneven, they can with less trouble Plane it again when the Stuff is all the way of an equal strength, than they can, if Crofs-grain'd Shoulders be added to any part of it.

Its use is for the striking of Lines square either to other Lines, or to straight sides, and to try the squareness of their Work by ; As if they would strike a Line square to a side they have already shot: They apply the inside of the Handle close to the side shot, and lay the Tongue flat upon the Work, than by the outerside of the Tongue, they draw with a Pricker a straight Line : This is called *Striking,* *or drawing of a Square.* Or, if they would Try the squareness of a Piece of Stuff shot on two adjoining sides, they apply the insides of the Handle and Tongue to the outsides of the Stuff, and if the outsides of the Stuff do all the way agree in Line with the insides of the Square, it is true Square. Or if they would try the inward squareness of Work, they apply the two outsides of the Square to the insides of the Work.

§. 16.

§. 16. *The manner of* Plaining *and* Trying *a piece of Stuff-fquare.*

WE will take, for Example, a Piece of Stuff called a Quarter, which is commonly two Inches thick, four Inches broad, and feven Foot long. To plane this Square, lay one of its broad Sides upon the Bench, with one of its ends fhov'd pretty hard into the Teeth of the Bench-hook, that it may lie the fteddier. Then with the Fore-Plane, as you were taught, § 2. *Numb.* 2. Plane off the roughnefs the Saw made at the Pit, and work that fide of the Quarter as ftreight in its length and breadth as you can with the Fore-Plane ; which you may give a pretty good guefs at, if the edge of the Iron have born all the way upon the Work, yet you may try by taking up your Work, and applying one end of it to one Eye, whilft you wink with the other, and obferve if any Hollow, or Dawks be in the length ; if not, you may conclude it pretty true: For the Work thus held, the Eye will difcern pretty near-ly. Or, for more certainty, you may apply the edge of the two-foot Rule, or rather a Rule fhot the full length of the Quarter to your Work, and if it agree all the way with the Rule, you may conclude it is ftraight in length. But if you find it not ftraight, you muft ftill with the Fore-Plane work off thofe Rifings that bear the edge of the Rule off any part of the Stuff: Then try if the Breadth be pretty ftraight ; if it be, (the Dawks the roughnefs the Fore-plane made excepted) the firft office of the Fore-plane is perform'd : If it be not, you muft ftraighten the Breadth as you did the Length.

But tho' this Quarter be thus plained ftraight in length and breadth, yet becaufe the Iron of the Fore-plane for its firft working the Stuff is fet

F Rank,

Rank, and therefore makes great Dawks in the Stuff, you muſt ſet the Iron of your Fore-plane finer, as you were taught, §. 3. *Numb.* 2. and with it then work down even almoſt to the bottom of thoſe Dawks: then try it again, as before, and if you find it try all the way, you may, with the Jointer, or Smoothing-plane, but rather with the Jointer, go over it again, to work out the irregularities of the fine Fore plane: For the Iron of the Fore-plane being ground to a Riſing in the middle, as has been ſhew'd, §. 2. *Numb.* 2. though it be very fine ſet, will yet leave ſome Dawks in the Stuff for the Jointer, or Smoothing-plane, to work out. Thus the firſt ſide of the Quarter will be finiſhed.

Having thus tryed one ſide of the Quarter ſtraight and flat, apply the inſide of the Handle to it, and if one of the adjoining ſides of the Quarter, comply alſo with the inſide of the Tongue all the way, you need only ſmooth that adjoining ſide: But if it do not ſo comply, that is, if it be not ſquare to the firſt ſide, which you will know by the riding of the inſide of the Tongue upon one of the Edges; or ſome other part between the Edges, you muſt, with the Fore-plane Rank-ſet, plain away that Stuff which bears off the inſide of the Tongue from complying all the way with it. But if the Riſings be great, you may, for quickneſs, hew away the Riſings with the Hatchet: but then you muſt have a care you let not the edge of your Hatchet cut too deep into the Stuff, leſt you either ſpoil your Stuff, by making it unſizeable, if it be already ſmall enough; or if it have ſubſtance enough, make your ſelf more labour to get out thoſe Hatchet-ſtroaks with the Plane than you need. Then take off the roughneſs the Hatchet made with the Fore-plane Rank-ſet, then fine ſet, and
laſt

laſt of all with the Jointer, or Smoothing-plane: So is the ſecond ſide alſo finiſhed.

To work the third ſide, ſet the Oval of the Gage exactly to that width from the Gage, that you intend the Breadth of the Quarter (when wrought) ſhall have, which, in this our Example, is four Inches, but will be ſomewhat leſs, becauſe working it true will diminiſh the Stuff: Therefore ſliding the Oval on the Staff, meaſure on your Inch-Rule ſo much leſs than four Inches, as you think your Stuff diminiſhes in working: Meaſure, I ſay, between the Oval and the Tooth, your ſize: If, at the firſt proffer, your Oval ſtand too far from the Tooth, hold the Oval in your Hand, and knock the Tooth-end of your Staff upon the Work-bench, till it ſtand near enough: If the Oval ſtand too near, knock the other end of the Staff upon the Work-bench till it be fit. Then apply the flat of the Oval to the ſecond wrought ſide of your Stuff, ſo as the Tooth may reach athwart the breadth of the Stuff upon the firſt ſide, and keeping the Oval cloſe againſt the ſecond ſide, preſs the Tooth ſo hard down, that by drawing the Gage in this poſture all along the length of the Quarter, the Tooth may ſtrike a Line. In like manner upon the ſide oppoſite to the firſt, *viz.* the fourth ſide, Gage another line oppoſite to the firſt gaged Line, and work your Stuff down to thoſe two gaged Lines on the third ſide, either with Plaining along, or with Hewing, and afterwards Plaining, as you were taught to work the ſecond ſide.

To work the fourth ſide, ſet the Tooth of the Gage to its exact diſtance from the Oval, *viz.* two Inches wanting ſo much as you think the Stuff diminiſh'd in working, and apply the flat of the O-val to each ſide of the firſt ſide, and Gage as be-fore two Lines, one on the ſecond, the other on

F 2 the

the third wrought fide. Work your Stuff then
down on the fourth fide to thofe two Gage lines,
either with Plaining alone, or with Hewing, and
afterwards Plaining, as you were taught to work
the fecond fide

§. 17. *To* Frame *two* Quarters *Square into one another.*

YOU muft take care in Mortefling and Tennanting, that as near as you can equallize
the ftrength of the fides of the Mortefs to the
ftrength of the Tenant. I do not mean that the
Stuff fhould be of an equal Subftance, for that is
not equalling ftrength : But the equalling ftrength
muft be confidered with refpect to the Quality,
Pofition and Subftance of the Stuff : As if you
were to make a Tennant upon a piece of Fur,
and a Mortefs to recieve it in a piece of Oak, and
the Fur and Oak have both the fame fize : The
Tennant therefore made upon this piece of Fur,
muft be confiderably bigger than a Tennant need
be made of Oak, becaufe Fur is much a weaker
Wood than Oak, and therefore ought to have a
greater Subftance to equallize the ftrength of Oak.
And for Pofition, the fhorter the Stuff that the
Tennant is made on, the lefs Violence the Tennant is fubject to. Befides, it is eafier to fplit
Wood with the Grain, than to break Wood crofs
the Grain ; and therefore the fame Wood when
pofited as a Tennant, is ftronger than the fame
Wood of the fame fize when pofited as a Mortefs :
for the injury a Mortefs is fubject to, is fpliting
with the grain of the Wood, which, without
good care, it will often do in working ; but the
force that muft injure a Tennant, muft offend it,
crofs the Grain of the Wood, in which Pofition
it will beft indure Violence.

When

When two pieces of Wood, of the fame quality and fubftance (as in this our Example) are
elected to make on the one a Tennant, and in the
other a Mortefs. If you make the Mortefs too
wide, the fides of the Mortefs will be weaker
than the fides that contain the Mortefs: And if
one be weaker than the other, the weakeft will
give way to the ftrongeft. when an equal Vio-
lence is offer'd to both. Therefore you may fee
a neceffity of equallizing the ftrength of one to
the other, as near as you can. But becaufe no
Rule is extant to do it by, nor can (for many
Confiderations, I think,) be made, therefore
this equallizing of ftrength, muft be referred to
the Judgment of the Operator. Now to the
Work.

The Mortefs to be made is in a Quarter four
Inches broad. In this cafe Workmen make the
Mortefs an Inch wide, fo that an Inch and an
half Stuff remains on either fide it. Therefore
your Stuff being fquar'd, as was taught in the
laft Section, fet the Oval of the Gage an Inch
and an half off the Tooth, and gage with it, on
either fide your Stuff, a ftraight line at that diftance from the end you intend the Mortefs fhall
be, then open your Compaffes to two Inches,
and prick off that diftance in one of the Lines,
for the length of the Mortefs ; then lay the infide of the Handle of the Square to one fide of
the Stuff, and upon both the pricks fucceffively,
and with your Pricker draw ftraight Lines through
them by the fide of the Tongue, fo fhall the
bounds of your Mortefs be ftruck out on the Quarter. If your Mortefs go through the Quarter,
draw the fame Lines on the oppofite fide of the
Quarter thus, Turn the Quarter, or its Edge,
and apply the infide of the Handle of the Square,
to the ends of the former drawn Lines, and by

F 3   the

the fide of the Tongue draw two Lines on the edge of the Quarter; then turn the Quarter again with its other broad fide upwards, and apply the infide of the Handle of the Square to the ends of the laſt Lines drawn on the edge, and by the fide of the Tongue, draw two Lines on this broad fide alſo. Theſe two Lines (if your Quarter was truly ſquar'd) ſhall be exactly oppoſite to the two Lines drawn on the firſt broad fide of the Quarter for the length of the Morteſs: And for the width of the Morteſs gage this fide alſo, as you did the firſt; then for the Tennant, gage on that end of the Quarter you intend the Tennant ſhall be made, the ſame Lines you did for the Morteſs. And becauſe the Quarter is two Inches thick, prick from the end two Inches, and applying the infide of the Handle of the Square to the fide of the Quarter, and the Tongue to that Prick, draw by the fide of the Tongue a Line through that fide the Quarter; then turn the other fides of the Quarter ſucceſſively, and draw Lines athwart each fide the Quarter, as you were taught to draw the oppoſite Lines for the Mortreſs.

Then place the edge of the Inch-Morteſs-Chiſſel with its Baſil from you, and the Helve bearing a little towards you, within one half quarter of an Inch of one end of the ſtruck Morteſs, and with your Mallet knock hard upon it, till you find the Baſil of the Chiſſel will no longer force the Chips out of the Morteſs; then remove the Chiſſel to the other end of the Morteſs, and work, as with the firſt end, till the Chips will void no longer: Then work away the Stuff between the two Ends, and begin again at one of the Ends, and then at the other, and work deeper into the Morteſs, then again between both; and ſo work deeper by degrees, till you have wrought the

Mor-

Mortefs through, or (if not through) to the intended Depth; then with the Mortefs-chiffel work nearer the drawn Lines at the ends of the Mortefs, (for before you were directed to work but within half a quarter of an Inch of the drawn Lines,) by laying light blows on it, till you have made it fit to pare fmooth with a narrow Paring-chiffel, and then pare the ends, as you were taught to work with the Paring-chiffel: Then with the broad **Paring**-chiffel, pare the fides of the Mortefs juft to the ftruck Lines; fo is the Mortefs finifhed.

To work the Tennant, lay the other Quarter on edge upon your Work-bench, and faften it with the *Holdfaft*, as you were taught Sect. I. Then with the Tennant, faw a little without the Struck-line towards the end: You muft not Saw juft upon the Struck-line, becaufe the Saw cuts rough: Befides, you muft leave fome Stuff to pare away fmooth to the Struck-line, that the *Stile* (that is, the upright Quarter) may make a clofe Joint with the *Rail* (that is) the lower Quarter: Saw therefore right down with the Tennant-Saw, juft almoft to the gaged Lines for the thicknefs of the Tennant, and have a care to keep the Blade of the Saw exactly upright. Then turn the oppofite Side of the Quarter upwards, and work as you were taught to work the firft Side.

Then with the Paring-chiffel, pare the Work clofe to the gaged Lines for the Tennant. Then try how it fits the Mortefs: If it be not pared enough away, you muft pare it where it bears, that is, fticks. But if you fhould chance to have made it too little, you have fpoiled your Work: Therefore you may fee how neceffary it is, not to make the Mortefs too wide at firft, or the Tennant too narrow.

Then with the Piercer pierce two holes through the Sides, or Checks of the Mortefs, about half an

Inch

Inch off either end one. Then knock the Tennant
ſtiff into the Morteſs, and ſet it upright, by applying the Angle of the outer Square, to the Angle the two Quarters make, and with your Pricker, prick round about the inſides of the Pierced
holes upon the Tennant. Then take the Tennant
out again, and Pierce two holes with the ſame
Bit, about the thickneſs of a Shilling above the
Pricked holes on the Tennant, that is, nearer the
Sholder of the Tennant, that the Pins you are to
drive in, may draw the Sholder of the Tennant
the cloſer to the flat ſide of the Quarter the Morteſs is made in. Then with the Paring-chiſſel
make two Pins ſomewhat Tapering, full big e-
nough, and ſetting the two Quarters again ſquare,
as before, drive the Pins ſtiff into the Pierced
holes.

If you make another Square, as you did this;
and make alſo a Tennant on each Un-tennanted
end of the Stiles, and another Morteſs on the
top and bottom Rails, you may put them together, and make ſquare Frames of them.

§. 18. *Of the* Miter Square. *And its Uſe.*

THe Miter Square marked E, hath (as the
Square) an Handle marked *a*, one Inch
thick, and three Inches broad, and a Tongue
marked *b*, of about the ſame breadth: The Handle and the Tongue (as the Square) have both
their Sides parallel to their own Sides. The Handle (as the Square) hath in the middle of its
narroweſt Side a Morteſs in it, of an equal depth,
the whole length of the Handle : Into this Morteſs is fitted one end of the Tongue, but the end
of the Handle is firſt Bereld off to make an Angle of 45 Degrees with its inſide. This Tongue
is (as the Square) Pin'd and Glewed into the
Morteſe of the Handle.

It

It is ufed for ftriking a Miter-line, as the Square is to ftrike a Square-line, by applying the infide of the Handle to the outfide of the Quarter, or Batten, you are to work upon ; and then by ftriking a Line by the fide of the Tongue : For that Line fhall be a Miter-line.   And if upon two Battens you ftrike two fuch Lines, and Saw and Pare them juft off in the Lines, when the flats of thofe two fawn ends are applied to one another, the ont and infide of the Battens, will form themfelves into the Figure of a Square.

Thus Picture Frames, and looking Glafs-frames, are commonly made, as by a more full Example you may fee in the next Section.

§. 19.   *Of the* Bevil.

AS the Square is made to ftrike an Angle of 90 Degrees, and the Miter an Angle of 45 Degrees, fo the Bevil (marked F) having its Tongue movable upon a Center, may be fet to ftrike Angles of any greater, or lefler numbers of Degrees, according as you open the Tongue wider from, or fhut it clofer to the Handle. It is ufed as the Square, and the Miter, and will perform the Offices of them both, though it be not purpofely made for either; but for the ftriking fuch Bevil-lines, as one part of your work muft be cnt away to, to make it join with another part of your Work : For Example,

We will propofe to make a Frame for a Picture, Looking-glafs, *&c.* containing eight ftraight Sides; You may quickly perceive that all the ends of thefe eight Sides muft be cut to Bevils, and what Bevils they muft be, you will find if you defcribe upon a fmooth flat Board, a Circle of any bignefs, but the larger the better : Divide this Circle into eight equal Parts, and from every point draw a Line to the Center : Draw alfo ftraight Lines from

from every point to its next Point : Then lay the inside of the Handle of your Bevil exactly upon any one of these straight Lines, so as the Angle made by the inside of the Handle, and the inside of the Tongue, lie exactly at the very Angle made by this straight Line, and the Semi-Diametral Line proceeding from the Center, and move the Tongue nearer, or farther off the Handle, till the inside of the Tongue and the inside of the Handle, lie exactly upon those two Lines, so shall your Bevil be set.

Then having fitted your Pieces to your Scantling, stick your Pricker as near the outward Corner of your Pieces as your Stuff will bear, and apply the inside of your Handle also to the outer sides of your Pieces, and so as the inside of the Tongue may be drawn home to the Pricker. For then Lines drawn on those Pieces by the inside of the Tongue, shall be the Lines the Pieces must be cut in, to make these eight Pieces join evenly together by the sides of each others Bevil: Then with the Strike-block smooth the ends of the Bevils, as you were taught in the Section of the Strike-block.

If you have a Board on the back-side of this Frame, you may Glew the back-sides of these Pieces, piece by piece to the Board; but first you must fit them to an exact Compliance of every Bevil with its Match, and when they are so fitted, drive two Nails close to the outside of every piece, but drive not the Nails deep into the Board, because when the Frame is set, and Glewed, or otherwise fastned, you must draw the Nails out again : For these Nails are only intended to serve for Fences to set, and fit each piece into its proper Place, before the whole Frame is fastned together. And should you not thus Fence them, though by your Eye you might judge you fitted the Bevils

exactly,

exactly, yet one piece being never fo little out of its due Pofition, would drive the next piece more out, and that the next, till at the laft, the laft piece would not join, but either be too fhort, or too long, or ftand too much out, or in, or elfe too open, or too clofe on the out, or infide.

But if you have no Board on the backfide, you muft, when you Saw the Bevilling Angles upon the fquare ends of pieces, not fawn quite through the depth of one end of every piece, but about half way through the depth, or thicknefs, and then with your Chiffel either fplit, or elfe pare, the up-per fide of the fquare end flat away to the Bevil, and fo leave part of the fquare end of your piece, to lap under the piece it is joined to. For Example,

In Fig. 3. Plate 5. *a b* is the fquare end of the piece, and *b c* is the Bevil you work the piece to. Therefore you muft work away fo much of the thicknefs of the fquare end, as is comprehended between *a* and *c*, fo that you will fee the Triangle *a b c*, is to be wrought away half way down the thicknefs of the Stuff, and fo will the Triangle *a b c* be left for the other half thicknefs of the Stuff. But that end of the piece marked 1, which joins to the piece marked 2, muft, upon its Bevil-ftroak, be fawn quite off, and its underfide muft have the fame Triangle wrought into it, juft fo fit as to re-ceive the Triangle in piece 2, and juft fo deep, as that when the Triangle on piece 2, is fitted into the Triangle in piece 1, the Superficies of both the pieces may be even with one another. And thus you may lap the ends of every piece into one an-other.

Thefe Triangles at the ends of the pieces you may Glew into one another, but if you think Glewing alone not ftrong enough, you may Pierce an hole near the inner edge of the Frame, becaufe the Triangle hath there moft Subftance of Stuff ;

and

and afterwards Pin it, as you are taught to Pin the Rail and Stile together in Sect. 17.

This way of Lapping over, is fometimes ufed alfo for fquare Miters, or other Angular Frames.

§. 20. *Of the* Miter-Box.

THere is another way ufed by Joiners that make many Frames, to fave themfelves the labour of Drawing, or ftriking out of Squares, Miters, and feveral Bevils upon their Stuff: And this is with a Tool called a *Miter-Box*, defcribed in Plate 5. Fig. 2. It is compofed of two pieces of Wood, of an Inch thick each, as A the upright piece, B the bottom piece. The Upright piece is nailed upright, faft upon the bottom piece. And this upright piece hath on its upper fide the Miter Lines ftruck with the, Miter Square, as *d e*, on the left hand, and *g h* on the right hand: On thefe two Miter Lines the edge of the Saw is fet, and a kerf made ftraight down the upright piece, as from *d e* on the left hand to *f*, and from *g h* on the right hand to *i*. In like manner any other Bevil is ftruck upon the upper fide of the upright piece with the Bevil, as *k l* on the left hand, and *n o* on the right. On thefe two Bevil Lines the edge of the Saw is fet, and a kerf made ftraight down the upright piece, as from *k* to *l m*, and from *g h* to *i*. You may make as many Bevils as you pleafe on the upright piece of the Miter Box ; Bevils to join Frames of either five, fix, feven, eight Sides, *&c.* and the manner to make them to any number of Sides, was in part taught in the laft Section. For as there you were directed to divide the Circle into eight equal Parts, becaufe eight was the number of Sides, we propofed to make that Frame confift of; So, if for any number of Sides you divide the Circle into the fame equal parts, and work as you were there directed, you may find what Bevil

vil the pieces muſt have that make a Frame that
conſiſts of any number of Sides.

So alſo for Sawing of any Batten, or other ſmall
pieces ſquare : Strike at the Point *a,* on the upper
ſide of the upright piece a line ſtraight athwart
it, to *b,* and Saw ſtraight down the upper piece,
to *c.*

The manner how theſe Kerfs are ſawn ſtraight
down with greateſt certainty is, thus, Apply the
inſide of the Handle of the ſquare to the upper
ſide of the upright piece, ſo as the Tongue lie
cloſe to that end of the Miter, Bevil, or ſquare
Line ſtruck through the upper ſide of the Miter-
Box, and with the Pricker ſtrike a Line cloſe by
the ſide of the Tongue, through that ſide of the
upright piece; Turn the Tongue to the other ſide
of the upright piece, and apply the inſide of the
Handle of the ſquare to the other end of the Miter, Bevil, or Square Line, and with the Pricker
ſtrike alſo a Line cloſe by the ſide of the Tongue
through that ſide the upright piece. Theſe two
Lines ſtruck on either *ſide* of the upright piece,
ſhall be a Line on each ſide in which the edge of
the Saw muſt run, to ſaw it ſtraight down.

§. 21.   *Of the* Gage.

THe *Gage* marked G (in *Plate* 4) The *Oval b*
is fitted ſtiff upon the *Staff c,* that it may be
ſet nearer or farther from the *Tooth a.* Its Office
is to *Gage* a Line parallel to any ſtraight ſide. It
is uſed for *Gaging* Tennants, and for *Gaging* Stuff
to an equal thickneſs.

When you uſe it, you muſt ſet the *Oval* to the
intended Diſtance from the *Tooth* : If the Oval
ſtand too near the Tooth, Hold the Oval in your
right hand, and knock the hinder end of the Staff
upon the Work-bench, till it remove to its juſt
Diſtance from the Tooth : If it ſtand too far off the
Tooth,

Tooth, knock the fore end of the Staff (*viz.* the
Tooth end) till it remove to its juſt Diſtance
from the Tooth : If the Oval ſlide not ſtiff enough
upon the Staff, you may ſtiffen it by ſtriking a
wooden Wedge between the Morteſs and the
Staff : So may you apply the ſide of the Oval next
the Tooth, to the ſide of any Table, or any o-
ther ſtraight ſide, with the Tooth Gage a Line
parallel (or of equal Diſtance) all the way from
that ſide.

§. 22.　*Of the* Piercer.

THe *Piercer* H, in *Plate* 4, hath *a* the *Head,* *b*
the *Pad, c* the *Stock, d* the *Bitt.* Its Office
is ſo well known, that I need ſay little to it.　Only, you muſt take care to keep the Bitt ſtraight to
the hole you pierce, leſt you deform the hole, or
break the Bitt.

You ought to be provided with Bitts of ſeveral
ſizes, fitted into ſo many Padds.

§. 23.　*Of the* Gimblet.

THe *Gimblet* is marked I, in *Plate* 4.　It hath a
Worm at the end of its Bitt.　Its Office is to
make a round hole in thoſe places of your work
where the *Stock* of the Piercer by reaſon of its own
Sholder, or a Sholder, or Butting out upon the
work will not turn about.　Its Handle is held in
a clutched hand, and its Bitt twiſted ſtiff into your
work.　You muſt have them of ſeveral ſizes.

§. 24.　*Of the* Augre.

THe *Augre* marked K in *Plate* 4, hath *a a* the
Handle, *b* the *Bitt.* Its Office is to make great
round holes. When you uſe it, the Stuff you work
upon is commonly laid low under you, that you
may the eaſier uſe your ſtrength upon it : For in
twiſting the Bitt about by the force of both your
Hands,

Hands, on each end of the Handle one, it cuts great Chips out of the Stuff. You muſt bear your ſtrength Perpendicularly ſtraight to the end of the Bitt; as with the Piercer.

§. 25. *Of the* Hatchet.

THe *Hatchet* marked L, in *Plate* 4. Its uſe is ſo well known (even to the moſt un-intelligent) that I need not uſe many Words on it, yet thus much I will ſay, Its uſe is to Hew the Irregularities off ſuch pieces of Stuff which may be ſooner Hewn than Sawn.

When the Edge is downwards, and the Handle towards you, the right *ſide* of its Edge muſt be Ground to a Bevil, ſo as to make an Angle of a-bout 12 Degrees with the left *ſide* of it : And af-terwards ſet with the Whetſtone, as the Irons of Planes, *&c.*

§. 26. *The Uſe of the* Saw *in general.*

IN my former *Exerciſes,* I did not teach you how to chuſe the Tools a Smith was to uſe ; Be-cauſe it is a Smith's Office to make them : And be-cauſe in thoſe *Exerciſes* I treated of making Iron-work, and Steel-work in general, and the making, and excellency of ſome Tools in particular, which might ſerve as a general Notion for the Know-ledge of all Smith's Workmanſhip, eſpecially to thoſe that ſhould concern themſelves with Smith-ing: But to thoſe that ſhall concern themſelves with Joinery, and not with Smithing ; It will be neceſſary that I teach them how to chuſe their Tools that are made by Smiths, that they may uſe them with more eaſe and delight, and make both quicker and nearer Work with them.

All ſorts of Saws, for Joiner's Uſe, are to be ſold in moſt Iron-monger's Shops, but eſpecially in *Foſter-lane, London:* Chuſe thoſe that are made

of

of Steel, (for fome are made of Iron) for Steel
of it felf is harder and ftronger than Iron : You
may know the Steel-*Saws* from Iron-*Saws* thus,
The Steel-*Saws* are generally ground bright and
fmooth, and are (the thicknefs of the Blade confidered) ftronger than Iron-*Saws* : But the Iron-
Saws are only Hammer-hardned, and therefore if
they could be fo hard, yet they cannot be fo
fmooth, as if the Irregularities of the Hammer
were well taken off with the Grindftone : See it be
free from flaws, and very well Hammered, and
fmoothly Ground, (that is, evenly Ground,) you
may know if it be well Hammered by the ftiff bending of it, and if it be well Ground, (that is, e-
venly Ground,) it will not bend in one part of it
more than in another ; for if it do, it is a fign
that part were it bends moft is, either too much
Ground away, or too thin Forged in that place :
But if it bend into a regular bow all the way, and
be ftiff, the Blade is good: It cannot be too ftiff,
becaufe they are but Hammer-hardned, and therefore often bow when they fall under unskilful
Hands, but never break, unlefs they have been often bowed in that place.   The Edge whereon the
Teeth are, is always made thicker than the Back,
becaufe the Back follows the Edge, and if the
Edge fhould not make a pretty wide Kerf, if the
Back do not ftrike in the Kerf, yet by never fo
little irregular bearing, or twifting of the Hand
awry, it might fo ftop, as to bow the *Saw* ; and
(as I faid before) with often bowing it will break
at laft.   When Workmen light of a good Blade
thus qualified, they matter not much whether the
Teeth be fharp or deep, or fet to their mind : For
to make them fo, is a Task they take to themfelves : And thus they perform it : They wedge
the Blade of the *Saw* hard into the *Whetting-
Block*, marked P, in *Plate* 4. with the Handle towards

wards their left Hand, and the end of the *Saw* to
the right, then with a three-fquare File they begin at the left hand end, leaning harder upon the
fide of the File on the right Hand, than on that
fide to the left Hand; fo that they File the upper-
fide of the Tooth of the Saw a-flope towards the
right Hand, and the underfide of the Tooth a little a-flope towards the left, or, almoft down-
right. Having filed one Tooth thus, all the reft
muft be fo filed. Then with the *Saw-wreft*, marked O, in *Plate* 4. they *fet* the Teeth of the Saw :
That is, they put one of the Notches marked *a a a*
of the *Wreft* between the firft two Teeth on the
Blade of the *Saw*, and then turn the Handle Horizontally a little about upon the Notch towards
the end of the *Saw*; and that at once turns the
firft Tooth fomewhat towards you, and the fecond Tooth from you : Then skipping two Teeth,
they again put one of the Notches of the *Wreft* between the third and fourth Teeth on the Blade of
the *Saw*, and then (as before) turn the Handle
a little about upon the Notch towards the end of
the *Saw*, and that turns the third Tooth fomewhat towards you, and the fourth fomewhat from
you : Thus you muft skip two Teeth at a time, and
turn the *Wreft* till all the Teeth of the *Saw* are *fet*.
This *Setting* of the Teeth of the *Saw* (as Workmen call it) is to make the Kerf wide enough for
the Back to follow the Edge : And is Set *Ranker*
for foft, courfe, cheap Stuff, than for hard, fine,
and coftly Stuff : For the *Ranker* the Tooth is fet,
the more Stuff is wafted in the Kerf : And befides,
if the Stuff be hard it will require greater Labour
to tear away a great deal of hard Stuff, than it
will do to tear away but a little of the fame Stuff.

The *Pit Saw*, is Set fo Rank for courfe Stuff, as
to make a Kerf of almoft a quarter of an Inch, but
for fine and coftly Stuff they fet it finer to fave

G   Stuff,

Stuff. The *Whip-Saw* is set somewhat finer than the *Pit-Saw* ; the *Hand-Saw*, and the *Compass-Saw*, finer than the *Whip-Saw* ; but the *Tennant-Saw*, *Frame-Saw*, and the *Bow-Saw*, &c. are set fine, and have their Teeth but very little turned over the Sides of their Blades : So that a Kerf made by them, is seldom above half a half quarter of an Inch.

The reason why the Teeth are filed to an Angle, pointing towards the end of the *Saw*, and not towards the Handle of the *Saw*, or directly straight between the Handle and end of the *Saw*, is, Because the *Saw* is designed to cut only in its Progress forwards ; Man having in that Activity more strength to rid, and Command of his Hands to guide his Work, than he can have in drawing back his *Saw*, and therefore when he draws back his *Saw*, the Work-man bears it lightly off the unsawn *Stuff* ; which is an ease to his Labour, and enables him the longer to continue his several Progressions of the *Saw*.

Master-Workmen, when they direct any of their Underlins to saw such a piece of Stuff, have several Phrases for the sawing of it : They seldom say *Saw that piece of Stuff* ; But *Draw the Saw through it* ; *Give that piece of Stuff a Kerf* ; *Lay a Kerf in that piece of Stuff* ; and sometimes, (but most unproperly,) *Cut*, or *Slit that piece of Stuff* : For the Saw cannot properly be said to cut, or slit the Stuff ; but it rather breaks, or tears away such parts of the Stuff from the whole, as the points of the Teeth prick into, and these parts it so tears away are proportionable to the fineness, or rankness of the setting of the Teeth.

The Excellency of Sawing is, to keep the Kerf exactly in the Line marked out to be sawn, without wriggling on either, or both sides ; And straight through the Stuff, as Work-men call it ;

that

that is, in a Geometrical Term, perpendicular
through the upper and under fide, if your Work
require it, as moſt Work does : But if your Work
be to be Sawn upon a Bevil, as ſome Work ſometimes is, then you are to obſerve that Bevil all the
length of the Stuff, *&c.*

§. 27. *The Uſe of the* Pit-Saw, *marked* M, *in* Plate 4.

THe *Pit-Saw* is not only uſed by thoſe Workmen that make ſawing Timber and Boards
their whole Buſineſs, but is alſo for ſmall matters
uſed by Joiners, when what they have to do, may
perhaps be as ſoon done at home, as they can carry or ſend it to the Sawyers. The manner of their
working is both alike, for if it be a Board they
would ſlit off a piece of Timber, or if they would
take any Square, Quarter, or Batten, *&c.* off, they
firſt ſet off their Scantlin : For Example, If it be
an Inch (or more, or leſs) they would take off
a piece of Stuff, they open the Points of their
Compaſſes to an Inch Meaſure on their Rule, and
ſo much more as they reckon the Kerf of the *Saw*
will make, and from on ſide of their Stuff they ſet
off at either end of the Stuff, the Diſtance of the
points of their Compaſſes ; at this Diſtance therefore they make with the points of their Compaſſes
a prick at either end of the Stuff; Then with
Chalk they whiten a Line, by rubbing the Chalk
pretty hard upon it ; Then one holds the Line at
one end upon the prick made there, and the other
ſtrains the Line pretty ſtiff upon the prick at the
other end ; then whilſt the Line is thus ſtrain'd,
one of them between his Finger and Thumb draws
the middle of the Line directly upright, to a convenient height (that it may ſpring hard enough
down) and then lets it go again, ſo that it ſwiftly applies to its firſt Poſition, and ſtrikes ſo
ſtrongly againſt the Stuff, that the Duſt, or At-

toms of the Chalk that were rubbed into the
Line, shake out of it, and remain upon the Stuff.
And thus also they mark the under side of their
Stuff: This is called *Lining of the Stuff*: And the
Stuff cut into those Lines shall be called *Inch-
Stuff*, because the Compasses that prickt the Stuff,
were opened wider by the width of the Kerf than
an Inch Measure upon the Rule : But had the
Compasses been opened but an Inch exactly, that
piece Sawn off should, in Workmen's Language,
have been called *Inch-prickt*, thereby giving to understand that it is half the breadth of the Kerf
thinner than an Inch : And thus they call all o-
ther Scantlins 2 *Inches*, 2½ *Inches*, 3 *Inches*, &c.
Sawn, or *Pricked*.

When two Work-men are not at hand to hold
the Line at both ends, he that Lines it, strikes one
point of his Compass, or sometimes a Pricker, or
a Nail aslope towards that end into the prick set
off, and putting the Noose at the end of his Line
over his Compasses, *&c.* goes to the other end,
and strains his Line on that prick, and strikes it
as before.

The Stuff being thus lined is fastned with
wedges over the *Pit*, (if the Joiner be accommodated with a *Pit*) if he have none, he makes shift
with two high Frames a little more than Man
high in its stead, (called *great Trussels*) with four
Legs, these Legs stand spreading outwards, that
they may stand the firmer: Over these two *Trussels* the Stuff is laid, and firmly fastned that it
shake not. Its outer side from whence the Pricks
were set off must be Perpendiculer, which you
must try by a Plumb-line, for should the top edge
of that side, hang never so little over the bottom
edge, or the bottom edge not lie so far out as the
top edge, the Scantlin you saw off would not be
of an equal thickness on the Top or Bottom : Because

caufe the Saw is to work exactly Perpendicular.
Then with the *Pit-Saw* they enter the one end of
the Stuff, the *Top-man* at the Top, and the *Pit-
man* under him : The *Top-man* obferving to guide
the *Saw* exactly in the Line: And withal drawing the *Saw* fomewhat towards him when the
Saw goes down ; and the *Pit-man* drawing it
with all his ftrength Perpendicularly down ; but
not fo low that the upper and lower Handles of
the *Saw* fink below both their Managements :
Then bearing the Teeth of the *Saw* a little off
the Stuff, the *Top-man* draws the *Saw* up again,
and the *Pit-man* affifts, or eafes him in it, and
thus they continue fawing on till the *Saw* has
run through the whole length upon the Stuff. But
when the Kerf is made fo long, that by the
working of the *Saw* the pieces of Stuff on either
fide will fhake againft one another, and fo more,
or lefs, hinder the eafie Progrefs of the *Saw*, they
drive a Wedge fo far in the Kerf as they dare do
for fear of fplitting the Stuff, and fo provide the
Saw freer and eafier Paffage through the Stuff :
This Wedging they continue fo oft as they find
occafion.

MECHA-

MECHANICK EXERCISES;

O R,

The Doctrine of *Handy-Works*

Continued in the Art of JOINERY.

§. 28. *The Use of the* Whip-Saw, *marked* N *in Plate* 4.

THE *Whip-Saw* is used by Joiners, to saw such greater pieces of Stuff that the *Hand-Saw* will not easily reach through ; when they use it, the Stuff is laid upon the *Truffel*, marked O in *Plate* 5. in the Angles of it. Then two Men takes each an Handle of the *Saw* ; He to whom the Teeth of the *Saw* points, drawing to him, and the other thrusting from him : And (as before) the *Saw* having run its length, is lifted gently over the Stuff to recover another stroak of the *Saw*.

§. 29. *The Use of the* Hand-Saw *marked* D, *the* Frame *or* Bow-Saw, *the* Tennant-Saw, *marked* O *in* Plate 4.

THese *Saws* are accommodated for a single Man's Use, and cut forward as the other *Saws* do. The Office of the Cheeks made to the *Frame-Saw* is, by the twisted Cord and Tongue in the middle, to draw the upper ends of the Cheeks closer together, that the lower end of the Cheeks

may

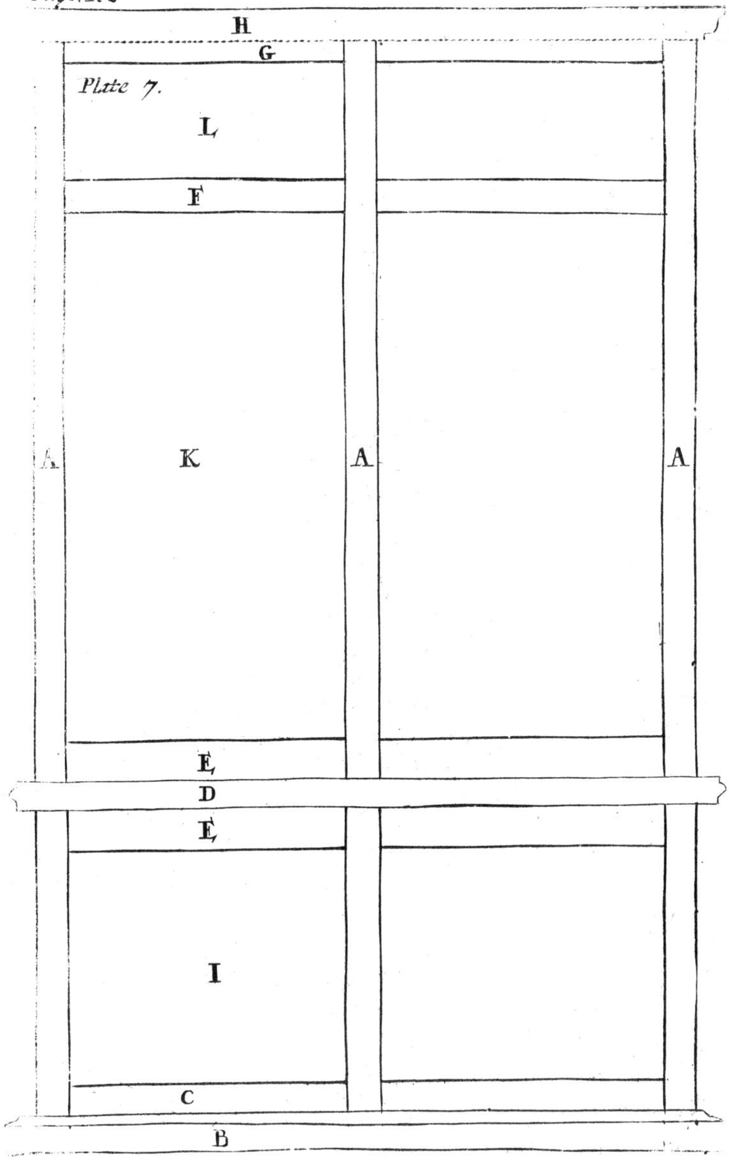

H

G

Plate 7.

L

F

A

K

A

A

E

D

E

I

C

B

may be drawn the wider afunder, and ftrain the Blade of the *Saw* the ftraighter. The *Tennant-Saw*, being thin, hath a Back to keep it from bending.

§. 30. *The Uſe of the* Compaſs-Saw, *marked* Q *in Plate* 4.

THe *Compaſs-Saw* fhould not have its Teeth *Set*, as other *Saws* have; but the edge of it fhould be made fo broad, and the back fo thin, that it may eafily follow the broad edge, without having its Teeth *Set* ; for if the Teeth be *Set*, the Blade muſt be thin, or elfe the Teeth will not bow over the Blade, and if it be thin, (confidering the Blade is fo narrow) it will not be ftrong enough to abide tough Work, but at never fo little an irregular thruſt, will bow, and at laſt break ; yet for cheapnefs, they are many times made fo thin that the Teeth require a fetting. Its Office is to cut a round, or any other Compaſs kerf ; and therefore the edge muſt be made broad, and the back thin, that the Back may have a wide kerf to turn in.

§. 31. *Of the* Rule *marked* D *in Plate* 5.

THe ufe of the *Rule* is to meafure Feet, Inches, and parts of Inches, which for that Purpofe, are marked upon the flat and fmooth fides of the *Rule*, and numbred with Inches, and hath every Inch divided into two halfs, and every half into two quarters, and every quarter into two half-quarters ; fo that every Inch is divided into eight equal parts ; And thefe Inches are numbred from one end of the *Rule* to the other ; which commonly is in all 24 Inches : Which is a Two-Foot *Rule*.

They have commonly both Board and Timber-meafure, *&c.* marked upon them, for the finding both the fuperficial and folid Content of Board or

Tim-

Timber : The ufe of which Lines and Tables ha-
vin been often taught by others, and being more
Mathematical than Mechanical, is unproper for
me to meddle with in this Place : But rather to
refer to thofe Books.

But the manual Ufe of it is, either to meafure
length with it, or to draw a ftraight Line by the
fide of it, or to Try the ftraightnefs or flatnefs
of their Work with. They Try their Work by
applying one of its Edges to the flat of the
wrought fide of their Work, and bring their Eye
as clofe as they can, to fee if they can fee light
between the edge of the *Rule* and their Work :
If they cannot, they conclude their Work is *Try*,
and well wrought.

§. 32. *Of the* Compaffes *marked* E *in* Plate 5.

a a THe *Joint*, *bb* the *Cheeks* of the Joint, *cc* the
Shanks, *dd* the *Points*. Their Office is to
defcribe Circles, and fet off Diftances from their
Rule, or any other Meafure, to their Work.

§. 33. *Of the* Glew-pot *marked* F *in* Plate 5.

THe *Glew-pot* is commonly made of good thick
Lead, that by its Subftance it may retain a
heat the longer, that the *Glew Chill* not (as
Work-men fay when it cools) when it is to be
ufed.

§. 34. *Of* Chufing *and* Boiling Glew.

THe cleareft, drieft, and moft tranfparent
Glew is the beft : When you boil it, break
it with your Hammer into fmall pieces, and put
it into a clean Skillet, or Pipkin, by no means
greafie, for that will fpoil the Clamminefs of the
Glew, put to it fo much Water as is convenient
to diffolve the Glew, and to make it, when it is
hot, about the thicknefs of the White of an Egg :

The

The quantity of Water cannot be affigned, becaufe of the different Quality there is in Glew: Keep it ftirring whilft it is melting, and let it not ftick to the fides or bottom of the Veffel : When it is well boiled, pour it into your Glew-pot to ufe, but let your Glew-pot be very clean. When it is cold, and you would heat it again in your Glew-pot, you muft take great care that it burn not to the fides or bottom of the Glew-pot, for that burning either turns to a thick hard skin, or elfe to a burnt Cinder-like Subftance, which if it mingle with the Glew, will fpoil it all ; becaufe by its Subftance it will bear the two Joints you are to Glew together, off each other.

When (with often heating) the Glew grows too thick, you may put more Water to it ; but then you muft make it very hot, left the Glew and Water do not wholly incorporate.

Some Joiners will (when their Glew is too thick, put Small-Beer into it, thinking it ftreng-thens it : I have tried it, and could never find it fo, but think it makes the Glew weaker, efpecial-ly if the Small-Bear chance to be new, and its Yeft not well fettled from it, or fo ftale, that it be either Draggy, or any whit mingled with the Settlings of the Cask.

§. 35. *Of ufing the* Glew.

Your Glew muft be very warm, for then it is thinneft, and as it chills, it thickens: With a fmall Brufh you muft fmear the Glew well upon the Joint of each piece you are to Glew together ; And before you fet them as they are to ftand, you muft joftle them one upon the other, that the Glew may very well touch and take hold of the Wood ; and that the Glew on each Joints may well incorporate. Then fit the two Joints as they muft ftand ; And when you fet them by to dry,

let

let the one stand upright upon the other ; For if
they stand a-flope, the weight of the Stuff when it
leans upon two extream Edges, may make one end
of the Joint *Open.*

§. 36.   Of *the* Waving Engine.

THe *Waving Engine* difcribed in *Plate* 5. *Fig.* 7.
Hath A B a long fquare Plank, of about feven Inches broad, five Foot long, and an Inch and
half thick : All along the length of this Plank, on
the middle between the two fides, runs a *Rabbet,*
as part of it is feen at C : Upon this Rabbet rides
a *Block* with a *Groove* in its under fide : This *Block*
is about three Inches fquare, and ten Inches long,
having near the hinder end of it a wooden Handle
going through it, of about one Inch Diameter, as
D E : At the Fore-end of this *Block* is faftned a
Vice, fomewhat larger than a great Hand-Vice,
as at F : The *Groove* in the *Block* is made fit to receive the Rabbet on the Plank.

At the farther end of the Plank is erected a
fpuare ftrong piece of Wood, about fix Inches
high, and five Inches fquare, as G. This fquare
piece hath a fquare wide Mortefs in it on the
Top, as at H. Upon the top of this fquare piece
is a ftrong fquare flat Iron Coller, fomewhat loofly fitted on, having two Male Screws fitted into
two Female Screws, to fcrew againft that part of
the wooden Piece un-morteffed at the Top, marked L, that it may draw the Iron Coller hard a-
gainft the Iron marked Q , and keep it ftiff againft
the fore-fide of the un-morteffed Piece, marked
L, when the piece Q, is fet to its convenient
heighth ; and on the other fide the fquare wooden
Piece is fitted another Iron fcrew, having to the
end of its fhank faftned a round Iron Plate which
lies within the hollow of this wooden piece, and
therefore cannot in Draft be feen in its proper
place ;

place; But 1 have defcribed it a part, as at M.
(Fig. 9.) Its Nut is placed at M, on the wooden
Piece. On the farther fide of the wooden Piece is
fitted a wooden Screw called a *Knob*, as at N.
Through the farther and hither fide of the fquare
wooden Piece is fitted a flat Piece of Iron, about
three quarters of an Inch broad, and one quarter
of an Inch thick, ftanding on edge upon the Plank;
but its upper edge is filed round: (the reafon you
will find by and by:) Its hither end comes through
the wooden Piece, as at O, and its farther end on
the oppofite fide of the wooden Piece.

Upright in the hollow fquare of the wooden
Piece ftands an *Iron*, as at Q, whofe lower end is
cut into the form of the Molding you intend your
work fhall have.

In the fore fide of this wooden Piece is a fquare
hole, as at R, called the *Mouth.*

To this Engine belongs a thin flat piece of hard
Wood, about an Inch and a quarter broad, and
as long as the *Rabbet*: It is disjunct from the Engine, and in Fig. 8. is marked S S, called the *Rack*:
It hath its under flat cut into thofe fafhioned
Waves you intend your Work fhall have : The
hollow of thefe Waves are made to comply with
the round edge of flat Plate of Iron marked O (defcribed before) for when one end of the Riglet
you wave, is, with the Vice, fcrewed to the plain
fide of the Rack, and the other end put through
the Mouth of the wooden Piece, as at T T, fo as
the hollow of the Wave on the under fide of the
Rack may lie upon the round edge of the flat Iron
Plate fet on edge, as at O, and the Iron Q, is
ftrong fitted down upon the Reglet : Then if you
lay hold of the Handles of the *Block* D E, and
ftrongly draw by them, the Rack and the Riglet
will both together flide through the Mouth of the
wooden Piece : And as the Rounds of the Rack
rid

rid over the round edge of the flat Iron, the Rack and Reglet will mount up to the Iron Q, and as the Rounds of the Waves on the under side of the Rack slides off the Iron on edge, the Rack and Reglet will sink, and so in a Progression (or more) the Riglet will on its upper side receive the Form of the several Waves on the under side of the Rack, and also the Form, or Molding, that is on the edge of the bottom of the Iron, and so at once the Riglet will be both molded and waved.

But before you draw the Rack through the Engine, you must consider the Office of the Knob N, and the Office of the Iron Screw M; For by them the Rack is screwed evenly under the Iron Q. And you must be careful that the Groove of the Block slip not off the Rabbet on the Plank : For by these Screws, and the Rabbet and Groove, your work will be evenly gaged all the way (as I said before) under the edge of the Iron Q, and keep it from sliding either to the right, or left Hand, as you draw it through the Engine.

§. 37. *Of* Wainscoting *Rooms.*

A A A (in *Plate* 7.) The *Stiles.* B The *Base,* C The *Lower Rail.* D The *Sur-Base.* E E The *Middle Rail,* or *Rails.* F The *Friese Rail.* G The *Upper Rail.* H The *Cornice.* I The *Lying Pannel.* K The *Large Pannel.* L The *Friese Pannel.*

In Wainscoting of Rooms there is, for the most part, but two heights of Pannels used ; unless the Room to be Wainscoting be above ten foot high, as some are eleven or twelve Foot high, and then three Heighths of Pannels are used : As I The *Lying Pannel,* above the *Base.* K The *Large Pannel* above the *Middle Rail* : And L The *Friese Pannel* above the *Friese Rail.*

The *Friese Rail* is to have the same breadth the *Margent* of the *Stile* hath ; The *Middle Rail* hath com-

commonly two breadths of the *Margent* of the *Stile,* viz. one breadth above the *Sur-bafe,* and the other below the *Sur-bafe.* And the *Upper* and *Lower Rails* have alfo each the fame breadth with the *Margent* of the *Stile.*

Thofe Moldings above the Prickt Line on the Top, as H, are called the *Cornice.*

Sometimes (and efpecially in low Rooms) there is no *Bafe* or *Sur-bafe* ufed, and then the *Middle* and *Lower Rail* need not be fo broad : For the *Middle Rail* need not be above a third part more than the *Margent* of the *Rail* : and the *Lower Rail* you may make of what breadth you fee convenient : They are commonly about three Inches and an half, or four Inches broad, yet this is no Rule : For fometimes Workmen make only a flat Plinth ferve.

You may (if you will) adorn the outer edges of the *Stiles* and *Rails* with a fmall *Molding* : And you may (if you will) Bevil away the outer edges of the *Pannels,* and leave a Table in the middle of the Pannel.

An Explanation of Terms *ufed among* Joiners

WHen I firft began to Print thefe Exercifes, I marked fome Terms in *Joinery* with *fuperiour Letters* (as Printers call them) thus a b c &c. intending, at the latter end of thefe Exercifes, to have explained the Terms thofe Letters referr'd to : But upon confideration that thofe Terms might often be ufed in this Difcourfe, when the Superiour Letter was out of fight, and perhaps its Pofition (where) forgotten ; I have changed my Mind, and left out the Superiour Letters beyond fol. 66. and inftead of thofe References give you this Alphabetical Table of Terms, by which you may always more readily find the Explanation, though you often meet with the Term.

A

A.

Architrave. See Plate 6. *l.* is the *Architrave Molding.*

Augre § 24. Plate 4. fig. K.

B.

Base. See Plate 6. *b.* And Plate 7. **B.**

Bead. See Plate 6. *a.*

Bed-molding. See Plate 6. *d.*

Basil. The *Basil* is an Angle the edge of a Tool is ground away to. See fol. 71.

Batten. Is a Scantling of Stuff either two, three or four Inches broad; and is seldom above an Inch thick: and the length unlimmitted.

Beak. The end of the Hold-fast. See fol. 60, 61.

Bench-screw. See Plate 4. A *g.* and fol. 60.

Bevil. Any sloping Angle that is not a square, is called a Bevil. See fol. 60. 85. § 19. and Plate 4. F.

Bitt. See § 22.

Bow saw. Plate 4. O.

C.

Capital. See Plate 6. *g.*

Cast. Stuff is said to Cast, or Warp, when by its own Drought or Moisture, or the Drought or Moisture of the Air, or other Accident, it alters its flatness and straightness.

Clamp. When a piece of Board is fitted with the Grain to the end of another piece of Board cross the Grain the first Board is *Clampt.* Thus the ends of Tables are commonly *Clampt* to preserve them from warping.

Compass-saw. See fol. 9. and Plate 4. fig. R.

Cornice. See Plate 6. *q.* and Plate 7. H.

Cross-grain'd-stuff. Stuff is Cross-grain'd when a Bough or some Branch shoots out on that part of the

the Trunk of the Tree ; For the *Bough* or *Branch*
fhooting forwards, the Grain of that branch
fhoots forwards alfo, and fo runs a-crofs the Grain
of the Trunk ; and if they be well grown together, it will fcarce be perceived in fome ftuff, but
in working ; yet in Deal-boards, thofe Boughs or
Branches are Knots, and eafily perceiv'd, and if
it grew up young with the Trunk, then inftead of
a Knot you will find a Curling in the *Stuff* when it
is wrought.

Curling-ftuff. If the Bough or Branch that fhoots
out of the Trunk of a Tree be large, and the ftuff
in that place fawn fomewhat a-flope, when that
fttuff comes under the Plane you will find a Turning about or Curling on that place upon the ftuff ;
and in a ftraight progrefs of the Plane the Iron
will cut with, and fuddenly *a-crofs* the Grain, and
that more or lefs as the Bough grew in the Youth
of the Tree, or grew more or lefs upright, or
elfe floping to the Trunk, or was fawn fo. Such
ftuff therefore is called *Curling-ftaff.*

D.

Door-cafe. Is the Fram'd work about the Door.
Double-Screw. See fol. 60. Plate 4. fig. *g.* on the
Work-bench A.

F.

Facia. See Plate 6. *b.*

Fence. See § 8. Ufe of the Plow, and Plate 4.
fig. B 6.

Fine-fet. The Irons of Planes are fet Fine, or
Rank. They are fet Fine, when they ftand fo
fhallow below the fole of the Plane, that in working they take off a thin fhaving. See § 3.

Flat Friefe. See Plate 6. *p.*

Fore-Plane. See § 2. and Plate 4. B 1.

Former. See § 10. and Plate 4. C 1. C 3.

Frame.

Frame. See fol. 59, 60.
Frame Saw. See § 28. and Plate 4. O.
Free-ſtuff. See §. 3.
Frieſe. See Plate 6. *p.*
Frieſe Pannel. See Plate 7. L.
Frieſe Rail. See Plate 7. F.
Frowy ſtuff. See § 3.

G.

Gage. See § 21. and Plate 4. G.
Gimblet. See § 23. and Plate 4. I.
Gouge. See § 14. C 6.
Groove. See fol. 69.

H.

Hammer-hard. See Numb. I. fol. 58.
Handle. See § 15. and Plate 4. D *a.*
Hard Stuff. See § 3.
Hatchet. See § 25. Plate 4. L.
Head. See § 22. Plate 4. H *a.*
Hold-faſt. See § 1. Plate 4. H *d.*
Hook. See § 1. Plate 4. A *b.*
Husk. See Plate 6. *n.*

I.

Inner-ſquare. See § 15. and Plate 4. D *d.*
Joint. See fol. 59.
Jointer. See § 4. and Plate 4. B 2.
Iron. See § 2. and Plate 4. B 1 *d.*

K.

Kerf. The Sawn-away ſlit between two pieces of ſtuff is called a Kerf. See fol. 95.
Knob. See § 36. fol. 104. and Plate 5. fig. 7. N.
Knot. See Plate 6. *o.*

L.

Large Pannel. See Plate 7. K.

Lying

Lying Pannel. See Plate 7. I.
Lower Rail. See Plate 7. H.

M.

Margent. See Plate 7. at A A A the flat breadth of the Stiles befides the Moldings, is called the Margent of the Stiles.

Middle Rail. See Plate 7. E E.

Miter. See fol. 64.

Miter Box. See § 20. and Plate 5. fig. 1.

Miter fquare. See § 18. and Plate 4. E.

Moldings. The feveral wrought-work made with Planes on Wood, is called *Moldings.* See Plate 6.

Molding Planes. See § 9.

Mortefs. Is a fquare hole cut in a piece of ftuff, to entertain a Tennant fit to it. See § 17.

Mortefs Chiffel. See § 13. and Plate 4. C 5.

Mouth. See § 2. B 7. *a* The Mouth.

O.

Ogee. See Plate 6. *c.*

Oval. See § 21. and Plate 4. G. *b.*

Outer Square. See § 15. and Plate 4. D *c.*

P.

Pad. See § 22. and Plate 4. H *b.*

Pannel. In Plate 7. I K L are Pannels, but diftin-guifhed by their Pofitions.

Pare. The fmooth cutting with the Paring-Chif-fel is called *Paring.*

Paring-Chiffel. See § 11. and Plate 4. C 2.

Plaifter. See Plate 6. *f.*

Peircer. See § 22. and Plate 4. H.

Pit-man The Saywer that works in the Pit, is called the Pit-man.

Pit-Saw. The Pit-faw is a great Saw fitted into a fquare Frame; as in Plate 4. M is a Pit-faw.

H   *Planchier.*

Planchier. In Plate 6. between *d* and *e* is the Planchier.

Plinth. See Plate 6.

Plow. See § 8. and Plate 4. B 6.

Pricker. Is vulgarly called an Awl: Yet for Joiners Use it hath moſt commonly a ſquare blade, which enters the Wood better than a round blade will; becauſe the ſquare Angle in turning it about breaks the Grain, and ſo the Wood is in leſs danger of ſplitting.

R.

Rabbet. See § 7.

Rabbet Plane. See § 7. and Plate 4. B 5.

Rack. See Plate 5. fig. 8. Read § 36.

Rail. See Plate 7. A A A.

Rank. The Iron of a Plane is ſaid to be *ſet Rank,* when its edge ſtands ſo flat below the Sole of the Plane, that in working it will take off a thick ſhaving. See § 3.

Rank-ſet. See Rank.

Range. The ſide of any Work that runs ſtraight, without breaking into Angles, is ſaid to *run Range:* Thus the Rails and Pannels of one ſtraight ſide of Wainſcoting is ſaid to *run Range.*

Return. The ſide that falls away from the foreſide of any Straight or Rank-work, is called the *Return.*

Riglet. Is a flat thin ſquare piece of Wood: Thus the pieces that are intended to make the Frames for ſmall Pictures, *&c.* before they are Molded are called *Riglets.*

S.

Saw-wreſt. See § 26. fol. 97. and Plate 4. O.

Scantlin. The ſize that your ſtuff is intended to be cut to.

Scribe.

Scribe. When Joiners are to fit a fide of a piece of Stuff againft the fide of fome other piece of Stuff, and the fide of the piece of Stuff they are to fit to is not regular; To make thefe two pieces of Stuff join clofe together all the way, they Scribe it, (as they phrafe it,) thus; They lay the piece of Stuff they intend to Scribe clofe a-gainft the other piece of Stuff they intend to Scribe to, and open their Compaffes to the wideft Diftance, thefe two pieces of Stuff bear off each other: Then (the Compaffes moving ftiff in their Joint) they bear the point of one of the fhanks a-gainft the fide they intend to Scribe to, and with the point of the other fhank they draw a Line up-on the Stuff to be Scribed; and then the points of the Compaffes remaining unremov'd, and your Hand carried even along by the fide of the piece to be Scribed to, that Line Scribed upon the piece intended to be Scribed, fhall be parallel to the irregular fide intended to be Scribed to: And if you work away your Stuff exactly to that Line, when thefe two pieces are put together, they fhall feem a Joint.

Shoot a Joint. See fol. 63.

Skew-former. See § 12. and Plate 4. C 4.

Smoothing Plane. See § 6. and Plate 4. B 4.

Sole. See Plate 4. B 7. *b a b.* The under fide of a Plane is called the *Sole.*

Square. See § 15. and Plate 4. D.

Staff. See § 21. and Plate 4. G *c.*

Staves. See § 8. and Plate 4. B 6. *a a.*

Stile. The upright Pieces AA in Pl. 7. are *Stiles.*

Stock. See § 22. and Plate 4. H *c.*

Stops. In Plate 6. *k k* are *Stops.*

Stuff. The Wood that Joiners work upon they call in general *Stuff.*

Sur-bafe. In Plate 7. D is the *Sur-bafe.*

Swelling-Friefe. In Plate 6. *r* is the *Swelling-friefe.*

T.

Table. In Plate 6. *f* is the *Table.*

Taper. All forts of Stuff or Work that is fmaller at one end than at the other, and diminifhes gradually from the biggeft end, is faid to be *Taper.*

Tennant. Is a fquare end fitted into a Mortefs. See § 17.

Tennant-Saw. In Plate 4. O. would be a Tennant-faw, were the flat of the Blade turned where the edge there ftands.

Tongue. See § 16. and Plate 4. D *b.*

Tooth. See § 21. and Plate 4. G *a.*

Top-man. Of the two Sawyers, the uppermoft is called the *Top-man.*

Tote. See § 2. and Plate 4. B 1 *a.*

Traverfe. See fol. 69.

Truffel. See fol. 100. and Plate 5. Fig. 3.

Try. See § 13.

V.

Vaws-Cornice. See Plate 6. *e.*

Upper Cornice. See Plate 6. *t.*

W.

Warp. The fame that *Caft* is.

Waving Engine. See § 46. and Plate 5.

Wedge. See § 2. and Plate 4. B 1. *c.*

Whetting-Block. See Plate 4. P.

Whip-Saw. See Plate 4. N.

Wreft. See § 26. and Plate 4. Q.

Thus much of Joinery. The next Exercifes will be of *Carpentry.*

MECHANICK EXERCISES;

O R,

The Doctrine of *Handy-Works*

Applied to the A R T of *House-Carpentry.*

BEING now come to exercise upon the *Carpenters* Trade, it may be expected, by some, that I should insist upon *Architecture*, it being so absolutely necessary for Builders to be acquainted with : But my Answer to them is, that there are so many Books of *Architecture* extant, and in them the Rules so well, so copiously, and so compleatly handled, that it is needless for me to say any thing of that Science : Nor do I think any Man that should, can do more than Collect out of their Books, and perhaps deliver their Meanings in his own Words. Besides, *Architecture* is a Mathematical Science, and therefore different from my present Undertakings, which are (as by my Title) Mechanick Exercises : yet because Books of Architecture are as necessary for a Builder to understand, as the use of Tools ; and left some Builders should not know how to enquire for them, I shall at the latter end of *Carpentry* give you the Names of some Authors, especially such as are Printed in the *English* Tongue.

Some may perhaps also think it had been more proper for me in these Exercises to have introduced *Carpentry* before *Joinery*, because Necessity, (the Mother of Invention) did doubtless compel

H 3 our

our Fore-fathers in the beginning to ufe the conveniency of the firft, rather than the extravagancy of the laft. I confefs, I confidered it my felf, and had in my own Reafon been perfuaded to it. but that I alfo confidered that the Rules they both work by are upon the matter in the fame, in *Sawing, Mortefling, Tenanting, Scribing, Paring, Plaining, Moulding,* &c. and likewife the Tools they work with the fame, though fome of them fomewhat ftronger for Carpenter's Ufe than they need be for Joiner's; becaufe Joiners work more curioufly, and obferve the Rules more exactly than Carpenters need do. And therefore I fay it was, that I began with Joinery before Carpentry; for he that knows how to work curioufly, may, when he lifts, work flightly; when as they that are taught to work more roughly, do with greater difficulty perform the curious and nice work. Thus we fee Joiners Work their Tables exactly flat and fmooth, and fhoot their Joint fo true, that the whole Table fhews all one piece: But the Floors Carpenters lay are alfo by Rule of Carpentry to be laid flat and true, and fhall yet be well enough laid, though not fo exactly flat and fmooth as a Table.

Yet though the Rules Joiners and Carpenters work by are fo near the fame, and the Tools they work with, and Stuff they work upon, the fame; yet there are many Requifites proper to a Carpenter, (efpecially a Mafter Carpenter) that a Joiner need take little notice of, which, after I have defcribed the Carpenters Tools that are not expreft among the Joiners, I fhall fpeak to.

§ 1. *Of feveral Tools ufed in Carpentry, that are not ufed in Joinery. And firft of the* Ax.

THe *Ax* marked *A* in *Plate* 8. is (as you fee) different from what the Joiners Hatchet is,

both

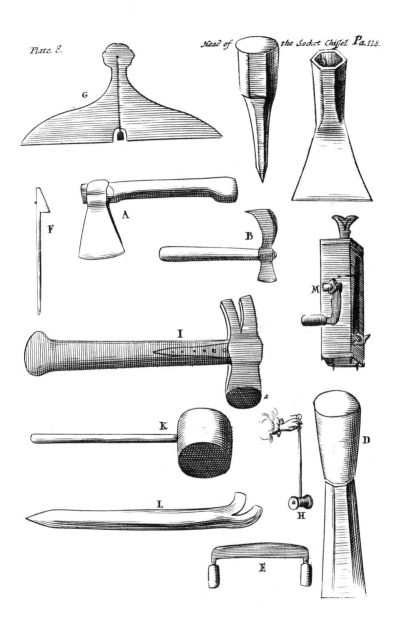

Plate. 8.

Head of the Socket Chisel *Pa. 118.*

G

A

F

B

I

M

a

K

H

D

L

E

both in Size and Form ; theirs being a light Hatchet, with a Bafil edge on its left fide, becaufe it is to be ufed with one hand, and therefore hath a fhort Handle : But the Carpenter's *Ax* being to hew great Stuff, is made much deeper and heavier, and its edge tapering into the middle of its Blade. It hath a long Handle, becaufe it is ufed with both their Hands, to fquare or bevil their Timbers.

When they ufe the Ax, the Timber hath commonly fome Bauk or Log laid under it near each end, that the edge of the Ax may be in lefs danger of ftriking into the ground, when they hew near the bottom of the Timber. And they commonly ftand on that fide the Timber they hew upon.

§ 2. *Of the* Adz, *and its ufe.*

THe *Adz* marked *B* in *Plate* 8. hath its Blade made thin, and fomewhat arching. As the Ax hath its edge parallel to its Handle, fo the *Adz* hath its edge athwart the Handle, and is ground to a Bafil on its infide to its outer edge : Wherefore when it is blunt they cannot well grind it, unlefs they take its Helve out of its Eye.

Its general Ufe is to take thin Chips off Timber or Boards, and to take off thofe Irregularities that the Ax by reafon of its Form cannot well come at ; and that a Plane (though rank fet) will not make riddance enough with.

It is moft ufed for the taking off the Irregularities on the framed Work of a Floor, when it is framed and pin'd together, and laid on its place ; for that lying flat under them, the edge of the Ax being parallel to its Handle (as aforefaid) cannot come at the Irregularities to take them off ; but the *Adz* having its edge athwart the Handle will. Again, upon fome Pofts framed upright, and range with other framed Work clofe to it,

H 4   the

the edge of the Ax cannot come at the Irregularities for the reason aforesaid, but the *Adz* will. And
the like for the Irregularities of framed Work on
a Ceiling, *&c.*

When they work upon the framed Work of a
Floor, they take the end of the Handle in both
their Hands, placing themselves directly before
the Irregularity, at a small Distance, stradling a
little with both their Legs, to prevent Danger
from the edge of the *Adz*, and so by degrees hew
off the Irregularity. But if they hew upon an Upright, they stand directly before it.

They sometimes use the *Adz* upon small thin
Stuff, to make it thinner, (but this is many times
when the Ax, or some other properer Tool, lies
not at hand) and then they lay their Stuff upon
the Floor, and hold one end of it down with the
Ball of the Foot, if the Stuff be long enough; if
not, with the ends of their Toes, and so hew it
lightly away to their size, form, or both.

§ 3. *Of Carpenters* Chissels *in general.*

THough Carpenters for their finer Work use
all the sorts of *Chissels* described in the Art of
Joinery yet are not those sorts of *Chissels* strong e-
nough for their rougher and more common Work,
and therefore they also use a stronger sort of *Chissels*;
and distinguish them by the name of *Socket-Chissels*:
For whereas those *Chissels* Joiners use have their
wooden Heads made hollow to receive the Iron
Sprig above the Shoulder of the Shank, Carpenters have their Shank made with an *hollow Socket*
at its Top, to receive a strong wooden Sprig
made to fit into the *Socket*, with a square Shoulder above it, the thickness of the Iron of the
Socket, or somewhat more ; which makes it much
more strong, and able to endure the heavy blows
of the *Mallet* they lay upon the head of the *Chis-*
sel.

fel. And the Shanks and Blades are made ſtrong-er for Carpenter's Uſe than they are for Joiners.

Of theſe *Socket-Chiſſels* they have of the ſeveral ſorts deſcribed in Joinery, though not all ſeverally diſtinguiſhed by their Names; for they call them *Half-Inch, Three-quarter-Inch Chiſſels, Inch and Half, Two-Inch,* to *Three-Inch Chiſſels,* according to the breadth of the Blade. But their Uſes are the ſame mentioned in Joinery, though the manner of uſing them be ſomewhat different too: For, as I told you in Joinery, the Joiners preſs the edge of the Blade into the Stuff, with the ſtrength of their Shoulders, but the Carpenters with the force of the blows of the Mallet. And the Joiners guide their *Chiſſels* differently from what the Carpenters do their *Socket-Chiſſels*; for the Joiners hold the Shank and Blade of their *Chiſſels,* as I deſcribed in Joinery, *Sect.* 11. but the Carpenters hold the Shank of their *Chiſſels* in their clutched left Hand, and beat upon the Head with the *Mallet* in the right. See the Figure of *Socket-Chiſſel* in *Plate* 8. C. with its Head *a* out of the Socket.

§ 4. *Of the* Ripping-Chiſſel, *and its Uſe.*

THe *Ripping-Chiſſel* deſcribed in *Plate* 8. D. is a *Socket-Chiſſel,* and is about an Inch broad, and hath a blunt Edge. Its Edge hath not a *Baſil,* as almoſt all other *Chiſſels* have, and therefore would more properly be called a *Wedge* than a *Chiſſel.* But moſt commonly Carpenters uſe an old caſt off *Chiſſel* for a *Ripping-Chiſſel.*

Its Office is not to cut Wood, as others do, but to *rip* or *tear* two pieces of Wood faſtned together from one another, by entering the blunt Edge of it between the two pieces, and then knocking hard with the Mallet upon the head of the Handle, till you drive the thicker part of it between the two pieces, and ſo force the power that holds
them

them together (be it Nails, or otherwife) to let
go their hold: For its blunt Edge fhould be made
of Steel, and well tempered, fo that if you knock
with ftrong blows of the Mallet the *Chiffels* Edge
upon a Nail (though of fome confiderable Subftance) it may cut or brake it fhort afunder. If
you cannot, at once, placing the *Ripping-Chiffel,*
part the two pieces, you muft ufe two *Ripping-
Chiffels,* placing the fecond at the remoteft entrance in the breach, and driving that home, will
both open the breach wider, and loofen the firft
Ripping-Chiffel, fo that you may take it again, and
place it farther in the breach : And fo you muft
continue edging farther and farther, till you have
feparated your intended pieces.

It is fometimes ufed when Carpenters have com-
mitted Error in their Work, and muft undo what
they did, to mend it. But it is generally ufed in all
Alterations, and old Work.

§ 5. *Of the* Draw-knife, *and its Ufe.*

THe *Draw-knife* defcribed *Plate* 8. E. is feldom
ufed about Houfe-building, but for the making of fome forts of Houfhold-ftuff; as the Legs
of Crickets, the Rounds of Ladders, the Rails to
lay Cheefe or Bacon on, *&c.*

When they ufe it, they fet one end of their
Work againft their Breaft, and the other end a-
gainft their Work-bench, or fome hollow Angle
that may keep it from flipping, and fo preffing
the Work a little hard with their Breaft againft
the Bench, to keep it fteddy in its Pofition, they
with the Handles of the *Draw knife* in both their
Hands, enter the edge of the *Draw-knife* into the
Work, and draw Chips almoft the length of their
Work, and fo fmoothen it quickly.

§ 6. *Of*

§ 6. *Of* Hook-Pins, *and their ufe.*

THe Hook-Pin is defcribed *Plate* **8.** F. *a* the *Pin,* *b* the *Hook,* *c* the *Head.* Its Office is to pin the Frame of a Floor, or Frame of a Roof together, whilft it is framing, or whilft it is fitting into its Pofition. They have many of thefe *Hook-Pins* to drive into the feveral Angles of the Frame. Thefe drive into the Pin-holes through the Morteffes and Tennants, and being made Taper, do with a Hammer ftriking on the bottom of it knock it out again; or they moft commonly ftrike under the Hook, and fo knock it out. Then if the Frame lie in its place, they pin it up with wooden Pins.

§ 7. *Of the* Level, *and its ufe.*

THe *Level* defcribed in *Plate* **8.** G. *a a* the *Level,* *b* the *Plumbet,* *c* the *Plumb-line,* *d d* the *Perpendicular* mark'd from the top to the bottom of the Board. The *Level* is from two to ten Foot long, that it may reach over a confiderable length of the Work. If the *Plumb-line* hang juft upon the *Perpendicular* *d d,* when the *Level* is fet flat down upon the Work, the Work is *Level*: But if it hang on either fide the *Perpendicular,* the Floor, or Work, muft be raifed on that fide, till the *Plumb-line* hang exactly upon the *Perpendicular.*

§ 8. *Of the* Plumb-line, *and its ufe.*

THe *Plumb-line* is defcribed in *Plate* **8.** H. *a* the *Line-Rowl,* *b* the *Line.* It is ufed to try the upright ftanding of Pofts, or other Work that is to ftand Perpendicular to the Ground Plot ; and then they draw off fo much Line as is neceffary, and faften the reft of the Line there, upon the *Line-Rowl* with a Slip-knot, that no more Line turn off. They hold the end of the Line between
their

their Finger and Thumb half the Diameter of the *Line-Rowl* off one corner of the Poft, or Work ; and if the *Line* and Corner of the Poft be parallel to each other, the Poft is upright : But if the Poft be not parallel to the *Line*, but its bottom ftands more than half the Diameter of the *Line-Rowl* from the *Line*, the Poft hangs fo much over the bottom of the Poft on that fide the *Line* bears off, and muft be forced backwards till the fide of the Poft and the *Line* become parallel to each other: But if the bottom of the Corner of the Poft ftands out from the top of the *Line*, the Poft muft be forced forwards to comply with the *Line*.

§ 9. *Of the* Hammer, *and its Ufe.*

THe *Hammer* is defcribed in *Plate* 8. I. *a* the *Face*, *b* the *Claw*, *c c* the *Pen* at the return fides of the *Claw*. This Tool was forgot to be defcribed in *Joinery*, though they ufe *Hammers* too, and therefore I bring it in here. Its chief Ufe is for driving Nails into Work, and drawing Nails out of Work.

There is required a pretty skill in driving a Nail ; for if (when you fet the point of a Nail) you be not curious in obferving to ftrike the flat face of the *Hammer* perpendicularly down upon the perpendicular of the Shank, the Nail (unlefs it have good entrance) will ftart afide, or bow, or break ; and then you will be forced to draw it out again with the *Claw* of the *Hammer*. Therefore you may fee a reafon when you buy a *Hammer*, to chufe one with a true flat *Face*.

A little trick is fometimes ufed among fome (that would be thought cunning Carpenters) privately to touch the Head of the Nail with a little Ear-wax, and then lay a Wager with a Stranger to the Trick, that he fhall not drive that Nail up to the Head with fo many blows. The ftranger ſtranger thinks he ſhall aſſuredly win, but does aſſuredly loſe ; for the *Hammer* no ſooner touches the Head of the Nail, but inſtead of entring the Wood it flies away, notwithſtanding his utmoſt care in ſtriking it down-right.

§ 10. *Of the* Commander, *and its Uſe.*

THe *Commander* is deſcribed in *Plate* 8. K.   It is indeed but a very great wooden *Mallet*, with an Handle about three foot long, to uſe in both the Hands.

It is uſed to knock on the Corners of Framed Work, to ſet them into their poſition.   It is alſo uſed to drive ſmall wooden Piles into the ground, &c. or where greater Engines may be ſpared.

§ 11. *Of the* Crow, *and its Uſe.*

THe *Crow* is deſcribed in *Plate* 8. L. *a* the *Shank,* *b b* the *Claws, c* the *Pike-end.*   It is uſed as a *Lever* to lift up the ends of great heavy Timber, when either a Bauk, or a Rowler, is to be laid under it ; and then they thruſt the *Claws* between the Ground and the Timber, and laying a Bauk, or ſome ſuch Stuff behind the *Crow,* they draw the other end of the Shank backwards, and ſo raiſe the Timber.

§ 12. *Of the* Drug, *and its Uſe.*

THe *Drug* deſcribed in *Plate* 9. A. is made ſomewhat like a low narrow Carr. It is uſed for the carriage of Timber, and then is drawn by the Handle *a a,* by two or more Men, according as the weight of the Timber may require.

There are alſo ſome Engines uſed in Carpentry, for the management of their heavy Timber, and hard Labour, *viz.* the *Jack,* the *Crab,* to which belongs Pullies and Tackle, &c. Wedges, Rowlers, great Screws, &c. But I ſhall give you an
account

account of them when I come to the explanation of Terms at the latter end of *Carpentry.*

§ 13. *Of the* Ten-foot Rod, *and thereby to measure and describe the* Ground-plot.

WE shall begin therefore to measure the *Ground-plot,* to which Carpenters use a *Ten-foot Rod* for Expedition, which is a Rod about an Inch square, and ten foot long ; being divided into ten equal parts, each part containing one foot, and is divided into 24 equal parts, and their Sub-divisions.

With this *Rod* they measure the length and breadth of the *Ground-plot* into Feet, and if there be odd Inches, they measure them with the *Two-foot Rule.* Their measure they note down upon a piece of paper, and having considered the situation of the Sides, *East, West, North* and *South,* they draw on paper their several Sides accordingly, by a small Scale, either elected, or else made for that purpose. They may elect their *Two-foot Rule* for some plots ; for an Inch and an half may commodiously serve to set off one Foot on some small *Ground-plots,* and then you have the Inches to that Foot actually divided by the Marks for the half quarters on the *Two-foot Rule.* But this large Scale will scare serve to describe a *Ground-plot* above ten Foot in length, because a small sheet of Paper is not above 15 or 16 Inches long, and therefore one sheet of Paper will not contain it, if the *Ground-plot* be longer : Therefore if you make every half quarter of an Inch to be a Scale for two Inches, a sheet of Paper will contain 20 Foot in length : And if you make every half quarter of an Inch to be a Scale for four Inches, a sheet of Paper will contain 40 Foot. And thus by diminishing the Scale, the sheet of Paper will contain a greater number of Feet.

But

But having either elected, or elſe made your Scale, you are to open your Compaſſes to the number of Feet on your Scale your *Ground-plot* hath in length, and then transfer that Diſtance to your paper, and to draw a ſtraight Line between the two points, and mark that ſtraight Line with *Eaſt, Weſt, North* or *South*, according to the ſituation of that ſide of the *Ground-plot* it repreſents.   Then a-gain open your Compaſſes to the number of Feet on your Scale one of the adjoining Sides contains, and transfer that Diſtance alſo to your paper, and draw a Line between the two points, and note its ſituation of *Eaſt, Weſt, North* or *South*, as before. Do the like by the other Sides ; and if either a Quirk, or any Addition, be added to the Build-ing, on any ſide of your *Ground-plot*, you muſt de-ſcribe it alſo proportionably.

Then you are to conſider what Apartments, or Partitions, to make on your *Ground-plot*, or ſecond, or third Story, and to ſet them off from your Scale, beginning at your intended Front. As for Example , Suppoſe your *Ground-plot* be a Long-ſquare, 50 Foot in length, and 20 Foot wide : This *Ground-plot* will contain in its length two good Rooms, and a Yard behind it 10 Foot long. If you will, you may divide the 40 Foot into two equal parts, ſo will each Room be 20 Foot ſquare : Or you may make the Rooms next the Front deeper, or ſhallower, and leave the remainder for the Back-Room : As here the Front-Room is 25 Foot, and the Back-Room 15 Foot deep, and a ſetting off of 8 Foot broad and 10 Foot long tak-ing out of the Yard, for a Buttery below Stairs (if you will) and Cloſets above Stairs over it. But what width and depth ſoever you intend your Rooms ſhall have, you muſt open your Compaſſes to that number of Feet on your Scale, and ſet off that Diſtance on the *Eaſt, Weſt, North* or *South,*

Line,

Line, according to the Situation of that fide it reprefents on your *Ground-plot.* If you fet it off the
Eaft Line, you muft alfo fet it off on the *Weft* ; if
on the *North* Line, you muft alfo fet it off on the
South Line : Becaufe between the two Settings off
on the *Eaft* and *Weft* Lines, or *North* or *South*
Lines, you muft draw a ftraight Line of the length
of your intended Partition. And in this manner
you muft from every Partition draw a Line in its
proper place on the Paper, by meafuring the Diftances each Partition muft have from the outfide
of the *Ground-plot.*

And thus you are alfo to defcribe by your Scale
your Front, and feveral fides of the Carcafe ;
allowing the *Principal Pofts , Enterduces , Quar-
terings, Braces, Gabies, Doors, Windows,* and *Ornaments,* their feveral Sizes, and true Pofitions by
the Scale : Each fide upon a Paper by it felf : Unlefs we fhall fuppofe our Mafter-Workman to underftand *Perfpective* ; for then he may, on a fing-
gle piece of Paper, defcribe the whole Building,
as it fhall appear to the Eye at any affigned Sta-
tion.

§ 14. *Of* Foundations.

HAving drawn the *Draft,* the Mafter-Workman is firft to caufe the Cellars to be dug,
if the Houfe fhall have Cellars. And then to try
the Ground, that it be all over of an equal firm-
nefs, that when the weight of the Building is fet
upon it, it may not fink in any part. But if the
Ground be hollow or weaker in any place, he
ftrengthens it, fometimes by well ramming it
down, and levelling it again with good dry Earth,
Lime-Core, Rubbifh, *&c.* or fometimes with ramming in Stones, or fometimes with well Planking
it ; or moft fecurely by driving in Piles. But
driving in of Piles is feldom ufed for Timber
Houfes,

Houfes, but for Stone, or Brick Houfes, and that
but in few places of *England* neither, but where
the Ground proves *Fenny*, or *Moorifh*. Therefore
a farther account fhall be given of Foundations,
when I come to exercife upon *Mafonry*, &c.

Then are the Celler-Walls to be brought up by
a *Brick-layer* with *Brick*; for fmall Houfes two
Bricks thick, for bigger two and an half Bricks
thick, or three or four Bricks thick, according to
the bignefs of the Houfe, and quality of the
Ground, as I fhall fhew when I come to Exercife
on *Bricklaying*.

But if the Houfe be defigned to have no Cellars
(as many Country-Houfes have not) yet for the
better fecuring the Foundation, and preferving
the Timber from rotting, Mafter-Workmen will
caufe three, or four, or five courfe of Bricks to be
laid, to lay their *Ground-plates* upon that Foundation.

The Foundation being made good, the Mafter-
Workman appoints his Under-Workmen their feveral *Scantlins*, for *Ground-plates*, *Principal Pofts*,
Pofts, *Breffummers*, *Girders*, *Trimmers*, *Joyfts*, &c.
which they cut fquare, and frame their Timbers
to, as has been taught in the feveral Exercifes upon Joinery, (whither I refer you) and there fet
them up, each in its proper place, according to
the Draft.

The Draft of a Foundation I have defcribed in
Plate 10, according to a Scale of eight Foot in an
Inch; where you have the Front A B 20 Foot
long, the fides A C and B D 50 Foot long. The
Shop, or firft Room, E E 25 Foot (as aforefaid)
deep. I make the firft Room a Shop, becaufe I in-
tend to defcribe *Shop-windows*, *Stalls*, &c. though
you may Build according to any other purpofe :
The *Kitching*, or *Back-Room* F F 15 Foot deep. A
Buttry or *Clofet*, taken out of the *Yard*, marked G,

I   10 Foot

10 Foot deep, and 8 Foot wide: H a *Setting off* in the *Yard*, 4 Foot fquare for the *Houfe of Office.* I *Leaving way* in the Shop for a *Stair-Cafe* 6 Foot, and 11 Foot. K The *Yard.* L The *Sink-hole* 1 Foot fquare. M *Leaving way* in the *Kitching* 6 Foot deep, and 4 Foot wide for the *Chimneys.*

I do not deliver this Draft of Partitions for the moft Commodious for this Ground-plot, nor is the Houfe fet out defigned for any particular Inhabitant; which is one main purpofe to be confidered of the Mafter-Workman, before he make his Draft; for a Gentleman's Houfe muft not be divided as a Shop-keeper's, nor all Shop-keepers Houfe a-like; for fome Trades require a deeper, others may difpence with a fhallower Shop, and fo an Inconvenience may arife in both. For if the Shop be fhallow, the Front Rooms upwards ought to be fhallow alfo: Becaufe by the ftrict Rules of *Architecture,* all Partitions of Rooms ought to ftand directly over one another: For if your Shop ftands in an eminent Street, the Front Rooms are commonly more Airy than the Back Rooms; and always more Commodious for obferving publick Paffages in the Street, and in that refpect it will be inconvenient to make the Front Rooms fhallow: But if you have a fair Profpect backwards of Gardens, Feilds, *&c.* (which feldom happens in Cities) then it may be convenient to make your Back-Rooms the larger for Entertainment, *&c.* But I fhall run no farther into this Argument; for I fhall leave the Mafter-Workman to confult Books of *Architecture,* and more particularly the Builder, which, in this cafe, they ought all to do.

MECHA-

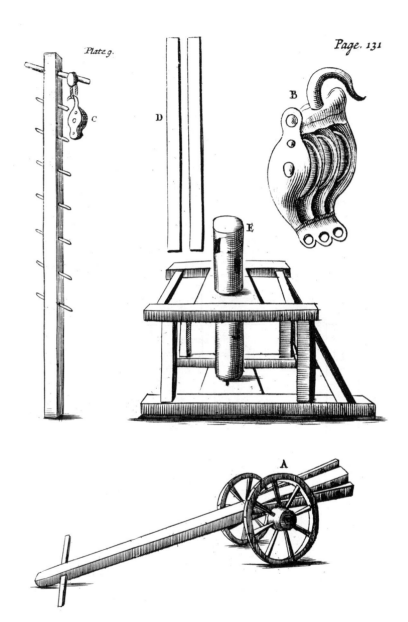

Plate 9.

Plate 10

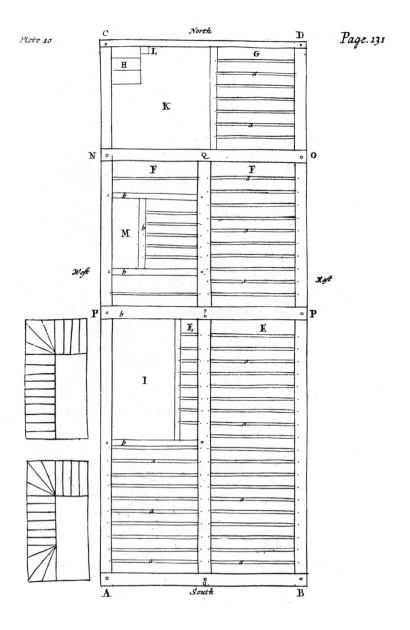

MECHANICK EXERCISES;

OR,

The Doctrine of *Handy-Works*

Continued in the ART of *House-Carpentry.*

A C, B D, C D, N O, *Ground-plates, Wall-plates,*
   Brefummers, Lintels, the Thickness of the Wall.
A B, *Also a Ground-plate, or Ground-fell.*
P P, *The Summer.*
Q Q Q, *Girders.*
I, *The Well-houle for the Stairs, and Stair-cafe.*
M, *Leaving a way for the Chimnies.*
b b, *Trimmers for the Chimny-way and Stair-cafe.*
a a a a, *Joyfts.*

§ 15. *Of* Framing *for the* Floors.

THE four Plates, A B, A N, N O and B O, lying on the Foundation, are called *Ground-plates.* They are to be of good Oak, and for this fize of Building about eight Inches broad, and fix Inches deep. They are to be framed into one another with Tennants and Morteffes. The longer Ground-plates A N and B O are commonly tennanted into the Front and Rear Ground-plates A B and N O, and into thefe two fide-Ground-plates are Morteffes made for the Tennants at the ends of the Joyfts, to be fitted fomewhat loofly in, at about ten Inches diftance from one another, as in the Draft. Thefe Ground-plates are to be bor'd with an Inch and half *Augre,* and well pinned into

one

one another with round Oaken Pins, made tapering towards the point,and so strong, that with the
hard blows of a Mallet, they may drive stiff into
the *Augre-hole*, and keep the Tennant firmly in the
Mortess.   The manner of making a Tennant and
Mortess is taught in *Joiuery*, p. 85.   But because
the Stuff *Carpenters* work upon, is generally heavy
Timber, and consequently not so easily managed as
the light Stuff Joiners work upon ; therefore they
do not at first pin their Tennants into their Mor-
tesses with wooden Pins, lest they should lie out of
square, or any other intended Position : But laying
a *Block*, or some other piece of Timber, under the
corner of the Frame-work to bear it hollow off the
Foundation, or what ever else it lies upon, they
drive *Hook-pins* (described in *Plate* 8. § 6.) into the
four *Augre-holes* in the corners of the Ground-
plates , and one by one fit the Plates either to a
Square, or any other intended Position : And when
it is so fitted, they draw out their *Hook-pins*, and
drive in the wooden Pins (as aforesaid) and taking away the wooden *Blocks* one by one from under the corners of the Frame, they let it fall into
its place.

But before they pin up the Frame of Ground-
plates,they must fit in the *Summer* marked P P,and
the *Girders* Q Q, and all the *Joysts* marked *a a a a*,
&c and the *Trimmers* for the *Stair-case*, and *Chimny-
-way* marked *b b*, and the binding *Joysts* marked
c c, for else you cannot get their Tennants into
their respective Mortess-holes. But they do I say fit
all these in, while the Frame of Ground-plates lies
loose, and may, corner by corner,be opened to let
the respective Tennants into their respective Mor-
tesses, which when all is done, they Frame the
Raising-plates just as the *Ground-plates* are Framed ;
and then Frame the Roof into the *Raising-plates*
with *Beams*, *Joysts*, &c.

The

The *Summer* is in this Ground-plate placed at 25 Foot diſtance from the Front, and is to be of the ſame Scantlin the principal Plates are of, for Reaſons as ſhall be ſhewn hereafter : And the *Girders* are alſo to be of the ſame Scantlins the *Summers* and *Ground-plates* are of, though according to the nice Rules of *Architecture*, the *Back-Girder* need not be ſo ſtrong as the *Front-Girder*, becauſe it Bears but at 14 Foot length, and the *Front-Girder* Bears at 24 Foot length : Yet Carpenters (for uniformity) generally make them ſo, unleſs they build an Houſe by the Great, and are agreed for the Sum of Money, &c.

The *Joyſts* Bearing at 8 Foot (as here they do) are to be 7 Inches deep, and 3 Inches broad.

The *Trimmers* and *Trimming Joyſts* are 5 Inches broad and 7 Inches deep, and theſe *Joyſts*, *Trimmers* and *Trimming Joyſts*, are all to be pinned into their reſpective Morteſſes ; and then its flatneſs try'd with the Level, as was taught § 7.

§ 16. Of ſetting up the Carcaſs.

THough the *Ground-plates*, *Girders*, &c. be part of the Carcaſs, yet I thought fit in the laſt Section they ſhould be laid, before I treated of the Superſtructure, which I ſhall now handle. The four Corner Poſts called the *Principal Poſts* marked A A, ſhould be each of one piece, ſo long as to reach up to the *Beam* of the *Roof*, or *Raiſing-plate*, and of the ſame Scantlin the *Ground-plates* are of, *viz.* 8 Inches broad, and 6 Inches thick, and ſet with one of its narroweſt ſides towards the Front. Its lower end is to be Tennanted, and let into a Morteſs made near the corner of the *Ground-plate* Frame ; and its upper end hath alſo a Tennant on it, to fit into a Morteſs made in the Beam of the Roof, or *Raſing-piece*.

I 3
At

At the heighth of the firſt Story in this Principal Poſt, muſt be made two Morteſſes, one
to receive the Tennant at the end of the Breſſummer that lies in the Front, and the other
to entertain the Tennant at the end of the
Breſſummer that lies in the Return-ſide.

Two ſuch Morteſſes muſt alſo be made in this
Principal Poſt at the height of the ſecond Story,
to receive the Tennant at the ends of the Breſſummers for that Story.

Though I have ſpoken ſingularly of one Principal Poſt, yet as you work this, you muſt work
all four Principal Poſts ; and then ſet them plumb
upright, which you muſt try with a Plumb-line
deſcribed in *Plate* 8 §. 8.

Having erected the Principal Poſts upright,
you muſt enter the Tennants of the Breſſummers into their proper Morteſſes, and with a
Nail or two (about a ſingle Ten or a double
Ten) tack one end of a deal Board, or ſome
other like piece of Stuff to the Breſſummer, and
the other end to the Fram'd Work of the
Floor, to keep the Principal Poſts upright, and
in their places   Then ſet up the ſeveral Poſts
between the Principal Poſts ; but theſe Poſts
muſt be Tennanted at each end, becauſe they
are to be no longer than to reach from Story
to Story, or from Entertiſe to Entertiſe, and
are to be framed into the upper and under Breſſummer. If the Entertiſes be not long enough,
they ſet up a Principal Poſt between two or three
Lengths, to reach from the Ground-plate up to
the Raiſing-plates.

It is to be remembred. that the Breſſummers and Girders are laid flat upon one of
their broadeſt ſides, with their two narroweſt
ſides Perpendicular to the Ground-plot ; but
the Joyſts are to be laid contrary : For they
are

are Framed fo as to lie with one of their narroweft fides upwards, with their two broadeft
fides Perpendicular to the Ground-plot. The
reafon is, becaufe the Stuff of the Breffummers
and Girders are lefs weakned by cutting the
Morteffes in them in this Pofition, than in the
other Pofition; for as the Tennants for thofe
Morteffes are cut between the top and bottom
fides, and the flat of the Tennants are no broader
than the flat of the narroweft fide of the Joyfts;
fo the Morteffes they are to fit into, need be
no broader than the breadth of the Tennant,
and the Tennants are not to be above an Inch
thick, and confequently the Morteffes are to
be made with an Inch Mortefs-Chiffel, as was
fhewn in *Joinery*, p. 86. for great care muft be taken
that the Breffummers and Girders be not weakned
more than needs, left the whole Floor dance,

Thefe Tennants are cut through the two narroweft fides, rather than between the two
broadeft fides, becaufe the Stuff of the Girders
retains more ftrength when leaft of the Grain
of the Stuff is cut: And the Tennants being
made between the narroweft fides of the Joyces,
requires their Mortefs-holes no longer than the
breadth of that Tennant : And that Tennant
being but an Inch thick, requires its Mortefs
but an Inch wide to receive it ; fo that you
Mortefs into the Girder no more than three
Inches wide with the Grain of the Stuff, and
one Inch broad contrary to the Grain of the
Stuff. But fhould the Tennant be cut between
the two broad fides of the Joyfts, the Mortefs
would be three Inches long, and but one Inch
broad, and confequently, you muft cut into the
Girder three Inches crofs the Grain of the Stuff,
which would weaken it more than cutting fix
Inches with the Grain, and one Inch crofs.

But it may be objected that the Tennants of
the Joyſts being ſo ſmall, and bearing at an Inch
thickneſs muſt needs be too weak.

Anſwer, Firſt, Though the Tennants be indeed but an Inch thick, and three Inches broad ;
yet the whole Bearing of the Joyces do not
ſolely depend upon their Tennants ; becauſe the
Girders they are framed into, prove commonly ſomewhat Wainny upon their upper ſides ,
and the Joyſts are always ſcribed to project over
that Waynnineſs , and ſo ſtrengthen their Bearing
by ſo much as they project over the Roundneſs or
Waynnineſs of the upper ſide of the Girder.

Secondly, The Floor is boarded with the length
of the Boards athwart the Joyſts, and theſe
Boards firmly railed down to the Joyſts, which
alſo adds a great ſtrength to them.

Thirdly, The Joyſts are ſeldom made to Bear
at above ten Foot in length, and ſhould by
the Rule of good Workmanſhip, not lie above
ten Inches aſunder at the moſt : So that this
ſhort Bearing and cloſe diſcharging of one another, renders the whole Floor firm enough for
all common Occupation. But if the Joyces do
Bear at above ten Foot in length, it ought to
be the care of the Maſter-workman to provide
ſtronger Stuff for them, *viz.* Thicker and Broader. If not, they cut a Tusk on the upper ſide of
the Tennant, and let that Tusk into the upper
ſide of the Girders.

Having erected the Principal Poſt, and other
Poſts, and fitted in the Breſſummers, Girders,
Joyſts, *&c* upon the firſt Floor, they pin up
all the Frame of Carcaſs-work. But though the
Girders and Joyſts deſcribed for this firſt Floor,
lie proper enough for it ; yet for the ſecond
Story, and in this particular Caſe, the Joyſts
lie not proper for the ſecond Story ; becauſe

in

in the fecond Story we have defcribed a *Balcony*.

Therefore in this Cafe you muft frame the Front-Breffummer about feven Inches lower into the Principal Pofts : Becaufe the Joyfts for the fecond Floor are not to be Morteffed into the Breffummer to lie even at the top with it, but muft lie upon the Breffummer, and project over it fo far as you defign the *Balcony* to project beyond the Upright of the Front : And thus laying the Joyfts upon the Breffummer renders them much ftronger to bear the *Balcony*, than if Joyfts were Tennanted into the Front of the Bref-fummer, and fo project out into the Street from it.

But the Truth is, Though I have given you a Draft of the Joyfts lying athwart the Front and Rear for the firft Floor, you may as well lay them Range with the two fides on the firft Floor. But then the Breffummer that reaches from Front to Rear in the middle of the Floor muft be ftronger : And Girders muft then be Tennanted into the Breffummer, and the Ground-plates at fuch a Diftance, that the Joyfts may not Bear at above ten Foot in length. And the Tennants of the Joyfts muft be Tennanted into the Girders, fo that they will then lie Range with the two Sides.

But, a word more of the Breffummer: I fay (as before) the Breffummer to Bear at fo great Length muft be ftronger, though it fhould be difcharged at the Length of the Shop, (*viz*. at 25 Foot) with a Brick Wall, or a Foundati-on brought up of Brick. But if it fhould have no Difcharge of Brick-work, but Bear at the whole 40 Foot in Length, your Breffummer muft be yet confiderably ftronger than it need be, were it to Bear but 25 Foot in Length ; be-caufe the fhorter all the Bearings of Timbers are, the firmer they Bear. But then the Fraim-ing Work will take up more Labour : And in

many

many Cafes it is cheaper to put in ftronger Stuff for long Bearings, than to put a Girder between, to Difcharge the Length of the Joyfts to be framed into the Girders.

But to make fhort of this Argument, I fhall give you the Scheme of Scantlins of Timber at feveral Bearings for *Summers, Girders, Joyfts, Rafters,* &c. as they are fet down in the Act of Parlia. for the Rebuilding the City of *London,* after the late dreadful Fire: Which Scantlins were well confulted by able Workmen before they were reduced into an Act.

Scantlins of Timber for the firft Sorts of Houfes

	Foot	Inches	Inches
For the Floor { Summers under—	15	12—and—	8
Wall-plates ———		7—and—	5

For the { Principal Rafters under—15 { at foot--8 } 6 Inch.
Roof { at top---5
Single Rafters ——— 4—and—3 Inches.

	Length Foot	Thickness	Depth
Joyfts to ———	10	3—and———	7 Inches
Garret Floors———	3	———	6

Scantlins of Timber for the other two Sorts of Houfes.

For the Floor:

		Breadth	Depth	Thickness	Depth
	Foot	Foot	Inches	Inches	Inches Inches
Summers	10--to--15—	11--and--8		Joyfts { 3 ——— 6
or Girders {	15 ——— 18	13 ——— 9	which { 3 ——— 7
which bear {	18 ——— 21	14 ——— 10	bear { 3 ——— 7
in length {	21 ——— 24	16 ——— 12	10 { 3 ——— 8
from {	24 ——— 26	17 ——— 14	Foot { 3 ——— 8

Inches   Inches

Principal Difcharges upon Peers { 13 and 12
in the firft Story in the Fronts { 15 ——— 13

Binding Joyfts with their { Thickness   Inches
Trimming Joyfts { 5 — depth equal to
their own Floors

Inches   Inches

Wall-plates, or Raifing Pieces and Beams { 10 and 6
{ 8 ——— 6
{ 7 ——— 5

Inches   Inches

Lintels of Oak in the { 1ft. and 2d. Story—8 and 6
{ 3d. Story——— 5 ——— 4

Length

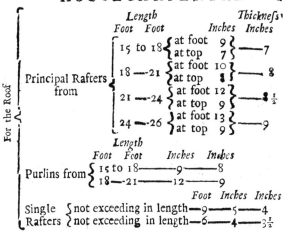

For the Roof

		Length			Thickness
		Foot Foot		Inches	Inches

Principal Rafters from
- 15 to 18 { at foot 9 } —— 7 / at top 7
- 18 —21 { at foot 10 } —— 8 / at top 8
- 21 —24 { at foot 12 } —— 8½ / at top 9
- 24 —26 { at foot 13 } —— 9 / at top 9

Length
Foot Foot Inches Inches

Purlins from { 15 to 18 ————9————8 / 18 —21————12————9

		Foot	Inches	Inches

Single { not exceeding in length —9——5——4
Rafters { not exceeding in length —6——4——3½

Scantlins for Sawed Timber and Laths, usually brought out of the West Country, not less than

Breadth Thickness
Foot Inches Inches

Single Quarters in length--8——3½——1¾
Double Quart. in length---8——4——3½
Sawed Joysts in length-----8——6——4

Laths in length ———— { 5 / 4 —1¼—1 quarter and ½ Inch

Inches

Stone Where Stone is used, to keep to these Scantlins——

First sort of Houses {
- Corner Peers——————————18 square
- Middle or Single Peers——————14 and 12
- Double Peers between House and House } 14 and 18
- Door-Jambs and Heads————————12 and 8

Foot Inches

2d & 3d sorts— {
- Corner Peers————————2—5 square
- Middle or Single Peers————18 square
- Double Peers between House and House } 24 and 18
- Door Jambs and Heads————————14 and 10

Foot Thickness

Scantlins for Sewers { 3 wide / 5 high } { Side-walls-1 Brick ½ / Arch-1 Brick on end } Bottom paved plain, and then 1 Brick on edge circular.

Gene-

General RULES.

IN every Foundation within the Ground add one Brick in thickneſs to the thickneſs of the Wall (as in the Scheme) next above the Foundation, to be ſet off in three Courſes equally on both ſides.

That no Timber be laid within twelve Inches of the fore-ſide of the Chimney-Jambs : And that all Joyſts on the back of any Chimney be laid with a Trimmer at ſix Inches diſtance from the Back.

That no Timber be laid within the Tunnel of any Chimney, upon Penalty to the Workman for every Default ten Shillings, and ten Shillings every Week it contiuues un reformed.

That no Joyſts or Rafters be laid at greater diſtances from one to the other, than twelve Inches ; and no Quarters at greater diſtance than fourteen Inches.

That no Joyſts bear at longer length than ten Foot ; and no ſingle Rafters at more in length than nine Foot.

That all Roofs, Window-frames, and Celler-floors be made of Oak.

The Tile-pins of Oak.

No Summers or Girders to lie over the Head of Doors and Windows.

No Summer or Girder to lie leſs than ten Inches into the Wall, no Joyſts than eight Inches, and to be laid in Lome.

But

But yet the *Carcaſs* is not compleated, till the *Quarters* and *Braces* between the *principal Poſts* and *Poſts* are fitted in ; the *Window-frames* made and ſet up, and the *principal Rafters, Purlins, Gables,* &c. are alſo fram'd and ſet up. The manner of their Pitch and Scantlins you will ſee in *Plate* 11. And the Reaſons for ſeveral *Pitches* you may find among Books of *Architecture.* But the Names of every Member you will find in the *Alphabetical Table* at the latter end of theſe Exerciſes on *Carpentry,* referred unto by Letters and Arithmetical Figures in the Plate aforeſaid.

But now we will ſuppoſe the Carcaſs is thus finiſhed. The Bricklayer is then to bring up the Chimnies, and afterwards to *Tile* the Houſe. And then the next Work the Carpenter has to do, is to bring up the *Stairs,* and *Stair-caſes,* and afterwards to *Floor* the Rooms, and *Hang* the *Doors,* &c. For ſhould he either bring up the Stairs and Stair-caſes, or Floor the Rooms before the Houſe is Tiled, or otherwiſe covered, if wet Weather ſhould happen it might injure the Stairs, Flooring, *&c.*

A, *The Ground-plate, or Ground-ſell.*

BB, BB, *The Principal Poſts.*

CC, *The Binding Intertiſes, or indeed, more properly Interduces, Breſſummers, Girders.*

D, *Beam of the Roof, Breſſummer, or Girder to the Garret Floor.*

EE, *Principal Rafters.* FF, *Breſſummers.*

G, *Plate or Raiſing-piece, alſo a Beam.*

a a, *Jaums or Door-poſts.* b b, *Braces.* c c, *Jaums.*

d, *Top-rail of the Balcony.*

e e, *Bottom-rail of the Balcony.*

fff, *Poſts of the Balcony.*

g g g, *Baniſters.*

h h, *Breſſummers for the Shop-windows.*

H, *King-*

H, *King-piece or Joggle-piece.*

i i, Struts.

k k, Top-beam, Coller-beam, Wind-beam, Strut-beam.

l l l, Door-head.

I I, *The Feet of the principal Rafters.*

K, *The Top of the Rafters.*

II K, *The Gable-end.*

LL, *Knees of the principal Rafters, to be made all of one piece with the principal Rafters.*

M, *The Fuſt of the Houſe.*

N N, *Purlins.*

O O, *Shop-windows.*

P P, *Flaps or Falls.*

m m m, Quarters.

n n, Jaums of the Window.

o o, Back and Head of the Window.

p p, Tranſums.

q q, Munnions.

r r, Furrings, or Shreadings.

V, *Single light Windows or Luteons.*

s s s, Rafters.

§ 16. *Of* Window-Frames.

IN Brick Buildings the *Window-Frames* are ſo framed, that the Tennants of the Head-ſell, Ground-ſell, and Tranſum, run though the outer *Jaums* about four Inches beyond them : And ſo they are ſet in a Lay of Morter upon the Brick-wall before the Peers on either ſide is brought up, at about three Inches within the Front; So that the Brick-work over the Head and about the Jaums defend it from the Weather. Then the *Bricklayer* brings up the Peers on both ſides, ſo that the four Ends or Tennants that project through the outer Jaums being buried and trimmed into the Brick-work become a Faſtning to the *Window-Frame.*

But

But if the Window-Frame ftands on a Timber-houfe, the Head and Ground-fell are fometimes Tennanted into Pofts of the Carcafs; and then the Pofts do the Office of the outer Jaums of the Window-Frame; and the Head and Ground-fell are then called *Entertifes*, and therefore both Head and Ground-fell, and Pofts or Jaums, are rabbetted about half an Inch on the outfide of the Front, to receive the Pane of Glafs that is fitted to it. And thus (as I faid) the Pofts become part of the Window-Frame.

But the better way is to frame a Window as the Brick-work Window, and to project it an Inch and a half beyond the fide of the Building, and to Plaifter againft its fides, for the better fecuring the reft of the Carcafs from the Weather.

The Window-Frame hath every one of its Lights Rabbetted on its outfide about half an Inch into the Frame, and all thefe Rabbets, but that on the Ground-fell, are grooved fquare, but the Rabbets on the Ground-fell is bevell'd downwards, that Rain or Snow, *&c.* may the freelier fall off it. Into thefe Rabbets the feveral Panes of Glafs-work is fet, and faftned by the Glafier.

The fquare Corners of the Frame next the Glafs is Bevell'd away both on the out and infide of the Building, that the Light may the freelier play upon the Glafs. And upon that Bevel is commonly Stuck a Molding (for Ornament fake) according to the Fancy of the Workman, but more generally according to the various Mode of the Times.

Of

§ 17. *Of* Stairs, *and* Stair-Cafes.

SEveral Writers of *Architecture* have delivered different Rules for the Height and Breadth of *Steps,* and that according to the feveral Capacities of the *Stair-Cafes.* They forbid more than fix, and lefs than four Inches for the Heighth of each Step, and more than fixteen, and lefs than twelve, for the Breadth of each Step. But here we muft underftand they mean thefe Meafures fhould be obferved in large and fumptuous Buildings: But we have here propofed an ordinary private Houfe, which will admit of no fuch Meafures, for want of room. Therefore to our prefent purpofe.

The firft and fecond Pair of Stairs the Steps fhall be about $7\frac{1}{3}$ Inches high, and 10 Inches broad. The third Pair of Stairs each Step may be about $6\frac{1}{2}$ Inches high, and $9\frac{1}{2}$ Inches broad. And for the fourth Pair of Stairs, each Step may be about 6 Inches high, and 9 Inches broad. But this Rule they do, or fhould follow, *viz.* to make all the Steps belonging to the fame pair of Stairs of an equal height; which to do, they firft confider the heighth of the Room in Feet and odd Inches, if any odd be, and multiply the Feet by 12, whofe Product, with the number of odd Inches, gives the fum of the whole Heighth in Inches ; which fum they divide by the number of Steps they intend to have in that Heighth, and the Quotient fhall be the number of Inches and parts that each Step fhall be high. Or, if they firft defign the Heighth of each Step in Inches, they try by Arithmetick how many times the Heighth of a Step they can have out of the whole Heighth of the Story, and fo know the number of Steps.

MECHA.

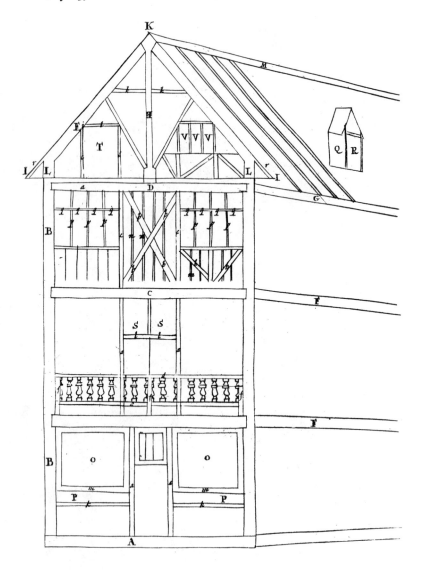

MECHANICK EXERCISES:

O R,

The Doctrine of *Handy-Works.*

Continued in the A R T of *Houfe-Carpentry.*

STAIRS are either made about a *Solid Newel*, or an *Open Newel*, and fometimes mixt, *viz.* with a Solid Newel for fome few Steps; then a ftraight or Foreright Afcent, with *Flyers* upon the fide of the fquare Open Newel, and afterwards a Solid Newel again. Than reiterate, *&c.*

The laft, *viz.* the *Mixt Newel'd Stairs*, are commonly made in our *Party-walled Houfes* in *London*, where no Light can be placed in the Stair-Cafe, becaufe of the Party-walls; fo that there is a neceffity to let in a *Sky-light* through the Hollow Newel: But this fort of Stair-Cafes take up more room than thofe with a fingle folid Newel; becaufe the Stairs of a folid Newel fpread only upon one fmall Newel, as the feveral Foulds of the Fans Woman ufe fpread about their Center: But thefe becaufe they fometimes wind, and fometimes fly off from that winding, take therefore the more room up in the Stair-Cafe.

The manner of projecting them, is copioufly taught in many Books of *Architecture*, whether I referr you: Yet not to leave you wholly in the

L dark,

dark, I fhall give you a fmall light into it. And firft of the *Solid Nowel.*

Winding Stairs are projeted on a round *Profile,* whofe Diameter is equal to the Bafe the Stair-Cafe is to ftand on, fuppofe fix foot fquare. This *Profile* hath its Circumference divided into 16 equal parts. The Semi-diameter of the *Profile* is divided into four equal parts, and one of them ufed for the Newel, and the reft for the length of the Steps: If you draw Lines from the Center through every one of the equal parts into the Circumference, the fpace between every two Lines will be the true Figure of a *Winding-Step.* And if they were all cut out and placed one above another, over the true place on the Profile round about the Newel, whofe Diameter is one quarter the length of a Step, you would by fupporting each Step with a *Raifer* have the modle of a true pair of *Winding-Stairs.* See Plate 10. Fig. 2.

Hollow Newel'd Stairs are made about a fquare Hollow Newel. We will fuppofe the *Well-hole* to be eleven foot long, and fix foot wide; and we would bring up a pair of Stairs from the firft *Floor* eleven Foot high; it being intended that a Skie-light fhall fall through the Hollow Newel upon the Stairs: We muft therefore confider the width and breadth of the Hollow Newel; and in this example admit it to be two foot and a half wide, and two foot broad: By the width I mean the fides that range with the Front and Rear of the Building, and by the breadth I mean the fides that range with the Party-walls.

I find (by the Rule aforefaid) that if I affign 18 Steps up, each Step will be feven Inches and one third of an Inch high.

You

You muſt Note, that the flying off, or elſe winding of theſe Steps will vary their places according as you deſign the firſt Aſcent. For if you make the firſt Aſcent as you come ſtraight out of the Street (as in Plate 10.) on the *South-ſide*, you will firſt aſcend upon a Pitch of *Flyers*, which Pitch (making an Angle of 38 deg. with the Floor) with ten Steps raiſe you ſix Foot high above the Floor, and bring you eight Foot towards the *North*-end of the *Well-hole*, by making each Step ten Inches broad.

But now you muſt leave *Flyers*, and make four Winding Steps. Theſe Winding Steps are made about a ſolid *Newel* (as hath been taught) and this *Newel* ſerves alſo for a *Poſt* to *Trim* the Stair-Caſe too. This Poſt ſtands upon the Floor, and is prolonged upwards ſo high, that Morteſſes made in it may receive the Tennants of the *Top* and *Bottom Rails* of the whole Stair-caſe for that Floor : Theſe four Winding ſteps aforeſaid, rounding one quarter about the Newel, turns your Face in your Aſcent now towards the *Eaſt*; theſe four ſteps are raiſed 2 foot, $5\frac{1}{3}$ Inches above the Flyers, ſo that (in all) your Stairs are now raiſed 8 foot $6\frac{2}{3}$ Inches. Here remains now only 2 foot $5\frac{1}{3}$ Inches to the *Landing place*, and theſe take up juſt four Flyers, which muſt be made as was taught before.

But now in your ſecond pair of Stairs, it will be proper to begin your Aſcent with your Face towards the *Weſt* : For landing by the firſt pair of Stairs with your Face towards the *Eaſt*, you turn by the ſide of the Rail on the ſecond Floor from the *Eaſt* towards the *North*, and at the further end of that Rail, you turn your Face again from the *North* towards the *Weſt*, and begin your Aſcent on the ſecond pair of Stairs.

Between

Between the Skie-light and the Afcent is a Poft fet upright to faften Rails into : (to bound the Stair-cafe) from the bottom of which, *viz.* on the fecond Floor you trim up three Flyers, and then turn off a quarter of a Circle, with Winding Steps : Then again, Flyers to your defigned pitch : And then again another quarter of a Circle with Winding Steps, *&c.*

The Rail thefe Steps are built upon, being at the beginning or bottom of the Afcent framed or otherwife faftned to the firft upright Poft, muft at its higher end be framed into the next Poft alfo, with a Bevel Tennant, as you were taught to frame *Quarters* into one another, *Numb.* 5. § 17. Only with this difference, that there you were taught to frame Square; but here you muft frame upon the *Bevel*, as you were taught, *Numb* 5. § 19. This Poft aforefaid bears upon the Floor, to make its Bearing the ftronger; and this Poft muft be continued to fuch an heighth, as it may alfo ferve to receive the Tennanted end of an upper and lower Rail framed into it. And between thefe *Bevelling Rails, Bannifters* make good the outfide of the *Stair-Cafe.*

Though I have here defcribed this Contrivance of a pair of Stairs, yet do I not deliver it as the beft Patern for this Building, or for thefe forts of Stairs, nor matters it to our purpofe whether it be or no; for (as I told you before) my undertaking is the *Doctrine of Handy-works*, not *Architecture*; but it's *Architecture* confiders the beft forming of all Members in a Building for the capacity of the Ground-Plot, and the Convenience of the intended Inhabitant; but Carpenters (as Carpenters) only work by directions prefcribed by the Architect.

Thefe therefore are the common Rules that thefe forts of Stairs, and indeed all others with

carving

carving according to the Profile or Ground-plot of the Stairs are made by. But thofe that will fee many Inventions may confult Books of *Architecture,* &c.

§ 18. *Of* Flooring *of* Rooms.

THough Carpenters never Floor the Rooms till the Carcafs is fet up, and alfo inclofed by the Plaifterer, left weather fhould wrong the Flooring ; yet they generally *Rough-plane* their *Boards* for Flooring before they begin any thing elfe about the Building, that they may fet them by to feafon: Which thus they do, they lean them one by one on end aflant with the edge of the Board againft a Bauk, fomewhat above the height of half the length of the Board, and fet another Board in the fame pofture on the other fide the Bauk, fo that above the Bauk they crofs one another : Then on the firft fide they fet another Board in that pofture, and on the fecond fide another, till the whole number of Boards are fet an end : Being fet in this pofture, there remains the thicknefs of a Board between every Board all the length, but juft where they crofs one another, for the Air to pafs through to dry and fhrink them, againft they have occafion to ufe them : But they fet them under fome covered Shed, that the Rain or Sun comes not at them ; for if the Rain wet them, inftead of fhrinking them, it will fmell them ; or if the Sun fhine fiercely upon them, it will dry them fo faft, that the Boards will *Tear* or *Shake,* which is in vulgar Englifh, *Split* or *Crack.*

They have another way to dry and feafon them, by laying them flat upon three or four Bauks, each Board about the breadth of a Board afunder, the whole length of the Bauks. Then they lay another Lay of Boards athwart upon

L 3 them,

them, each Board alſo the breadth of a Board aſunder; then another Lay athwart the laſt, till all are thus laid: So that in this poſition they alſo lye hollow for the Air to play between them.

Thus then, the Boards being Rough-plain'd and Seaſon'd. They try one ſide flat, as by *Numb.* 6. § 31. and both the edges ſtraight, as if they were to ſhoot a Joint; as by *Numb.* 4. § 4. and cut the Boards to an exact length, be-cauſe if the Boards are not long enough to reach athwart the whole Room, the ends may all lye in a ſtraight Line, that the ſtraight ends of o-ther Boards laid againſt them may make the truer Joint, and this they call a *Beaking Joint.* But before they lay them upon the Floor, they try with the *Level* (deſcribed § 7.) the flatneſs of the whole Frame of Flooring again, leſt any part of it ſhould be *Caſt* ſince it was firſt framed together; and if any part of the Floor lye too high, they with the *Adz* (if the eminency be large) take it off, as was ſhewed § 2. Or if it be ſmall, with the *Jack-Plain* in *Numb.* 4 § 2. till it lye level with the reſt of the Floor. But if any part of the Floor prove hollow, they lay a Chip, or ſome ſuch thing, upon that hollow place, to bare up the Board, before they nail it down.

All this being done, they chuſe a Board of the commoneſt thickneſs of the whole Pile for the firſt Board, and lay it cloſe again one ſide of the Room athwart the Joyſts, and ſo nail it firmly down with two Brads into every Joyſt it croſſes, each Brad about an Inch, or an Inch and a half within the edge of the Board.

If they ſhould lay more than an ordinary thick or thin Board at the firſt, they would have a greater number of Boards to work to a Level than

than they need, becaufe all the reft of the Boards muft be equalized in thicknefs to the firft.

Then they lay a fecond Board clofe to the firft. But before they nail it down they again try how its fides agrees with the fide of the firft, and alfo how its thicknefs agrees with the firft Board. If any part of its edge lye hollow off the edge of the firft Board, they fhoot off fo much of the length of the Board from that hollownefs towards either end, till it comply and make a clofe Joint with the firft. But if the edge fwell in any place, they plain of that fwelling till it comply as aforefaid.

If the fecond Board prove thicker than the firft, then with the *Adz* (as aforefaid) they hew away the under fide of that Board (moft commonly crofs the Grain, left with the Grain the edge of the *Adz* fhould flip too deep into the Board) in every part of it that fhall bare upon a Joyft, and fo fink it to a flat fuperficies to comply with the firft Board. If the Board be too thin, they underlay that Board upon every Joyft with a Cap, *&c.*

And as this fecond Board is laid, fo are the other Boards laid, if they be well affured the Boards are dry, and will not fhrink; but if they doubt the drinefs of the Boards, they (fometimes do, or fhould) take a little more pains; for after they have nailed down the firft Board, they will meafure the breadth of two other Boards, laying them by the fide of the firft. But yet they will not allow them their full Room to lye in, but after there edges are true fhot in a ftraight line, they will pinch them off about half a quarter of an Inch room more or lefs, according as they guefs at the well-feafonednefs of the Boards; by nailing down the fourth Board nearer to the firft Board by half a quarter

of

of an Inch (more or lefs) then the breadth of both Boards are. And though it be afterwards fomewhat hard to get thefe two Boards into that narrow room, *viz.* between the firft and fourth Board, yet they help themfelves thus : The under-edge of thefe Boards that are to join to each other, they Bevel fomewhat away, and then the firft and fourth Board being faft nailed down (as aforefaid) they fet the outer edges of thefe two Boards again the two nailed Boards, letting the inner edges of the two loofe Boards meet, and make an Angle perpendicular to the Floor.   Then with two or three Men jumping all at once upon that Angle, thefe two Boards with this force and reiterated jumps by degrees prefs flat down into the fuperficies of the Floor, or elfe with forcing Pins and Wedges, force them together : And then with Brads they nail them down, as they did the firft Board.   Thus afterwards they nail down a feventh Board, as they did the fourth, and then fit in the fifth and fixth Boards, as they did the fecond and third Boards. And fo on, nailing down every third Board, and forcing two others between it and the laft nailed Board, till the whole Floor be boarded.

But if thefe Boards are not long enough (as I hinted before) to reach through the whole Room, they examine how true the ends lye in a ftraight line with one another, by applying the edge of the Two-foot Rule to the ends, and where the ends of any Boards keep of the edge of the Two-foot Rule from complying with the whole range of ends, they with the *Chiffel* and *Mallet* cut off that irregularity , holding and guiding the Chiffel, fo that it may rather cut a-way more of the bottom then top of the Board, that fo the Boards joined to the ends of the firft

laid

laid Boards, may make on the Superficies of the Floor the finer and truer Joint.

Having thus Boarded the whole Room, notwithstanding they used their best diligence to do it exactly, yet may the edges of some Boards lye somewhat higher than the Board it lies next to ; therefore they peruse the whole Floor, and where they find any irregularities they plane them off with the Plane, *&c.*

§ 19. *The* Hanging *of* Doors, Windows, *&c.*

THe Floors being Boarded, the next work is to *Hang* the *Doors,* in which tho' there be little difficulty, yet is there much care to be taking, that the *Door* open and shut well.

If the *Door* have a *Door-Case* (as Chamber-Doors, and Closet-Doors commonly have) the *Jaums* of the Door-Case must stand exactly perpendicular, which you must try by the Plumbline, as by § 8. and the Head of the *Door-Case* or Entertise must be fitted exactly square to the *Jaums,* as you where taught *Numb.* 3. § 17, 18, 19. and the Angles of the *Door* must be made exactly square, and the *Rabbets* of the *Door* to fit axactly into the *Rabbets* of the *Door-Case.* But yet they commonly make the *Door* about one quarter of an Inch shorter than the insides of the *Jaums* of the *Door-Case,* least if the Boards of the Floor chance to swell within the sweep of the *Door,* the bottom of the *Door* should drag upon the *Floor.*

They consider what sort of *Hindges* are properest for the *Door* they are to *Hang.* When they have a *Street-door* (which commonly is to take off and lift on) they use *Hooks* and *Hindges.* In a *Battend-door, Back-door,* or other *Battend-door,* or *Shop-windows,* they use *Cross-Garnets.* If a *Framed Door, Side Hindges :* And for *Cupboard boards Doors,* and such like, *Duf-tails.* (See the description of these Hindges in *Numb.* 1. *Fig.* 1. 5, 6.) But what sort of Hindges soever they use, they have care to provide them of a strength proportionable to the size and weight of the *Door* they hang with them. Well-made Hindges I have described *Numb.* 1. *fol.* 20. whither to avoid repetition I refer you.

If they hang a *Street-door* (which is commonly about six *foot* high) they first drive the *Hooks* into the *Door-post,* by entring the Post first with an *Augure :* But the *Bit* of the *Augure,* must be less than the Shank of the *Hook,* and the hole boared not so long, because the Shank of the *Hook,* must be strongly forced into the Augure-hole, and should the Augure-hole be too wide, the Shank would be loose in it, and not stick strong enough in it. Therefore if the Shank be an Inch square, an half Inch-Augure is big enough to bore that hole with, because it will then endure the heavier blows of an Hammer, to drive it so far as it must go; and the stronger it is forced in, the faster the *Hook* sticks; but yet they are careful not to split the *Door-post.*

These *Hooks* are commonly drove in about Fifteen Inches and an half above the *Ground-sell,* and as much below the top of the *Door.* It is, or should be, their care to chuse the Pin of the lower *Hook* about a quarter of an Inch longer than that they use for the upper *Hook* (or else to make it so) because these *Doors* are commonly unweildy to lift off and on, especially to lift both the Hindges on both the *Hooks* at once. Therefore when the lower Hindge is lifted on the lower *Hook,* if the *Door* be then lifted perpendicularly upright, so high as the under side of the upper Hindge may just reach the top

of

of the upper *Hook,* you may the eafier flip the Eye of the upper Hindge upon the *Hook* ; whereas, if the lower *Hook* be either fhorter, or juft no longer than the other, inftead of lifting it readily upon the upper *Hook,* you may lift it off the lower *Hook,* and fo begin the labour again.

Having drove in the *Hooks,* they fet the *Rabbets* of the *Door* within the *Rabbets* of the *Doorpoft,* and underlay the bottom of the *Door,* with a Chip or two about half a quarter of an Inch thick, to raife the *Door* that it drag not. Then they put the Eyes of the Hindges over the Pins of the *Hooks,* and placing the Tail piece of the Hindges parallel to the bottom and top of the *Door,* they fo nail them upon.

This is the Rule they generally obferve for Hanging *Doors, Shop-windows,* &c. Only, fometimes inftead of Nailing the Hindges upon the Door, they *Rivet* them on, for more ftrength. And then, after they have fitted the Door, or Window, into its Rabbets, and laid the Hindges in there proper place and pofition (as aforefaid) they make marks in the Nail-holes of the Hindge with the point of their Compaffes upon the *Door,* and at thofe marks they Pierce holes, with a *Piercer-Bit,* that fits the fhank of the *Rivet* ; then they put the fhank of the *Rivet* thro' the holes made in the *Door* ; yet fo that the Head of the Rivet be on the outfide of the *Door* ; and they alfo put the end of the Shank into the Nail-hole of the Hinge, and fo whilft another Man holds the head of the Hatchet againft the Head of the Rivet, they with the *Pen* of their *Hammer* batter and fpread the flat end of the Shank over the Hole, as was fhewn *Numb.* 2. *fol.* 24, 25.

The

The Titles of fome Books of Architecture.

S *Ebaſtion Seirleo,* in Folio.
Hans Bloom's Five Collumns, Folio.
Vignola, in Folio.
Vignola, Or the *Compleat Architect,* in Octvo.
Scamotzi, Quarto.
Palladio, Quarto.
Sir *Henry Wotton's* Elements of Architecture, Quarto.

Theſe *Books* are all Printed in Engliſh: But there are many others extant in ſeveral other Languages, of which *Vitruvius* is the chief: For from his *Book* the reſt are generally derived; as *Philip Le Orm, Ditterlin, Marlois,* and many others, which being difficult to be had among *Book-ſellers,* and theſe ſufficient for information, I ſhall omit till another opportunity.

An Explanation of *Terms* uſed in *Carpentry.*

A

A *Dz,* Plate 8. B § 2.
Arch, Any work wrought Circular, as the top part of fome Window-frames, the top of fome great Gates, the Roof of Vaults, &c.
Architrave, See Numb. 6. Plate 6. 1. and Plate 6. A. § 1.
Ax, Numb. 7. Plate 8. A.

B

B *Ack* or *Hip-molding.* The backward Hips or *Valley-Rafters* in the way of an Angle for the back part of a Building.
Banniſter, Numb. 8. Plate 11. ggg.
Baſe, is commonly the Bottom of a Cullumn. See Numb. 6. Plate 6. *h.* and Plate 7. B.

Bate-

Batement, To abate or waſte a piece of Stuff, by forming of it to a deſigned purpoſe. Thus inſtead of asking how much was cut off ſuch a piece of Stuff, Carpenters ask what *Batement* that piece of Stuff had.

Batter, The ſide, or part of the ſide of a Wall, or any Timber that bulges from its bottom or Foundation, is ſaid to *Batter,* or *hang over* the Foundation.

Battlement, A flat Roof or Platform to walk on. But Battlements are more properly Walls built about the Platform to incloſe it, as is ſeen upon Towers for defence; part of the Battlement being Breaſt high that Muſquetiers may ſhoot over it, the other part Man high, to ſecure Men from the ſhot of their Enemies.

Bauk, A piece of Fir unſlit, from four to ten Inches ſquare, and of many lengths.

Bear, Timber is ſaid to *Bear* at its whole length, when neither a Brick-wall, or Poſts, &c. ſtand between the ends of it. But if either a Brick-wall or Poſts, &c. be Trimmed up to that Timber, than it is ſaid to Bear only at the diſtance between the Brick-wall or Poſt, and either end of the Timber. Thus Carpenters ask what

Bearing ſuch a piece of Timber has? The anſwer is 10, 12, 15, &c. Foot, according to the length of the whole Timber, or elſe according to the diſtance between either end of the Timber, and a

Bearer, viz. a Poſt or Brick-wall that is Trimmed up between the two ends of a piece of Timber, to ſhorten its *Bearing.*

Bond, When Workmen ſay make good Bond, they mean faſten the two or more pieces of Timber well together, either with Tennanting and Morteſſing, or Duff-tailing, &c.

Binding

Binding Joyſts, See Trimmers, or Plate 10. *b b b.*

Brace, See Plate 11. *b b b.*

Brad, is a Nail to *Floor Rooms* with, they are about the ſize of a Ten-penny Nail, but have not their heads made with a ſhoulder over their ſhank, as other Nails, but are made pretty thick towards the upper end, that the very top of it may be driven into, and buried in the Board they nail down, ſo that the tops of theſe Brads will not catch (as the Heads of Nails would) the Thrums of the Mops when the *Floor* is waſhing. You may ſee them at moſt Ironmongers.

Break in, Carpenters with their Ripping Chiſſel do often *Break in* to Brick-walls ; that is, they cut holes, but indeed more properly break the Bricks by force, and make their hole to their ſize and form.

Breſſummer, See Plate 11. CC, D, FF, *b b.*

Bring up, A Term moſt uſed amongſt Carpenters, when they diſcourſe *Bricklayers* ; and then they ſay, *Bring up* the Foundation ſo high, *Bring up* ſuch a Wall, *Bring up* the Chimnies, &c. which is as much as to ſay, Build the Foundation ſo high, Build the Wall, Build the Chimnies, &c.

Butment, The piece of Ground in the Yard marked G, in Plate 10. is a *Butment* from the reſt of the Ground-plot.

Buttreſs, That ſtands on the outſide a Wall to ſupport it.

C.

CAmber, A piece of Timber cut Arching, ſo as when a weight conſiderable, ſhall be ſet upon it, it may in length of time be reduced to a ſtraight.

Can-

Cantilevers, Pieces of Wood framed into the Front or other fides of an Houfe to fuftain the Molding and Eaves over it.

Carcafs, is (as it were) the Skelleton of an Houfe, before it is Lath'd and Plaftered.

Cartoufes. Ornamented *Corbels.*

Cleer Story Window, Windows that have no Tranfum in them.

Commander, See Numb. 7. Plate 8. K. and § 10.

Coping over, is a fort of hanging over, but not fquare to its upright, but Bevelling on its under fide, till it end in an edge.

Corbel, A piece of Timber fet under another piece of Timber, to difcharge its Bearing.

Crab, The Engine defcribed Plate 9. E. and BCD feveral of its Appurtenances, *viz.* B C C *Snatch Blocks.* D *Levers.* Its Office is to draw heavy Timber to a confiderable height.

Crow, See Plate 8. L. its Office is to remove heavy Timber, and therefore for ftrength is made of Iron.

Crown Poft, See Plate 11. H. Alfo the *King-Piece,* or *Joggle-Piece.*

D

D*Ifcharge,* A Brick-wall or a Poft trim'd up to a piece of Timber over charg'd for its Bearing, is a Difcharge to that Bearing.

Dormer, Plate 11. Q R.

Double Quarters, See *Quarter.*

Draft, The Picture of an intended Building difcribed on Paper, whereon is laid down the devifed Divifions and Partitions of every *Room* in its due proportion to the whole Building, See Numb. 7. § 13.

Drag, A *Door* is faid to *Drag* when either by its ill Hanging on its Hinges, or by the ill boarding of the *Room,* the bottom edge of the *Door* rides

rides (in its fweep) upon the *Floor.* See § 19.

Dragon-beams, are two ftrong Braces or Struts that ftands under a Breffummer, meeting in a an angle upon the fhoulder of the *King-piece.* In Plate 11, *i i* are *Dragon beams.*

Draw knife, defcribed Plate 8. E and § 5.
Draw Pins, defcribed Plate 8. F and § 6.
Drug, defcribed Plate 9. E and § 12.

E

ENter, When Tennants are put into Mortef- fes, they are faid to Enter the Morteffes.
Enterduce, or *Entertife,* defcribed Plate 11. CC.

F.

FEather-edge, Boards, or Planks, that have one edge thinner than another are called *Feather-edge* ftuff.

Fir-Pole, A fort of ftuff cut off of the Fir-tree, fmall and long, commonly from 10 to 16 Foot. They are fometimes ufed in flight Buil-dings, to ferve inftead of Bauks and Quarters.

Flyers, are Stairs made of an Oblong fquare Figure, whofe fore and backfides are parallel to each other, and fo are their ends ; the fecond of thefe *Flyers* ftands parallel behind the firft, the third behind the fecond, and fo are faid to fly off from one another.

Floor, in *Carpentry,* it is as well taken for the Fram'd work of Timber, as the Boarding over it.

Foot-pace, is a part of a pair of Stairs, where-on after four or fix fteps you arrive to a broad place, where you make two or three paces be-fore you afcend another ftep ; thereby to eafe the legs in afcending the reft of the fteps.

Furrings, The making good of the Rafters Feet in the Cornice.

Gable,

G

G*Able*, or *Gable-end*, in Plate 11. 11 K.

Gain, The bevelling fhoulder of a Joyft, or other Stuff: It is ufed for the Lapping of the end of a Joyft, &c. upon a Trimmer or Girder, and then the thicknefs of the fhoulder is cut into the Trimmer alfo Bevilling upwards, that it may juft receive that *Gain*, and fo the Joyft and Timber lye even and level upon their fuperficies. This way of working is ufed in a Floor or Hearth.

Girder, defcribed Plate 10 Q Q.

Ground Plate, defcribed Plate 11 A.

Ground Plate, The piece of Ground a Building is to be erected upon.

H.

H*Ang over*, See *Batter*.

Hips, defcribed Plate 11. EE, They are alfo called *Principal Rafters*, and *Sleepers*.

Hook-pin, defcribed Plate 8. F.

I.

J*Ack*, defcribed Plate 8. M. An Engine ufed for the removing and commodious placing of great Timber.

Jack-Plane, called fo by Carpenters, but is indeed the fame that Joyners call the *Fore-Plane*, See Numb. 4. § 2. and Plate 4. B. 1.

Jaums, Door Pofts are fo called: So are the upright outer Pofts of a Window frame, See Plate 11. *a a a a*, *c c*, *n n*.

Joggle-piece, See Plate 11. H.

Joyfts, See Plate 10. *a a a a*.

M   *Juffers*,

Juffers, Stuff, about 4 or 5 inches square, and of several Lengths.

K.

KIng-piece, See *Joggle-piece.*

Kerf, See *Explanation of Terms* in Numb. 6.

Knee, A piece of Timber growing angularly, or crooked, that is, a great Branch shooting out near the top of the Trunk of the Tree, and is so cut that the Trunk and the Branch make an angle; as in Plate 11. E L, being made out of one piece of stuff: It is called a *Knee-piece,* or *Knee-rafter.*

L.

LAnding-place, is the uppermost Step of a pair of Stairs, *viz.* The Floor of the Room you ascend upon.

Skirts, Projecting of the Eaves.

Level, See Plate 8. G and § 7.

Lever, See Plate 9. D.

Lintel, In Brick-buildings Carpenters lay a long piece of Timber over the Peers, to Trim with the Window-Frame; as well to bear the thickness of the Brick-wall above it, as to make Bond with the sides of the Walls.

Long-plane, The same that Joyners call a *Joynter.* See Numb. 4. B. 2. § 4.

Luthern, See *Dormer.*

M.

MOdillon, See *Cantelever.*

Molding, Moldings are stuck upon the edges of stuff to Ornament it: As on Chimney-pieces, the inner edges of Window-frames, Shelves, &c. See *Numb.* 4. §. 9.

Munnion,

Munnion, the upright Poſt that divide the ſeveral Lights in a Window-frame, are called
Munnions, See Plate 11. *q q q.*

N.

NEwel, the upright poſt that a pair of
Winding-ſtairs are turned about.

P.

PItch, The Angle a Gable-end is ſet to, is
called the *Pitch* of the Gable-end.

Planchier, An Ornament to which the Cornice
is faſtned.

Plate. A piece of Timber upon which ſome
conſiderable weight is framed, is called a Plate.
Hence *Ground-Plate,* Plate 11. A. *Window-plate,*
&c.

Plumb-line, deſcribed Plate 8. H § 8.

Poſts, See *Principal-Poſts.*

Prick-Poſts, Poſts that are framed into *Breſſummers,* between Principal-Poſts, for the ſtrength-
ning of the Carcaſs.

Principal-Poſts, The corner Poſts of a Carcaſs,
See Plate 11. B. B.

Profile, The ſame with *Ground-Plot.*

Projecture, is a jetting over the upright of a
Building: Thus *Balconies* project into the Street.

Puncheons, Short pieces of Timber placed under ſome conſiderable weight to ſupport it.

Pudlaies, Pieces of Stuff to do the Office of
Hand-Spikes.

Purlins, See Plate 11. NN.

Q.

QUarters are *ſingle* and *double. Single Quarters*
are Sawen ſtuff, two Inches thick, and four
Inches broad. The *Double Quarters* are ſawen
to Four Inches ſquare.

M 2

Quar-

Quartering, In the Front of the third Story in Plate 11. All the Work, except the Principal Posts, Jaums, and Window-frames, *viz.* the upright Triming, and the Braces is called *Quartering.*

Quirk, A piece taken out of any regular Ground-plot, or Floor: For example, the whole Ground-plot A B C D. in Plate 10. is a regular Ground-plot. But if the piece K be taking out of it, K shall be a *Quirk.*

R.

R*After,* See Plate 11. *cccc.*

Rail, Rails stand over and under Bannisters of *Balconies,* Stair-Cases, *&c.*

Raiser, is a Board set on edge under the Fore-side of a step.

Raising-piece, Pieces that lye under the Beams upon Brick or Timber by the side of the House.

Rellish, See *Projecture.*

Return, Either of the adjoining sides of the Front of an House, or Ground-plot, is called a *Return-side,* as in Plate 10. the Front is A B, the *Return-sides* to this Front is A C and B D.

Ridge, the meeting of the Rafters on both sides the House is called the *Ridge.*

Ripping-Chissel, See Plate 8. D § 4.

Roof, The Covering of a House: But the word is used in Carpentery for the Triming work of the Covering.

S.

S*cribe,* See Number 6. in *Explanation of Terms.*

Shake, Such stuff as is crackt either with the heat of the Sun, or the droughth of the wind, is called *Shaken Stuff.*

Shingles,

Shingles, Small pieces of Wood ufed to cover Houfes with, inftead of Tiles or Slates.

Shreadings, See Plate 11. the lower end of the Principal Rafters markt *rr* are called *Shreadings,* or *Furrings.*

Sleepers, The fame with *Purlins.*

Snatch-blocks, See Plate 9. B C C.

Socket-Chiffel, Defcribed Plate 8. and § 3.

Soils, or *Sells,* are either *Ground-Sells* defcribed Plate 11. A. or *Window Sells,* which are the bottom Pieces of Window Frames

Stair-Cafe, The inclofure of a pair of Stairs, whether it be with Walls, or with Walls and Railes and Bannifters, *&c.*

Stancheons, See *Puncheons.*

Strut, See *Dragon-beam.*

Summer, In Plate 10. P P is a *Summer,* where into the Girders are Tennanted.

T.

TEn-Foot-Rod, See § 13.

 Tranfom, The Piece that is fram'd a-crofs a double Light-window. See Plare 11. P P.

Trim, When workmen fit a piece into other Work, they fay they *Trim* in a piece.

Trimmers, See Plate 10. *b b b b.*

Trufs, See *King-piece,* or *Joggle-piece.*

Tusk, A Bevel fhoulder, made to ftrengthen the Tennant of Joyft, which is let into the Girder.

V.

VAlley Rafter, See *Back,* or *Hip-molding,*

W.

WEll-*hole*, See Plate 10. I.
　　　Wall-Plate, In Plate 10. A C, B D and
N O are *Wall-Plates*.

Thus much of *Carpentry.* The next *Exercises* will (God willing) be upon the Art of *Turning*, *Soft Wood*, *Hard Wood*, *Ivory*, *Brass*, *Iron*, &c. With several Inventions of *Oval-work*, *Rose-work*, *Rake-work*, *Angular-work*, &c.

MECHA-

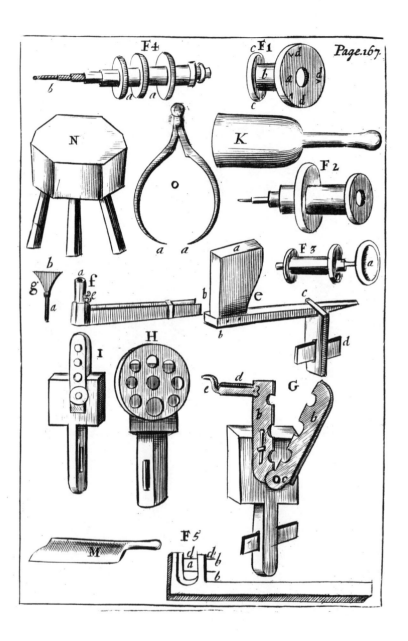

MECHANICK EXERCISES:

O R,

The Doctrine of *Handy-Works.*

Applied to the ART of *TURNING.*

Of Turning.

AS by placing one Foot of a pair of Compaffes on a Plane, and moving about the other Foot or point, defcribes on that Plane a Circle with the moving point; fo any Subftance, be it *Wood*, *Ivory*, *Brafs*, &c. pitcht fteddy upon two points (as on an *Axis*) and moved about on that *Axis*, alfo defcribes a Circle Concentrick to the *Axis:* And an Edge-Tool fet fteddy to that part of the outfide of the aforefaid Subftance that is neareft the *Axis*, will in a Circumvolution of that Subftance, cut off all the parts of Subftance that lies farther off the *Axis*, and make the outfide of that Subftance alfo Concentrick to the *Axis*. This is a brief Collection, and indeed the whole Sum of *Turning.*

Now, as there is different Matter, or Subftance, to be *Turned*, fo there is alfo different Ways, and different Tools to be ufed in *Turning* each different Matter.

M 4 The

The different Matters are *Soft Wood, Hard Wood, Ivory, Brass, Iron,* &c. each of which (when I have deſcribed the Turners Tools for ſoft Wood) I ſhall diſcourſe upon. But,

§ I. *Of the* Lathe.

THe *Lathe* is deſcribed in *Plate* 12. A. This Machine is ſo vulgarly known, that tho' it cannot be deſcribed in Draft, ſo as all its parts ſhall appear at one ſingle View, yet enough of it to give you the Names of its ſeveral Members, and their Uſes are repreſented, *viz.*

a a a a The *Legs* or *Stiles.*
b b The *Cheeks* or *Sides.*
c c The *Puppets.*
d The *Screw.*
d The *Pike.*
e The *Reſt.*
f The Handle of the *Screw.*
g The Tennants of the *Puppets,*
h The *Wedge.*
i The *Treddle.*
k The *Croſs-Treddle.*
l The *Pole.*
m The *String.*
n The *Horn.*

¶ 1. *Of the* Legs, *or* Stiles.

THe *Legs,* or *Stiles,* are commonly about two Foot and ten Inches high, and are ſet perpendicularly upright; having each of them a Tennant on its upperend, of the thickneſs the two *Cheeks* are to ſtand aſſunder: And on either ſide the Shoulder of theſe two *Tennants,* is laid one of the *Cheeks* cloſe to the ſides of the *Tennants,* and ſo pinned cloſe to the *Tennant,* as
was

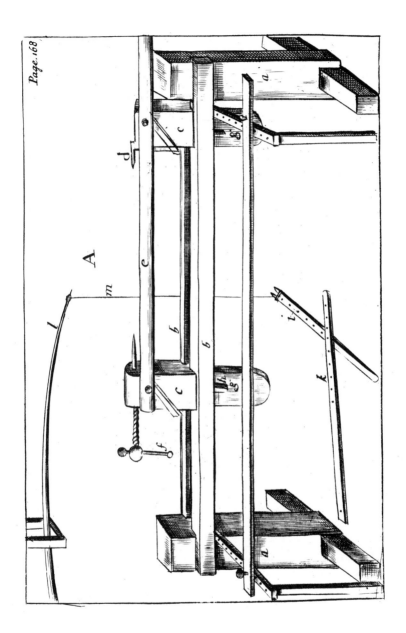

was taught *Numb.* 5. § 17. But a fteddier and more fecure way, is to have a ftrong Iron Screw made with a fquare Shank near the Head, that when it enters into a fquare hole made fit to it in the hithermoft *Cheek*, it may not twift about, but by the Turning about of an Iron Nut, upon the fore-end of the Screw, the Nut fhall draw the two Cheeks clofe to the two fides of the *Tennants*, or the upper ends of the *Legs*.

¶ 2. Of the Cheeks.

AS I told you, the Legs are to be fet up directly perpendicular, fo the *Cheeks* are to be faftned directly Horizontally upon them: And the *Legs* and *Cheeks* are to be faftned with *Braces* to the Floor, and other parts of the Room the *Lathe* ftands in, according to the convenience of the Room for faftning, that the whole *Lathe* may ftand as fteedy and folid as may be. For if with *Turning* large Work the ftrength of the Tread fhould make the *Lathe* tremble, you will not be able to make true and neat Work; but the Tool will job into fofter parts of the Stuff, and fly off where a Knot or other harder parts of the Stuff comes to the Tool.

¶ 3. Of the Puppets.

THe *Puppets* are fquare pieces of Wood, of a Subftance convenient to the light or heavy work they intend to *Turn:* And *Turnners* will rather have their *Puppets* too ftrong than too weak; becaufe, though the *Puppets* be very ftrong, yet they can turn light work with them; whereas if they be weak they cannot turn Heavy work with them: For the weight of heavy unequal tempered Stuff running about, will be apt both to fhake the *Puppets*, aud loofen the
fmall

ſmall hole of the *Wedge* in the **Tennant** ; by
either of which Inconveniences the Work in the
Lathe may tremble, as aforeſaid.

And though no ſize for the height of the *Puppets* can be well aſſerted, becauſe of the ſeveral
Diameters of Work to be *Turned*, yet Workmen
generally covet to have their *Puppets* as ſhort as
they well can, to bear their Work off the *Cheeks*
of the *Lathe*, becauſe theſe *Puppets* ſtand in the
firmer, and are leſs ſubject to looſen. But then,
if the Diameters of the work be large, the *Puppets* may be too ſhort to **Turn** that work in : For
the *Pikes* of the *Puppets* muſt ſtand ſomewhat
more than half the Diameter of the Work a-
bove the ſuperficies of the *Cheeks*. Therefore
Turners have commonly two or three pair of
Puppets to fit one *Lathe*, and always ſtrive to uſe
the ſhorteſt they can to ſerve their Work, unleſs the ſhortneſs of the *Legs* of the *Lathe*, makes
the work fall too low for the pitch of the Workman that is to work at the *Lathe*. Therefore
in the making of the *Lathe*, the height of the
Legs with relation to the intended Work, and
height of the Work-man, are to be well confidered.

At the lower end of theſe *Puppets* are made
two *Tennants*, of ſuch a thickneſs, that they
may eaſily ſlide in the *Grove* between the two
Cheeks, and ſo long, that a *Morteſs* through it
of the length of the *Cheeks* depth, and a ſufficient ſtrength of Wood below it may be contained. Into this *Morteſs* is fitted a Tapering-
Wedge, ſomewhat leſs at the fore end, and bigger at the hinder end than the *Morteſs*, that as
it is forced into the *Morteſs* with a *Mallet*, or a
Maul, it may draw the bottom Shoulder of the
Puppet cloſe and firmly down upon the *Cheeks*,
that they may neither joggle or tremble in working.   ¶ 4. *Of*

¶ 4. *Of the Horn.*

UPon the Right Hand *Puppet* on the out fide near the top of it, is hung the Tip-end of an *Horn* with its Tip downwards, to hold Oyl in, and ought to have a Wooden round *Cover* to fit into it, that neither Chips or Dirt get in to fpoil the Oyl; and in the handle of the *Cover* fhould be fitted a wooden *Butten,* which may ferve for an *Handle* to the *Cover :* And through this *Butten* fhould be faftned an Iron Wyer, to reach almoft to the bottom of the *Horn :* This Wyer ftands always in the Oyl, that fo oft as the Workman has occafion to oyl the Centers of the Work, to make his Work flip about the eafier, he takes the wooden *Cover* by the *Button,* Wyer and all, and with the end of the Wyer, oyls his Center-holes, and pops his Wyer and *Cover* again into the *Horn* againft he has occafion to ufe it the next time.

¶ 5. *Of the* Pikes *and* Screw.

NEar the upper end of one of thefe *Puppets* is faftned a ftrong Iron *Pike,* but its point is made of tempered Steel : And near the upper end of the other *Puppet* is fitted an Iron *Screw* quite through a *Nut* in the *Puppet,* whofe point is alfo made of Temper'd Steel. This Iron *Pike* in one *Puppet,* and the *Screw* in the other *Puppet* are fo fitted into the *Puppets,* that their Shanks lye in a ftraight Line with one another, and both their points lie alfo in that ftraight Line pointing to one another : And in the Head of the Iron *Screw* is a Hole where into is fitted an Iron *Handle* about feven or eight Inches long, with a round *Knob* at each end of it that it flip

not

not through the hole in the Head. This Iron *Handle* is to turn about the *Screw* forward or backward as your purpose fhall require.

Upon the points of this *Screw* and *Pike* the Centers of the Work are pitcht, and afterwards fcrewed with the *Screw* hard, and fo far into the Stuff, that it may not flip off the points in working, efpecially if it be foft Wood, and the work large and heavy.

Alfo, near the upper end of thefe *Puppets*, upon that fide the Workman ftands when he works, the Wood of the *Puppets* is wrought a-way to fquare flat fhoulders fomewhat below the *Pikes*, that the *Reft* may (if occafion be) lye near the *Pikes*, and bear fteddy upon the *Shoulders*.

¶ 6. *Of the* Reft.

THe *Reft* is a fquare piece of Stuff about an Inch, or an Inch and half thick, and two Inches, or two and an half broad, and fomewhat longer than the diftance between the *Puppets*. Its Office is to reft the Tool upon, that it may lie in a fteddy pofition while the Workman ufes it.

¶ 7. *Of the* Side-Reft.

BUt befides this *Reft*, *Turnners* have another *Reft*, called the *Side-reft*. This they ufe when they *Turn* the flat fides of Boards; be-caufe the flat fides of Boards ftanding athwart the *Pikes*, and this *Reft* ftanding alfo athwart the *Pikes*, they can the more conveniently reft their Tool upon it. It is marked *e* in plate 13. and is in the *Plate* disjunct from the *Lathe*; as well becaufe it and the Common *Reft* cannot both together be expreft in Picture, as alfo be-caufe it is made to take off and put on as oc-cafion requires.   The

The *Reſt* is marked *a*, and is a piece of an Oaken plank, or Elm plank, about two Inches think, and ſtands ſo high above the *Cheeks* of the *Lathe* as the *points* of the *Pikes* do, or ſometimes a little higher: Its Breadth is about a Foot, or more, or leſs, as the Work requires, or the Workman fancies. The Bottom of it is firmly nailed to one ſide of a Quarter of Oak, or Elm, of about three Inches ſquare, and two Foot, or two Foot and an half long, cloſe to one end, as you ſee in the Figure at *b*, ſo as the *Reſt* ſtand upright to the piece of Quarter. This piece of Quarter is as a *Tennant* to ſlide into a ſquare Iron Collar marked *e* ; this ſquare Iron Collar is made ſo long as to reach through the depth of the *Cheeks* of the *Lathe*, and to receive the Quarter or Tennant thruſt through it above the *Cheeks*, and a *Wedge* under the *Cheeks* marked *d*, which *Wedge* (when ſtiff knock'd up) draws the *Tennant* ſtrong and firmly down to the *Cheeks*, and conſequently keeps the *Side-reſt* ſteddy on any part of the *Cheeks*, according as you ſlide the *Collar* forwards or backwards towards either *Pike*, or as you thruſt the *Reſt* nearer or farther to and from the *Pikes*.

Some *Turners* for ſome Work, inſtead of a plank for this *Reſt*, faſten to one end of the Quarter or *Tennant*, a long Iron with a round Cilindrick *Socket* in it, as at the Figure marked *f* in Plate 13, *a* is the *Socket* of about an Inch, or an Inch and an half Diameter, to reach within two or three Inches as high as the *Pikes*, and into this *Socket* they put a long round Iron *Shank*, as in Figure *g* of the ſame *Plate*, *a* is the *Shank*, and at the top of this *Shank* is made the *Reſt*, marked *b*. This *Shank* (I ſay) ſlips eaſily into the *Socket*, that it may be raiſed, or let down, as occaſion requires. and by the

help

help of a *Screw* through the *Socket* at *e*, may . be faftned at that length.

The *Reft*, (by reafon of its Round *Shank*) may be alfo turned with its upper edge more or lefs oblique or athwart the Work, or elfe parallel to the Work, according as the purpofe may require.

Near one end of the *Reft* is fitted and faftned a piece of Wood about an Inch fquare, and ten or twelve Inches long: This piece of wood is fitted ftiff into a fquare Hole or Mortefs made in the *Puppet*, a little above the *Shoulder* for the *Reft*, to fet the *Reft* to any diftance from the *Pikes*, which, with the ends of wooden *Screws* entred into wooden *Nuts* on the further fide of the *Puppet*, and coming through againft the *Reft*, keeps the *Reft* from being thruft nearer to the work when the Workman is working.

¶ 8. *Of the* Treddle *and* Crofs-Treddle.

ABout the middle between the ends, is placed a wooden *Treddle* about two Inches and an half broad, an Inch thick, and three Foot long, and fometimes three and an half, to four Foot long. The hinder end of it is faftned to the Floor, with a piece of Leather (fometimes a piece of the Upper-leather of an old Shoe, which piece of Leather is nailed to the under-fide of the hinder end of the *Treddle*, fo as to leave Leather enough beyond the end of the *Treddle* to nail down upon the Floor; which *Treddle* being thus nailed down, will move upwards, as the Spring of the *Pole* draws up the *String*; the *String* being alfo faftned to the fore-end of the *Treddle*.

The

The hinder end of the *Treddle* is nailed down about a foot, or a Foot and an half behind the *Lathe*, and about the middle between both the *Legs*, fo that the fore-end of the *Treddle* reaches beyond the fore-fide of the *Lathe*, about a Foot and an half, or two Foot. And Note, that the farther the Fore-end of the *Treddle* reaches out beyond the Fore-fide of the *Lathe*, the greater will the fweep of the Fore-end of the *Treddle* be, and confequently it will draw the more *String* down; and the more *String* comes down at one *Tread*, the more Revolutions of the Work is made at one *Tread*, and therefore it makes the greater riddance of the Work.

But then again, if the Fore-end of the *Treddle* reach too far before the Fore-fide of the *Lathe*, it may draw the end of the *Pole* fo low as to brake it: And it will alfo be the harder to *Tread* down, becaufe the power commanding (which is the weight of the *Tread*) lies fo far from the weight to be commanded, which is the ftrength of the *Pole*, augmented by the diftance that the end of the *Treddle* hath from the Work in the *Lathe*; fo that you may fee, that the nearer the Fore-end of the *Treddle* lies to the Perpendicular of the Work in the *Lathe*, the eafier the *Tread* will be : And fome *Turners* that *Turn* altogether fmall Work, have the Fore-end of the *Treddle* placed juft under their work; fo that their *String* works between the *Cheeks* of the *Lathe:* But then the Sweep of the *Treddle* being fo fmall, the *Pole* draws up but a fmall length of *String*, and confequently makes the fewer Revolutions of the Work in one *Tread*, which hinders the riddance of the Work ; unlefs with every Spring of the *Pole*, they fhould lift their Treading Leg fo high, as to tire it quickly

quickly with bringing it down again, after it is raifed to fo uncommodious a pofition.

This *Treddle* hath a fquare Notch in the middle of the further end, about an Inch and an half wide, and two Inches long, that the end of the *String* may be wound either off or on the Wood on either fide the Notch, to lengthen or fhorten the *String*, as the different Diameters of the Work fhall require.

About the midde of the *Treddle* is fixed a round Iron *Pin* about half an Inch in Diameter; fo as to ftand upright about an Inch and an half, or two Inches long above the *Treddle.* And under the *Cheeks* is alfo fixed down the *Crofs-Treddle*, which is fuch another piece of Wood as the *Treddle* is, but longer or fhorter, according to the length of the *Lathe :* And in the middle of the Breadth of the *Crofs-Treddle,* is made feveral holes all a-row to receive the Iron *Pin* fet upright in the *Treddle.* Thefe holes are commonly boared about two or three Inches affunder, that the *Pin* or the *Treddle* may be put into any one of them, according as the *String* is to be placed nearer to or further off either end of the *Lathe.*

¶ 9. Of

¶ 9. *Of the* Pole.

THe *Pole* is commonly made of a *Fir-pole*, and is longer or fhorter, or bigger or fmaller, according to the weight of the Work the Workman defigns to *Turn:* For the thicker the *Pole* is, the harder muft the *Tread* be to bring it down; and for this reafon, if the *Pole* prove too ftrong for their common or continued Work, they will weaken it by cutting away (with a Draw-knife, defcribed *Numb.* 7. Plate 8. E, and § 5.) part of the fubftance off the upper and under fides of the Pole.

The thick end of this *Pole* is nailed (or indeed rather pinned) up to fome Girder, or other Timber in the Ceiling of the Room, with one fingle Nail or a Pin, that the *Pole* may move upon that Nail, or Pin, as on a Center, and its thin end pafs from one *Puppet* to the other, as the Work may require. And at about a diftance or more, is alfo nailed up to fome Joyfts, or other Timbers of the Ceiling, two *Cheeks* of a convenient ftrength, and at the lower end of thefe two *Cheeks* is nailed a Quarter or Batten to bear the *Pole*, though the weight of a *Tread* be added to it, as you may fee at *n n* in Plate 12.

¶ 10. *Of the* Side-Reft.

BUt it fometimes happens that the Ceiling of the Work-room is not high enough for the *Pole* to play upwards and downwards; therefore in fuch cafe, they place the thin end of the *Pole* at fome confiderable diftance off the *Lathe*, either before or behind it, and fo make the Spring of the *Pole* Horizantal towards the *Lathe*, conveying and guiding the *String* from the *Pole* to the Work by throwing it over a

N   *Rowlox*

Rowler, moving on two Iron *Center-pins* faſtned at both ends, and placed parallel to the *Cheeks* of the *Lathe,* above the Work as high as they can ; and thus every *Tread* draws the *Rowler* a-bout : But ſhould the *Rowler* not move about upon theſe Irons Pins, the *String* every *Tread* would both cut a Groove in the *Ruler,* and fret it ſelf more or leſs upon the *Rowler.*

¶ 11. *Of the* Bow.

SOme *Turuners* that work light Work, ſuch as *Cane-heads, Ink-horns,* &c. for which they need ſcarce remove the *Puppets* off their *Lathe,* uſe a common *Bow,* ſuch as Archers uſe. The middle of this *Bow* they faſten over Head, with its *String* Horizontally downwards, and in the middle of that *String* they faſten another *String* perpendicularly downwards, whoſe other end they faſten to the *Treddle,* and the *String* wound round their Work brings it about.

¶ 12. *Of the* Great Wheel.

BUt when *Turuners* work heavy Work, ſuch as the Pole and *Tread* will not Command, they uſe the *Great Wheel.* This Wheel is ſo commonly known, that I ſhall need give you no other Deſcription of it than the Figure it ſelf, which you may ſee in *Plate* 14. a. It is turned about with one, and ſometimes with two Iron *Handles,* according as the weight of the Work may require.

Its *String* hath both its ends ſtrong and neat-ly faſtned together, not with a Knot, but lapt over one another about three Inches in length, and ſo is firmly whipt about with ſmall Gut, that it may the eaſier paſs over the narrow *Groove* in the edge of the *Rowler.* This *String* is laid in the *Groove* made on the edge of the Wheel,

Wheel, and alfo in the *Groove* of the Work. But before it is laid upon both, one part of the *String* is lapt over and croffes the other, and the *String* receives the Form of a Figure of Eight (only one of its Bows or Circles becomes no bigger than the *Groove* in the Work, and the other as big as the *Groove* in the *Wheel*.)

Then the whole Frame wherein the *Wheel* is fixed is removed farther off the *Lathe*, that the *String* may draw tight upon the Work.

The reafon why the *String* thus croffes it felf, is, becaufe it will touch and gird more upon the *Groove* of the Work, and confequently (as was faid before ¶ 14.) will the better command the Work about.

The manner of Turning this *Wheel*, is as the manner of Turning other *Wheels* with *Handles*.

Befides the commanding heavy Work about, the Wheel rids Work fafter off than the Pole can do; becaufe the fpringing up of the Pole makes an intermiffion in the running about of the Work, but with the *Wheel* the Work runs always the fame way; fo that the Tool need never be off it, unlefs it be to examine the work as it is doing.

When the Wheel is ufed, its Edge ftands athwart the *Cheeks* of the *Lathe*.

¶ 13. *Of the* Treddle-Wheel.

THis is a *Wheel* made of a round Board of about two Foot and an half Diameter, conveniently to ftand under the *Cheeks* of the *Lathe*. It alfo hath a *Groove* on its Edge for the *String* to run in; it hath an Iron *Axis* with a *Crook* or *Crank* at one end: And on this *Crook* is flipt the Noofe of a *Leather Thong*, which having its other end faftned to a *Treddle*, does, by keeping

ing

ing exact time in *Treads*, carry it swiftly about without intermission.

But the length of the *Thong* must be so fitted, that when the *Wheel* stands still, and the *Crook* at the end of the *Axis* hangs downwards, the end of the *Treddle* to which the *Thong* is fastned may hang about two or three Inches off the Ground: For then, giving the *Wheel* a small turn with the Hand, till the *Crook* rises to the highest, and passes a little beyond it; if just then (I say) the Workman gives a quick *Tread* upon the *Treddle* to bring the *Crook* down again with a jerk, that *Tread* will set it in a motion for several revolutions; and then if he observes to make his next *Tread* just when the *Crook* comes about again to the same position, it will continue the motion, and cause of the motion, and keep the *Wheel* always running the same way, if he punctually times his *Treads*.

The *Treddel Wheel* is used for small work only, as not having strength enough to carry heavy Work about, such as *Cane-heads, Small Boxes,* &c. and it is fitted below the *Cheeks* between the *Puppets*, as the *Bow* is above.

Besides these Inventions to carry about the Work in the *Lathe,* there are many more; as with a great *Iron Wheel,* having Teeth on its edge, which Teeth are to fall into an Iron *Nut* upon an Iron *Axis,* pitcht upon the *Pikes* of the *Puppets* of the *Lathe,* or fitted into *Collars,* &c.

Also, for very heavy Work, as Guns, great Mortars, &c. *Wheels* turn'd with *Wind, Water,* or *Horses,* to carry the Work about. Of which more in their proper places.

§ 14. *Of*

¶ 14. *Of the* String.

UPon the thin end of the *Pole* is wound a confiderable Bundle of *String*, that as a *Mandrel* requires to be bigger than ordinary, or the Work heavier, they may unwind fo much of the *String* as will compafs the *Mandrel* twice, or (if the Work be heavy) thrice; the eafier to carry it about.

This *String* is made of the Guts of Beafts (moft commonly of Sheep, and fpun round of feveral thickneffes, of which the Workman chufes fuch fizes as are apteft for his Work; for large and heavy Work, very thick, but for fmall and light work, thin: And there are feveral reafons for his Choice; for a thin *String* will be too weak for heavy Work; but if it were not too weak for heavy work, it would be apt to mark foft wood more than a thick *String* would, when they are forc'd to fhift the *String*, and let it run upon the Work. Befides, a thin *String* (though it were ftrong enough) would not fo well bring heavy Work about; becaufe being fmall, but little of the *String* touches the wood to command it, unlefs they wind it the oftner about the Work, which both takes up time, and hazards the breaking of the *String*, by the fretting of the feveral twifts againft one another.

Now a thick *String* is uncommodious for fmall work; becaufe having a ftrength and ftubbornnefs proportionable to its fize, it will not comply clofely to a piece of Work of fmall Diameter, but will be apt to flip about it, unlefs both *Pole* and *Tread* be very ftrong; and then, if the Center-holes be not very deep, and the *Pikes* fill them not very tight, and the *Puppets* alfo not very well fixt, the ftrength of the

String

String will alter the Center-holes; especially, when the work is upon soft Wood, or else it will endanger the breaking the work in its weakest place.

¶ 15. Of *the* Seat.

PArallel to the *Cheeks* on the inside the *Lathe* is fitted a Seat, about two and an half Inches square, and the whole length of the *Lathe*; having an Iron Pin faltned on either end the underside of it: It lies upon two *Bearers* of Wood, that are faltned athwart the outer sides the *Legs*, (or else to set it higher) the outer ends of the *Cheeks*, according to the height of the person that works at the *Lathe*. These Bearers reach in length so far inwards, as that they may be capable to bear the Seat so far off from the *Lathe*, as in the Diameter of the *Work* they intend to *Turn* in the *Lathe*, and also the bulk of the Workman that stands between the *Lathe* and it, may be contained.

It is not called a Seat, because it is so; but because the *Workman* places the upper part of his *Buttocks* against it, that he may stand the steddier to his *Work*, and consequently guide his Foot the firmer and exacter.

The two *Bearers* have several Holes made in them, from within sixteen Inches off the *Lathe*, to the ends of them, that the Iron Pins faltned in the ends of the *Seat*, may be removed nearer or farther off the *Lathe*, according to the greatness or smallness of the Diameter of their Work.

Having thus described the parts of a Common *Lathe*, I shall now follow with their other Tools also.

§ II. *Of*

§ II. *Of* Gouges.

GOuges are marked B B in *Plate* 15. They do the Office of *Fore-plains* in *Joynery*, and the *Jack-plains* in *Carpentry*, and ferve only to take off the Irregularities the *Hatchet*, or fometimes the *Draw-knife* leaves, after the work is hewed or drawn pretty near a Round with either of them: And therefore as the *Fore-plain* is made with a Corner-edge, only to take off the Irregularities of a Board, fo the *Gouge* that it may alfo take off the Irregularities or Extuberancies that lye fartheft from the *Axis* of the Work, and alfo frame pretty near the hollow Moldings required in the *Work*, precede the *Smoothing-Chiffels*. And that the *Gouge* may the more commodioufly and effectually do it, the Blade of this Tool is formed about half round to an edge, and the two extream ends of this half round a little floped off towards the middle of it, that a fmall part about the middle may the eafier cut off the prominencies that are not concentrick to the *Axis*, and fo bring the *Work* into a Method of Formation.

The hollow edge is ground upon the Corner of a *Grind-ftone*, which in fhort time wears the outfide of that Corner to comply and form with the hollow of the *Gouge*. It is afterwards fet upon a round *Whet-ftone*, that fits the hollow of the edge, or is fomewhat lefs. But they do not fet their *Gouges* or *Chiffels* as (I told you in *Numb.* 4. § 10.) the Joyners do; for *Turnners* Tools being fomewhat unweldy, by reafon of their fize, and long Handles, they lay the *Blade* of the *Gouge* with its convex fide upon the *Reft* of the *Lathe*; and fo with the *Whet-ftone* in their right hand they rub upon the *Bafil* the *Grind-ftone* made, and as they rub, they often turn

N 4   another

another part of the hollow of the edge to bear
upon the round of the *Whet-ſtone*, till they have
with the *Whet-ſtone* taken off the roughneſs of
the *Grind-ſtone*.

Of theſe *Gouges* there are ſeveral ſizes, *viz.*
from a quarter of an Inch, to an whole Inch,
and ſometimes for very large *Work*, two Inches
over.

The *Handles* to theſe *Gouges* (and indeed to
all other *Turning Tools*) are not made as the
Handles of *Joyners* or *Carpenters Tools* are, but
tapering towards the end, and ſo long that the
Handle may reach (when they uſe it) under
the Arm-pit of the *Work-man*, that he may
have more ſtay and ſteddy management of the
Tool.

MECHA-

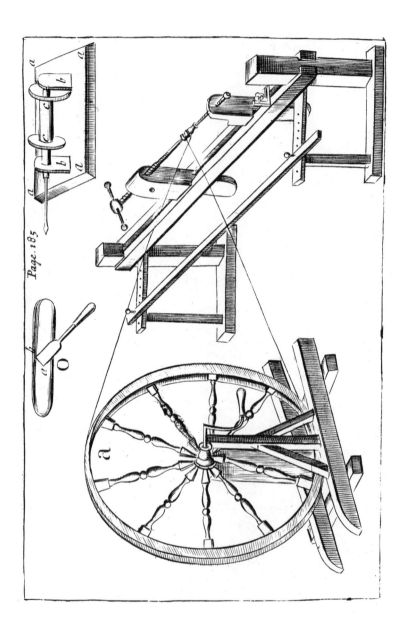

Page. 185

MECHANICK EXERCISES:

O R,

The Doctrine of *Handy-Works*.

Applied to the ART of TURNING.

§ III. *Of Flat Chiffels.*

THE *Flat Chiffels* are marked C C in *Plate* 15. Thefe do the Office of *Smoothing Plains* in *Joyning* and *Carpentry*; for coming after the *Gouges* they cut off the prominent Rifings that the *Gouges* leaves above the hollow.

The edges of thefe *Flat Chiffels* are not ground to fuch a *Bafil* as the *Joyners Chiffels* are, which are made on one of the Flat fides of the *Chiffels*, but are *Bafil'd* away on both the flat fides; fo that the edge lyes between both the fides in the middle of the *Tool:* And therefore either fides of the *Tool* may indifferently be applied to the Work; which could not well be, fhould the edge lye on one of the fides of the *Tool:* Becaufe, if they fhould apply the *Bafil* fide of the *Tool* to the Work, the thicknefs of the *Bafil* would bear the edge of the *Tool* off: And fhould they apply that fide of the *Tool* the edge lyes on to the *Work*, the fwift coming about of the *Work* would (where a fmall irregularity of

Stuff

Stuff fhould happen) draw or jobb the fuddain
edge into the Stuff, and fo dawk it; which if
the Stuff be already fmall enough, would now
be too fmall, becaufe in *Turnings*, all Irregularities muft be wrought fmooth down.

Of thofe *Flat Chiffels* there are feveral fizes,
viz. from a quarter of an Inch, one Inch, two
Inches, to three Inches broad, according to the
largnefs of the *Work.*

Thefe are Set with the *Whet-ftone* as the *Gouges*
are, only they often turn the *Gouges* upon the
round fide, becaufe they would fmoothen all the
hollow edge; but thefe are laid flat upon the
Reft, and with a flat *Whet-ftone* rubbed on the
Bafil, as the *Gouge* was with the Round.

§ IV. *Of* Hooks.

THe *Hook* is marked D in *Plate* 15. As the
   Gouge is ufed when the Work lyes before
the *Workman,* viz. parallel to its *Axis,* and cuts
right forwards, fo the *Hook* is ufed when the
Work ftands on the right or left fide the *Workman,* as the flat fides of Boards to be Turned do;
and therefore this *Work* may be faid to lye athwart its *Axis.* And the *Hook* is made fo as to
cut on the right or left fide a Board, and to
take off the extuberances from the plain of the
Board. But though this *Tool* does the Office
of a *Gouge,* yet it is more difficult for a *Workman* to ufe than a *Gouge,* becaufe it is made
thinner and flenderer than a *Gouge,* that its edge
cutting at a greater Bearing from the *Reft,* may
the eafier come at the Stuff it works upon, and
the farther the edge that cuts lyes from the *Reft,*
the more difficult it is for a *Workman* to guide
it, becaufe it is then more fubject to tremble;
efpecially fince (as aforefaid) the edge of the
Hook is and muft be thinner than the edge of the
Gouge.   Thefe

These *Tools*, as also the *Gouges*, and *Flat-Chif-fels*, are all about ten or twelve Inches long without the Handles.

The *Hooks* when they want sharpening cannot be *ground* as the *Gouges* and *Chiffels* are ; but they must be first softned in the Fire and turned straight, and then brought to an edge, and by heating again red hot turned into its form : Then must it be hardned and tempered as you were taught, *Numb.* 3. *fol.* 57, 58. Yet do not *Workmen* proceed thus with their *Hook* every time it grows bluntish, but only when the edge is either by long use, or bad Temper, grown so thick, that this following way will not help them : For they *Whet* the outer edge with a *Whet-stone* as they do other *Tools.* But because they cannot come at the inner edge of the *Hook* with a *Whet-stone*, unless the *Hook* be very wide, and the *Whet-stone* very thin, they make use of a piece of Temper'd Steel, as sometimes the thin side of a *Chiffel*, or the back of a *Knife*, and so with the edge of the Square, scrape along the hollow edge of the *Hook*, and force the edge as much to the outside of the *Hook* as they can. Thus *Butchers* wear at their Girdles small round Rods of Steel well tempered and polisht, that they may with quick dispatch whet their *Knives* upon it, by forcing the edge forwards upon the Blade, or pressing down the Shoulder that hinders the edge Entrance ; for their Steels being so well polisht, cannot properly be said to wear away any part of the Shoulder that should hinder the edge from doing its Office.

§ V. Of

§ V. *Of* Grooving Hooks, *and* Grooving Tools.

THe *Grooving Hook* is marked E in *Plate* 15, and hath its Tooth of different forms, according to the Fashion of the *Groove* to be made on the Plain of the Board; for sometime its Tooth hath a flat Edge, sometimes a round Edge, sometimes a point only, and sometimes two points, or other Forms as aforesaid.

Its whole Blade is made much stronger than the *Gouge* and *Chiffels*, and hath the fides of its Edge more obtufe to make it the stronger.

The *Flat Tools* work the Boards Flat either to the Plain of the Board, or to a Flat Groove in the Board.

The *Round Edge* cuts an half-round hollow in the Board.

The Point cuts a fine Hollow Circle or Swage in the Flat of the Board; and being made Triangular, hath three Edges each, of which cuts the Ridges fmooth down that the *Hook* left upon the Board.

The *Two-point Grooving-Hook* cuts two fine hollow Circles or Swages on the Plain of the Board.

The *Grooving-Hooks* do not work as the *Hooks* do, for the Hooks cut the Wood; but thefe do but indeed fcrape off the Extuberancies, or fret into the Wood, and therefore they are very feldom ufed to foft Wood, becaufe its being loofe, will not endure fcraping without leaving a roughnefs upon the Work; but hard Wood, or Ivory (for the Reafon converted) will.

§ VI. *Of*

§ VI. *Of* Mandrels. *And* ¶ 1. *Of* Flat Mandrels.

Mandrels are marked F 1. F 2. F 3. F 4. in *Plate* 15. There are different sorts of *Mandrels,* and the sizes of them also different, according to the sizes of the Work.

1. *Broad Flat Mandrels* marked F 1. in *Plate* 15. with three or more little Iron *Pegs,* or *Points* near the Verge of its Flat : And these are used for the *Turning* Flat Boards upon. For the back-side of a Board placed Flat upon it, will when screwed up tight between the *Pikes,* by help of the Irong *Pegs,* remain in its place and position, whilst the Flat side of the Work is working upon.

Behind the Backside of this *Mandrel* (and indeed all other *Mandrels*) is fitted a long *Shank,* or *Rowler,* for the *String* to be wound about while the Work is *Turning.* This *Rowler* must be so large in Diameter, that the *String* wound about it may command the *Work* about. If the *Work* be large and heavy, the *Rowler* must be bigger than if the *Work* be light ; for else the *String* will not command it about : But if the Diameter of the *Rowler* be smaller, the work comes so much swifter about. The *Rowler* must also be so long between its *Shoulders,* that it may conveniently contain so many Diameters of the *String* as shall be necessary to wind about it.

This whole *Mandrel* is marked F 1. in *Plate* 15. *a.* The *Round Flat,* or *Face,* of the *Mandrel. b.* The *Rowler. c c* The *Shoulders* of the *Rowler. d d d* The *Pegs.*

¶ 2. *Of* Pin-Mandrels.

2. Mandrels are made with a long *Wooden Shank,* to fit stiff into a round hole that is made in the Work that is to be *Turned.* This

Mandrel

Mandrel is called a *Shank*, or *Pin-Mandrel*, and is marked F 2. in Plate 15. And if the hole the *Shank* is to fit into be very fmall, and the Work to be faftned on it pretty heavy, then *Turners* faften a round Iron *Shank*, or *Pin*, of the fize of the Hole it is to be fitted into, and faften their Work upon it. Thefe *Mandrels* with Iron *Shanks* are ufed by *Turnners* that *Turn* Bobbins, or fuch like Work : Becaufe a *Wooden Shank* to fit the fmall Hole though the work would not be ftrong enough to carry the work about.

¶ 3. *Of* Hollow-Mandrels.

3. THere is another fort of *Mandrels* called *Hollow Mandrels*, defcribed F 3. Plate 15. It is both a *Hollow-Mandrel*, and alfo ufed to *Turn* hollow *Work* in it. This *Mandrel* hath but one Center-hole belonging to it, *viz.* at the *Rowler* end or Neck; but it hath a *Shank*, which fupplies the Office of another Center-hole, *a* the hollow, *b* the *Shank*, or *Neck*. The *Hollow* is made fo wide, that the *Work* intended to be *Turned* hollow in it may fit very ftiff into it, and fo deep that it may contain the intended *Work*.

When it is ufed, it is pitcht upon the Center at the farther end of the *Rowler*, and hath its *Shank* put into one of the Holes of the *Joint-Coller* defcribed in Plate 13. *fig. G.* that will beft fit it; which Hole ftanding directly againft the *Pike* in the hinder *Puppet*, and receiving the *Shank* into it, guides the *Mandrel* about, as if it were pitcht upon two Centers: And the *Work* being forced ftiff into the Hollow of this *Mandrel*, will be carried about with it, expofing the Fore-fide of the work bare and free from the *Joynt-Coller*, and not impeded by *Spikes* from coming at the *work*; fo that with the *Hook*,

Grooving

Groving-Hook, Gonge, or *Flat-Chiſſel,* according as your *work* requires, you may come at it to *Turn* your intended Form.

Hollow Mandrels are alſo uſed in *Collers* that open not with a *Joynt* ; but then the *Spindle* is made of Iron, and hath a *Screw* juſt at its end, upon which is ſcrewed a Block with an hollow, in it, made fit to receive the *work* ſtiff into it.

¶ 4. *Of the* Screw-Mandrel.

4. A Nother ſort of *Mandrel* is called the *Screw-Mandrel,* and is marked F 4. in Plate 15. *a* the *Rowler* of the *Mandrel, b.* the *Shank,* or *Screw,* is made of Iron, having its two ends Round, and in the middle between the Round ends a Square the length of the *Rowler,* and this Square is fitted ſtiff into a Square-hole made through the middle of the *Rowler* that it turn not about in the Square-hole. In each Flat-end of this Iron *Shank,* or *Spindle,* is made a Center-hole, wherein the *Pikes* of the *Puppets* are pitcht when this *Mandrel* is uſed. This Iron *Shank,* or *Axis,* muſt be made very ſtraight, and ought to be turned upon the two Center-holes for exactneſs ; becauſe on one of the round ends, or ſometimes on both, a Screw, or indeed ſeveral Screws of ſeveral Diameters is made. That Screw next the end of the *Shank* is the ſmalleſt, *viz.* about three quarters of an Inch over, and takes up in length towards the middle of the *Shank,* about an Inch, or an Inch and an half ; and ſo far from the end of the *Shank* it is of an equal Diameter all the way ; and on this por-tion of the *Shank* is made a *Male-ſcrew* of the fineſt Thread. The next Inch and half (wrought as before) hath another *Male-ſcrew* ; but about half a quarter of an Inch more in Diameter than the former, and hath its Threads courſer. Ano-ther

ther Inch and half hath its Diameter ftill greater, and its Threads yet courfer.   And thus you
may make the *Shank* as long as you will, that
you may have the more variety of fizes for
Screws.

Thefe forts of *Mandrels* are made for the making of *Screws* to *Boxes,* and their *Lids,* as fhall
be fhewed in the next Paragraph.

¶ *Of* Sockets, *or* Chocks, *belonging to the*
Screw-Mandrel.

TO this *Screw-Mandrel* belongs fo many *Sockets*
as there are feveral fizes of *Screws* on the
Shank.   They are marked F 5. in *Plate* 15. *a*
the *Socket* or *Chock:* *b b,* the Wooden *Pin,* *c* the
Stay, *d d* the *Notch* to flip over the *Male-fcrew.*

Thefe *Hollow* Sockets have *Female-Screws* in
them, made before the Notch to flip over the
Male-fcrew of the *Screw-Mandrel* is cut. The
manner of making *Female-fcrews* is taught *Numb.*
2. *fol.* 29, 30, 31. only inftead of a *Tap* (ufed
there) you ufe the feveral and different fizes of
Screws made on the *Screws-Mandrel* to do the
Office of a *Tap* into each refpective *Socket;*
which *Sockets* being only made of hard Wood,
it will eafily perform, though the *Shank,* or
Axis be but Iron.

Therefore (as aforefaid) to each of the *Male-
fcrews* on the *Screw-Mandrel* is fitted fuch a
Socket, that you may chufe a *Thread* Courfer or
Finer as you pleafe; but this *Female-fcrew* is
open, or hath a *Notch* on one fide of it, that it
may flip over the *Male-fcrew,* and the Threads
of each other fit into each others *Grooves;* and
when they are thus fitted to one another, the
further or open fide of the *Male-fcrew* is gaged
in, or pin'd on the *Female-fcrew* with a wooden
Pin thruft through two oppofite Holes, made
for

for that purpofe in the *Cheeks* of the wooden Sockets, that it fhake not.

When the *Treddle* comes down in working, and the *Socket* is fitted on its proper *Screw*, and pinn'd ftiff upon it, and the Stay held down to the *Reft* of the *Lathe,* then will the *Socket,* and confequently the *Stay* flide farwards upon the *Male-fcrews* ; fo that a Tool held fteddy on any part of the *Stay,* and applied to the out or in-fide of your *Work,* that Tools point will de-fcribe and cut a Screw, whofe Thread fhall be of the fame finenefs that the Screw and the Shank is of.

§ VII. *Of* Collers.

THere are feveral fafhion'd *Collers* ; As the *Joynt-Coller* marked G, the *Round-Coller* mar-ked H, and the *Coller* marked I, in Plate 13.

The *Joynt-Coller* is made of two Iron *Cheeks* marked *b b,* which moving upon a Joint *c* at the Bottom, may be fet clofe together, or elfe opened as the two infides of the *Joynt-Rule* Car-penters ufe to do. On the inner Edge of each *Cheek* is formed as many half-round holes or Semi-circles as you pleafe, or the length of the *Cheeks* will conveniently admit : Thefe Semicir-cles are made of different Diameters, that they may fit the *Shanks* or *Necks,* of different fiz'd *Mandrels :* And thefe Semi-circles muft be made fo exaƐtly againft each other on the edges of the *Cheeks,* that when the two *Cheeks* moving upon their *Joynt* are clapt clofe together, the Semi-circles on both the *Cheeks* fhall become a per-feƐt round hole, or circumference.

Near the top of one of thefe *Cheeks* is faftned with a *Center-pin,* a fquare Iron Coller marked *d,* with a fmall *Handle* to it marked *e.* This fquare Coller is made to contain the breadth of

O both

both the *Cheeks* when they are fhut together, and to hold them fo faft together, that they fhall not ftart affunder ; and yet is made fo fit, that it may flip off and on both the *Cheeks.*

This *Joynt-Coller* may ferve to do the Office of the other two *Collers*, and its one particular Office too : Yet to fave the Charge of the price of this Tool, *Turners* feldom ufe them, but make fhift with either of the other, or fometimes with a hole made in a Board only : But its particular Office is to hold a *Mandrel*, whofe Neck is fitted to one of its Holes, and the work they are to *Turn* is required to ftand out free from the outer Flat of the *Cheeks* of the *Coller*, the better to come at it with the *Tool* ; fuch as are deep Boxes, or deep Cups, *&c.*

MECHA-

MECHANICK EXERCISES:

O R,

The Doctrine of *Handy-Works*.

Applied to the ART of *TURNING*.

§ VIII. *Of the* Mawl.

THE *Mawl* is marked K in Plate 13. The Figure of it there is Description sufficient: Its Office is to knock and un-knock the Wedge in the *Puppets*; and to knock upon the back of the *Cleaving Knife*, when they split their Wood for their Work. The *Joyner's Mallet* would supply the Office of this Tool; but use has made the *Mawl* more handy for them: Besides when one is batter'd to shivers, they can quickly, of a Chump of Wood, accommodate themselves with another.

§ IX. *Of the* Hatchet, Draw-knife *and* Cleaving-knife.

THe *Hatchet* is marked L in Plate 4. It is of the same sort that *Joyners* use; which I described *Numb.* 5. § 25. and therefore refer you thither. And the *Draw-knife* is described in *Numb.* 7. § 5. Plate 8. marked E. The *Cleaving-knife* marked M in Plate 13. needs no other Description than that Figure.

Q 2 § 10. *Of*

§ X. *Of the* Chopping-Block.

THe *Chopping-Block* is marked **N** in **Plate 13.**
It is made of a piece of *Elm-Tree* placed
with its Grain upwards and downwards as it
grew. It hath three Leges in it, that ftand
ftradling out from the underfide of the *Block* to
the Floor, and of fuch an height, as the Workman may have moft Command of the Work.
See the Figure. Sometimes *Turnners* ufe inftead
of it, a piece of the Trunk of a Tree, of about
a Foot and an half, or two Foot, in length from
the Ground, or more or lefs.

§ XI. *Of the* Callippers.

THe *Callippers* is marked **O** in *Plate* 13. As
common Compaffes (defcribed *Numb.* 6.
§ 32.) are for meafuring Diftances upon a plain
Superficies ; fo *Callippers* meafure the diftance of
any round *Cilindrick* Conical Body, either in
their Extremity, or any part lefs than the Extream : So that when Workmen ufe them, they
open the two points *a a* to their defcribed width,
and *Turn* fo much ftuff off the intended place,
till the two points of the *Callippers* fit juft over
their Work ; fo fhall their Work have juft the
Diameter in that place, as is the diftance between the two points of the *Callippers*, be it
either Feet or Inches, *&c.*

§ XII. *Of the* Drill-Bench.

THere is yet another Tool, or rather a *Machine*
ufed by fome *Turnners*, called a *Drill-Bench*.
It is defcribed in Plate 14. *a a a a* a thick Board,
about three Inches thick, five Inches broad, and
eighteen Inches long, *b b* two Stiles placed towards either end, and faftned upright. In the
hithermoft Stile is a *Coller* defcribed § 7. and
Plate

Plate 13. H. or any of the other *Collers* : And in the further *Stile* is fitted a square flat tempered piece of Steel having a Center-hole in the middle of it, and is placed juft againſt the Center or middle point of the Hole of the *Coller*, *c c* the *Rowler*, whoſe hither end is *Turned* away, ſo as it juſt fit into the *Coller*, and at the further end of it, it hath a temper'd *Steel Pin*, to be placed in the Center-hole : And in the middle of the hither end of it, it hath a *Piercer-Bit* faſtned ſtraight in, ſo that it lie in a true ſtraight Line, with the *Axis* of the *Rowler*. Of theſe *Rowlers* they have ſeveral, and *Bits* of different ſizes fitted into them, that upon all occaſions they may chuſe one to fit their purpoſe.

On the under-ſide, about the middle of the *Bench*, is fitted and faſtned athwart it a ſquare Iron *Coller*, deep enough to reach through the *Cheeks* of the *Lathe*, and ſo much deeper as it may receive a Wooden *Wedge*, ſuch a one as belongs to one of the *Puppets :* And by the force and ſtrength of the *Wedge*, the whole *Drill-bench* is drawn down and faſtned athwart the *Cheeks* of the *Lathe*.

When it is uſed, it ſtands athwart the *Cheeks* of the *Lathe* (as aforeſaid) with the point or end of the *Bit* towards you ; and then the *String* being turned twice or thrice about the *Rowler*, will (with *Treading* on the *Treddle*) turn the *Rowler* and its *Bit* forcibly about, and cauſe it to enter ſwiftly into a piece of Wood that ſhall be preſt forwards upon the *Bit*.

When they uſe it, they hold the piece of Wood they intend to *Drill*, or *Pierce*, faſt in both their Hands, right before them, and preſs it forwards upon the *Piercer-Bit* ; ſo that by its running about, it cuts a ſtraight round hole into the Wood, of what length they pleaſe,

Bu

But while the *Pole* is riſing after every *Tread*, they preſs not againſt the *Piercer-Bit*, ſo that it is diſ-ingaged from doing its Office in the Wood; but in that while, they nimbly give the Wood a turn in their hands, of about one third part of its Circumference; which makes the *Bit* very ſucceſſive *Tread*, go the ſtraighter through the middle of the Wood: And thus they reiterate *Treads*, and keep the Wood turning in their Hands, till the *Bit* is enter'd deep enough.

Thus much of the *Tools* uſed in common *Turning:* I ſhall proceed to the Working a Pattern or two in ſoft Wood; which being well underſtood, may render a Practicer capable of moſt common Work.

§ XIII. *Of* Turning *a* Cilinder *in ſoft Wood.*

THE ſoft Wood *Turners* Uſe is commonly either *Maple, Alder, Birch, Beech, Elm, Oak, Fir,* &c. and for ſome particular purpoſes each of theſe ſorts are beſt.

The firſt Pattern we purpoſe ſhall be a *Cilinder* two Inches over, and eight Inches long: Therefore you muſt chuſe a piece of Wood at leſt two Inches and a quarter over, leſt you want Stuff to work upon: Nay, if your Stuff prove ſhaken, or otherwiſe unſound, or your Center be not very exactly pitcht, you may want yet more Stuff; and that according as it proves more or leſs faulty, or as the Centers are more unequally pitcht. But ſuppoſing the Stuff good, you may take a piece of two Inches and a quarter over, as I ſaid before, and about ten or eleven Inches long. For though the length of the *Cilinder* be but eight Inches, yet you muſt cut your Stuff long enough to make a Groove at one end of it beſides, for the *String* to run in. If your Stuff be ſomewhat too big for your

Scantlin,

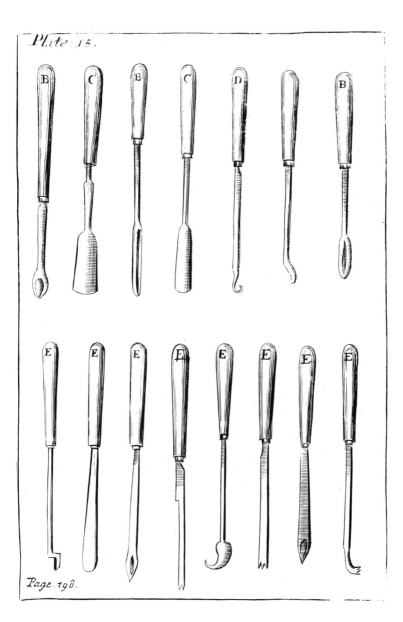

Plate 15.

Page 198.

Scantlin, and not round enough to go into the *Lathe*, you muſt *Hew* it pretty near with the *Hatchet* to make it ſizable, and afterwards ſmoothen it nearer with a *Draw-knife*, as you were taught, *Numb.* 7. § 5.

But if you have not Stuff at hand near your ſize, then you muſt Saw off your length from a Billet, or ſome other piece of Stuff, and with the *Cleaving-knife* and the *Mawl*, ſplit it into a ſquare piece near the ſize, and with the *Draw-knife* round off the Edges to make it fit for the *Lathe*.

Then ſet your *Puppets*, and wedge them right up, ſo as the *Points* of your *Spikes* ſtand pretty near the length of your Work aſſunder, and move the *Pole*, ſo as the end of it may hang o-ver between the *Pikes*, and alſo fit the Iron *Pin* in the *Treddle* into a proper *Hole* in the *Croſs-Treddle*, ſo as the end of the *Treddle* may draw the *String* below the Work into pretty near a ſtraight Line with the ſtring above the Work: And take the Work in your Right Hand, and put it beyond the *String* before you, and with your Left Hand wind the *String* below the Work, but once about the Work, left it ſhould be too ſtrong for your ſhallow Centers, as you ſhall underſtand by and by, and then with a pretty ſtrength preſs the middle of one end of your Work over the Point of one of the *Pikes*, and ſo make a hole in your Work for one of the Cen-ter holes: Then ſcrew your Pike wider or cloſer, according as the length of your Work requires, and pitch the other end of your Work upon the other Pike alſo, and ſcrew your Work a little lightly up: Then try how the Centers are pitcht, by Treading the *Treddle* lightly down; and if you find the Centers are well pitcht, you may without more ado ſcrew up your Work tight:

But

But if your Centers, or either of them be not well pitcht, you muft alter them. You may know when they are well pitcht, by treading foftly upon your *Treddle*, and holding your Finger fteddy on the *Reft*, direct the point of it pretty clofe to the Work: For if in a Revolution of your Work, its Out-fide keeps it an equal diftance from the end of your Finger, you may conclude your Work is well pitcht. But if you find one fide of your Work comes nearer your Finger than the other fide, you muft with your *Flat Chiffel*, or *Gouge*, (or what is neareft at hand) knock foftly, or hard, upon that fide that comes neareft to your Finger, till you have forc'd the *Pikes* into the true Centers at the end of your Work; and then you may boldly fcrew it hard up: But you muft be fure to fcrew it hard up; becaufe it is foft Wood you purpofe to work upon, and the ftrength of the *Pole* may endanger the drawing or removing the Centers, if the *Pikes* have not good hold of them.

Having found your Centers, take your Work again off the *Pikes*, and wind the *String* once or twice more about your Work, that your *String* (as I faid in *Numb.* 10. § 1. when I wrote of the *String*) may the better command it, and then wind off or no more *String* at the end of your *Pole*, or end of your *Treddle*, or both, if your Work require it, till the *Pole* draws the *Treddle* up a little above half the length of the *Legs* of the *Lathe*. For about the height your Leg may without fudden trying, command the *Pole* down again.

But before you begin to work upon the Stuff, I fhall inform you how to *Tread* the *Treddle*, in which you may obferve this General Rule; That the nearer the Fore-end of the *Treddle* you *Tread*, the eafier you bring down the *Pole*; but then

the

the *Pole* in its Spring rafes your Leg the higher,
and may draw the upper fide of the your Thigh
againft the underfide of the *Cheek* of the *Lathe*,
and with reiterated Rifings Gawl, and alfo tire
your Thigh.

Place therefore your Foot fteddy upon the
Treddle, fo far forward as you can, to avoid the
Poles rifing from drawing your Thigh againft the
underfide of the *Lathe*; and Tread the *Treadle*
nimbly down, but not quite fo low as to knock
againft the Floor : Then abate the weight of your
Tread, and let the *Pole* draw the *Treddle* up, but
ftill keep your Foot fteddy, and lightly Bearing
upon the *Treddle:* For then your fucceeding
Treads will prove eafier to your Leg and Thigh,
and you will with your Foot the better and
quicker command the *Treddle*. Then Tread a-
gain nimbly down as before, and keep this train
of Treading till your Work be finifh'd, or that
you may have occafion to ftop and exaime how
rightly you proceed.

In all fmall Work the *Tread* is lightly and
nimbly performed ; but in large and heavy work
the *Tread* comes flow and heavily down.

This being premifed, you may begin with your
Gouge; lay the round fide of it upon the *Reft*,
and take the Handle of it in your Right Hand,
and lay the Fore and Middle Fingers of your
Left Hand upon the Hollow of the *Gouge* near
the Work, mounting the Edge about a quarter
of an Inch above the *Axis* of your Work, and
finking your Right Hand a little; for in this
pofition the *Gouge* cuts beft : And thus cut down
on your Work near one end, a *Groove* for your
String to run in: The *Groove* may be about an
Inch, or an Inch and an half long; but it matters not much what depth. Then flip your
String into the *Groove*, and if you find the *String*
will

will not flip eafily, you may put your Foot under the *Treddle* and lift it a little up, that the
String when no weight is hanged to it, may flide
the eafier into the *Groove.*

And by the way you may take notice, that
the deeper you cut down the *Groove,* the oftner
will your Work come about every Tread; becaufe the *String* that comes down every Tread,
meafure a fmall Circumference oftener than it
does a greater Circumference: But then the work
is not fo ftrongly carried about; becaufe it hath
a lefs portion of the *String* to command it. This
I hint, not that in this our fmall propofed Pattern it is very confiderable: For if you only cut
the *Groove* down but fo low as there may be a
Shoulder at the end, and another againft the
Work, to keep the *String* from flipping out of
the Groove, it will be fufficient: But in heavy
Work this *Groove* ought to be cut with difcretion.

Now come to the Forming of your Work,
and hold your *Gouge,* as you were taught before,
but fomewhat lightly againft your Work, beginning at one end, and fliding your *Gouge* gradually to the other, cutting with its Edge all the
way you go, and bearing fomewhat ftiff againft
the Work every Tread you make on the *Treddle:*
And withdrawing it again a little lightly from
the *work* every Spring of the Pole. And thus by
Ufe you muft habituate your felf to let the edge
of your *Tool* bear upon the Work when the Pole
and *Treddle* comes down, and to draw it back
juft off the Work, as the Pole and *Treddle* goes
up. And thus you muft continue till you have
rough-wrought all your work from end to end.

If you have not at firft brought your Work
clean; that is, if you have not gone deep e-
nough with your *Gouge* to take off all the Rifings

fings of the Stuff the *Draw-knife* left, even with the fmalleft part of your Work, you muft in like manner (as before) work it over again. But you muft have a fpecial Care you take not too much Stuff away on any part of the whole Work : For this propofed Pattern being a *Cilin-der*, if you take but a fmall matter to much a-way from any part, and make it fmaller than your given meafure there, the whole Work will be fpoiled, as being fmaller than the propofed Diameter; which to know, you may by open-ing the Points of your *Callippers* to two Inches on your *Rule* (the propofed Diameter of your *Cilinder*) try if the Points at that diftance will juft flip over the deepeft *Grooves* of your Work (for we will not fuppofe that the *Grooves* are of an equal depth with the Rough-working of the *Gouge*) without ftraining the Joint, for then your Work is juft fizeable: If not, work over again as before, &c. But we will now fuppofe you have not taken too much away, but have made a due procefs with your *Gouge*. Therefore now proceed, and ufe a *Flat Chiffel*, about an Inch and an half broad, to take off the Irregu-larities the *Gouge* left.

Take the Handle of it in your Right Hand, as you did the *Gouge*, and clafpfing the *Blade* of it in your Left Hand, lean it fteddy upon the *Reft*, holding the Edge a little aflant over the Work, fo as a Corner of the thin fide of the *Chiffel* may bear upon the *Reft*, and that the Flat fide of the *Chiffel* may make a fmall Angle with the *Reft*, and confequently with the Work; (which is pa-rallel to the *Reft*) for fhould you fet the edge of the *Chiffel* parallel to the Work, it might run too faft into the Work, and dawk it. Therefore you muft fet the *Chiffel* in fuch a pofition, that the lower, Corner, or near the lower Corner of the edge,

edge, may cut lightly upon the Work : But this
pofition is beft defcribed by a Figure, which to
that purpofe I have inferted in *Plate* 14. at O,
where you may perceive in, or near, what pofition the *Chiffel* muft be fet to cut the Work ;
and how the edge of the *Chiffel a b* lying aflant
the Work, and the further Corner of the edge of
the *Chiffel b* being fomewhat mounted, as the
Work comes about, the Bottom, or near the
Bottom, of the edge of the *Chiffel* is only capable to cut a narrow Shaving off the Work : And
juft in this manner you muft keep the *Chiffel*
fteddy bearing upon the Work, as the *Pole* comes
down, and withdrawing it from the Work as the
Pole Springs up (as you were taught to ufe the
Gouge) and at the fame time fliding it forwards
from one end of the Work to the other, till it be
wrought down all the way to its true Diameter
between the points of the *Callippers* : For then a
ftraight *Ruler* applied to your Work, the outfide
of your purpofes *Cilinder* will be formed.

Only the ends muft be cut down fquare to the
length : Therefore open the points of your Compaffes to the diftance of eight Inches on your
Rule, and prick that diftance hard off upon your
Work, that the points of your *Compaffes* may
leave vifible marks, by placing one point as near
one end as you can, to leave Stuff enough to cut
ftraight down all the way ; that is, to cut it
fquare down at right Angles with the outfide of
the Work. Which to do, you muft hold the
Handle of the *Flat Chiffel* in your Right Hand
(as before) and clafp the Blade of it in your
Left, and lay one of the thin fides of it upon the
Reft, fo that the edge may ftand upright, or very near upright againft the Work. Then fink
your Right Hand fomewhat below the Level of
the *Reft*, that the lower Corner of the edge of
the

the *Chiſſel* may mount, and being thruſt ſteddy
againſt the Work, juſt in the mark one Point of
the *Compaſſes* made, Tread the *Treddle,* and cut
a pretty deep Circle into the Stuff. But you
muſt have a care you do not direct the cutting
Corner of the *Chiſſel* inwards, but rather outwards, leſt you make the end hollow inſtead of
Flat: For if you do take off too little at firſt,
you may by degrees cut it down to a Flat afterwards. As you cut deeper into the Stuff, you
muſt turn the Flat of the *Chiſſel,* and with it cut
down the Shoulder juſt at the end on the outfide the mark, for elſe that may hinder the Corner of the edge of the *Chiſſel* for coming at the
Work.

Note, That if you hold not the edge of the
Chiſſel truly before the Work, but direct it inwards, and if you hold it not very ſteddy, and
have a good guidance of it, the quick coming
about of the Work, may draw the edge of the
Chiſſel into it inwards and run a dawk on *Cilinder,* like the Grooves of a *Screw,* and ſo ſpoil
your Work: For being once wrought to the true
ſize, you cannot afterwards take any more off to
cleanſe it, &c.

The other end muſt be cut down as this.

§ 14. *Of*

§ 14. *Of* Turning Flat Boards.

IF your Board be thick enough, you may boar
a round Hole in the middle of it ; and turn
a *Mandrel* with a *Pin* a very little Tapering, to
fit hard and ftiff into the round Hole : And if
the *Hole* and *Pin* be proportionable in fize to the
weight of the Board, the *Pin* will carry it about.
But you muft be very careful the *Hole* be boarded exaɛtly ftraight through the middle, and not
inclining on either fide the Board, more to any
part of the Verge than to another ; but that the
middle of the *Hole* be exaɛtly the Center of the
Board the whole thicknefs through. This *Pin-
Mandrel* is defcribed *Numb.* 11. § 6. and *Plate*
13.

If your Board be not thick enough to be faftned upon a *Pin-Mandrel,* or that your Work will
not admit of an Hole to be bored through the
middle of it, you may ufe the *Flat-Mandrel* defcribed *Plate* 13. F 2. And then you muft with
your *Compaffes* find the Center on the backfide of
the Round Board (with feveral proffers if need
require) till you have found it, and prick there
an Hole for a mark : Then open the points of
your *Compaffes* to about the thicknefs of a Shilling wider than the Semidiameter of the *Flat-
Mandrel* ; and with the points of your *Compaffes*
at that diftance defcribe a Circle on the back-
fide of the Board to be turned, by placing one
Foot in the prick-mark, and turning about the other
Foot. By this Circle you may pitch the Center of
the Board exaɛtly upon the Center of the *Flat-
Mandrel :* For the points of the *Compaffes* being
opened about the thicknefs of a Shilling wider
than the Semidiameter of the *Flat-Mandrel :* will
(when

(when you have pitcht the Center of the Board
on the Center of the *Mandrel*) place the outer
Verge of the *Mandrel* the thickneſs of a Shilling round about within the Circle deſcribed on
the the backſide of the Board: And when it is
thus pitcht, you may, by laying the Board flat
down, knock upon the *Rowler* end of the *Mandrel*, and drive the *Pegs* in the flat of the *Mandrel* into the Board, and ſo hold it ſteddy upon
the *Mandrel :* Then find the Center on the Foreſide of the Board alſo, as you were taught to
find the Center on the backſide, and put your
Board and *Mandrel* upon the *Pikes* of the *Puppets*, and ſcrew them hard up, as you have been
taught before.

Sometimes *Turners* uſe this *Flat-Mandrel* without *Pegs*, and then they chalk the Flat ſide of it
very well, and clap the backſide of the Board to
it, which will (if the Board to be *Turned* be
not too heavy, but be well ſcrewed up between
the *Pikes*) keep the Board ſteddy from ſlipping
from its ſet-poſition, till you work it.

If in going about of your Work you find it
Wabble, that is, that one ſide of the Flat incline
either to the Right or Left Hand, you muſt with
ſoft Blows of an Hammer, or other Tool at
hand, ſet it to right, and then again ſcrew it
hard up : For ſo often as you thus ſtrike upon
the Verge to ſet the Board true, you force the
Steel point of the *Pike* more or leſs (according
to the ſoftneſs of the Wood) towards that ſide
of the Verge you ſtrike upon ; and therefore you
may perceive a reaſon for ſcrewing up the *Pike*
ſo oft as you knock upon the outer Verge of the
Board.

But we will now ſuppoſe the Board well pitcht
and faſtned on the *Mandrel* and Center ; therefore take the *Side-Reſt* deſcribed in § 1. *Numb.*
10. ¶

10. ¶ 7. and *Plate* 82. at the Figure e, and f g, and fit it fo into the *Lathe*, as the upper edge of it may ftand range, or parallel to the fide of the Board you are to work upon, and fo wedge it hard up.

Now you muft come to ufe the *Hook*, defcribed *Numb.* 12. § 5. and *Plate* 15. For this Tool is moft commodious to ferve you inftead of the *Gouge*, when the Work ftands athwart the *Pikes*; becaufe the end of the Blade of this Tool being on its Flat fide turned into a Circular Figure, and that Circular Figure turned a little backwards, one of the Edges of this Circular Figure will conveniently (though the Tool be not held ftraight before the Work) come at any part of the Flat of the Board, and fo by the Circulation of the Board againft the Edge of the *Hook*, cut off its irregular Extuberances.

In the ufing of this Tool, you muft place the end of the *Handle* under your Arm-pit, and hold your Left Hand on the upper fide of the Blade of the Tool clofe to the *Reft*, and your Right Hand clofe befides your Left Hand under the Tool, and with both your hands clafp the Tool hard, and prefs it fteddy upon the *Reft*, and at the fame time hold it alfo fteddy, and yet lightly bearing againft the Work, that by the fwift coming about of the Work it draw not the Edge of the thin and tender Blade of the *Hook* into it.

You muft not hold the Blade of this Tool perpendicularly before the Work, *viz.* parallel to the *Pikes*, but aflant, fo as fomewhat above the middle of the Convex of the *Hook* may touch againft the Work. You may begin at the Verge, and fo lay feveral Grooves clofe by one another

till

till you come to the Center : But you muſt obſerve (as was ſaid before in the *Cilinder*) that
you lay all your *Grooves* of an equal depth into
the Board : For if you lay one deeper than the
reſt, and an Hollow may not properly be in that
place, you muſt again go over your work with
your *Hook*, to work that dawk out : And then
perhaps your Board may be made too thin for
its intended purpoſe. But this Craft of the
Hand muſt be acquired with ſome continued
Uſe and Practice, which will better inform your
Judgment what Errours you may be ſubject to
commit, than many words (though ſignificant)
upon this Doctrine. And this I'm ſure I found,
when I firſt practiſed upon *Turning.*

Having thus with the *Hook* rough-plain'd the
Board (for this *Hook* does in *Turning* the Office
of a *Fore-plain* in *Joynery*) you muſt uſe the *Tri-*
angular Grooving Tool, deſcribed in Turning § 5.
Plate 15. and with one of its Edges ſmoothen
down the ridges the *Hook* left on the Board.

But if your Work require any Molding near
the Verge, or any other part of it, you muſt
work that Molding as near as you can with the
Hook, eſpecially where Hollows are required ;
for that cuts faſter and ſmoother than any other
Tool, and moſt artificially forms an Hollow.

If a Flat be to be laid in the Board, you muſt
firſt uſe the *Triangular Point Tool,* and with it
ſtrike ſo many Threds as the breadth of the Flat
requires, and lay each Thred almoſt ſo deep
into the Board as you intend the Flat ſhall be :
And afterwards to ſmoothen it down, you muſt
uſe the *Flat Grooving Tool,* or a *Flat Chiſſel,*
and with either of them finiſh the Flat to its
intended Depth and Breadth. And where a
fine **Thred**, or Circle, is to be laid in the Board,

P you

you muft ufe the *Triangular Point Tool.* And thus as you fee occafion, you muft accommodate your felf with a Tool apt and proper for your purpofe, *viz.* fuch a Tool as will moft conveniently come at, and from the intended Work.

MECHA-

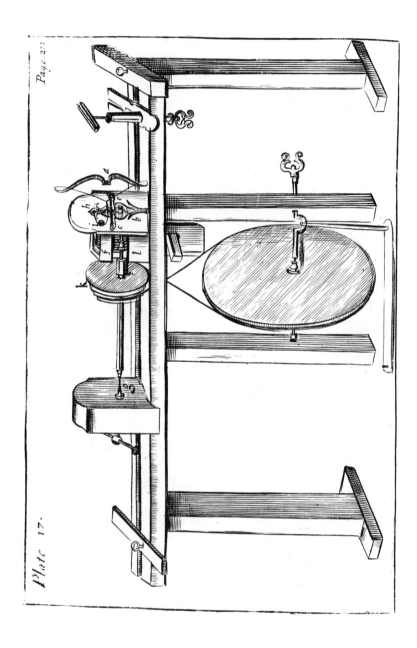

Plate 17.

MECHANICK EXERCISES:

OR,

The Doctrine of *Handy-Works*.

Applied to the ART of TURNING.

§ XV. *Of Turning* Hard Wood, *and* Ivory.

IF the Wood be very hard, as *Ebony*, *Lignum Vitæ*; or if it be *Ivory*, *Bone*, or *Horn* they are to Turn; they neither use the same Tools they do for soft Wood; because their edge is to tender: Nor do they use their other Tools as they do soft Wood. For the Tools made for Hard Wood are made with a stronger Point, Edge, &c. than they are for soft, as was said in Turning § 5. And they use them differently, because for Turning Soft Wood, they hold the Edge of the *Gouge* and *Flat Chissel*, at some considerable Distance from the *Rest*, mounting the Edge at such an Angle as will best cut off from the Work, as a great Chip as they can, or desire. And as they Turn the Work smaller, they guide the *Chissel* to follow the Work: But for Hard Wood, they raise the *Rest* near the Horizontal Plain of the *Axis* of the Work, setting it as close as conveniently they can to their Work, and lay their Tool flat and

steddy

fteddy upon the *Reft*; which being hard held in this pofition, does by the comming about of the Work, cut or tear off all the Extuberances the Tool touches in the fweep of the Work. So that (as I faid before) as in *Turning* foft Wood the Tool does fomewhat follow the Work; in *Turning* hard Wood the Work comes to the *Tool:* And therefore you may perceive a great reafon they have to keep the *Tool* fteddy: For fhould it in one fweep of the Work be thruft nearer the *Axis* in any place, it would there take off more than it fhould.

Having prepared the Work fit for the *Lathe*, either with Hewing, or as fome Hard Woods and Ivory may require, with Rafping, they pitch it between the *Pikes*, as before has been fhewn, or fuch Work as it may be, as Boxes, and generally all Hollow Work, they fit into *Collers*, either by fcrewing the *Mandrel* on an Iron *Axis*; or fitting it with fome other of the *Mandrels* defcribed in Turning § 6. as is proper for it: As fometimes they fit the Work tight into an *Hollow Mandrel*, and the tight fitting in holds it whilft it is working upon: And fometimes, if the Work be very thin, they fix it on a *Flat Mandrel* with Cement; But they are always either to chufe one of the *Mandrels* defcribed already in Turning § 6. or elfe contrive (as they often do) fome other *Mandrel* convenient to the opportunity that accidentally their Bufinefs may require. For the Work (whether it be pitcht on the *Pikes*, or fitted into *Hollow Mandrels*, or otherwife) muft run very fteddy and tight.

But having thus fitted it into the *Lathe*, they begin to work with the *Sharp-pointed Grooving Tool*, or elfe with the *Triangular Grooving Tool*,

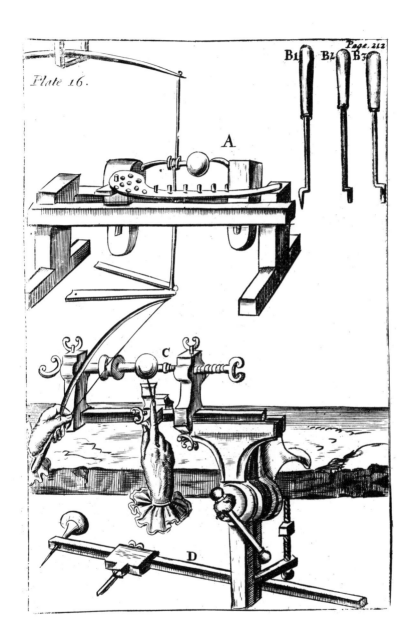

Plate 16.

A

B1 B2 B3

C

D

and with the point of either of thefe *Tools* break
the Grain of the Wood, by laying fmall Grooves
upon its Surface, till they have pretty well
wrought away Extuberances, and brought the
Work tollerably near an intended fhape, by
ftreightning, hollowing, and leaving Rifings in
their feveral proper places.

Afterwards with edg'd *Grooving Tools* of a proper Breadth, they cut down and fmoothen away
the Extuberances left by the *Sharp-pointed Grooving Tool*, or the *Triangular Grooving Tool*, and
bring the Work into a perfeÊt fhape. Which
done, they fmoothen the work with the Edge of
a piece of a Blade of a broken Knife, bafil'd a-
way, by following the Work with it: That is,
holding the bafil'd Edge of the Knife clofe againft
the Work while it comes about: For then its
fharp Edge fcrapes or fhaves off the little roughnefs the groffer *Tools* left upon the Work.

Laftly, they hold either a piece of Seal-skin
or *Dutch* Reeds (whofe outer Skin or Filme
fomewhat finely cuts) pretty hard againft the
Work, and fo make it fmooth enough to polifh.

Hard Wood they polifh with *Bees-wax*, viz.
by holding *Bees-wax* againft it, till it have fuff-
ciently toucht it all over; and prefs it hard into it by holding hard the edge of a Flat piece of
hard Wood made fizable and fuitable to the
Work they work upon, as the Work is going a-
bout. Then they fet a Glofs on it with a very
dry Woollen Rag, lightly fmear'd with *Sallad
Oyl.*

But *Ivory* they polifh with Chalk and Water,
and afterwards dry it with a Woollen Rag, and
a light touch of *Sallad Oyl*; which at laft they
rub off again with a dry Woollen Rag, and fo
fet a Glofs on it.

If there be a Screw to be made upon the thin Edge of an *Ivory,* or *Hard Wood,* or *Brafs Box,* they ufe the *Screw-Mandrel,* and its *Socket,* defcribed in Turning 6. ¶ 4. and 5. as is fhewn at the latter end of that Section.

§ XVI. *Of* Turning *long and flender Work of* Ivory.

SOme *Turners* to fhew their Dexterity in *Turning,* and make others that know not the way how it is done admire their Skill, *Turn* long and flender Sprigs of *Ivory,* as fmall as an Hay-ftalk, and perhaps a Foot or more long : Which perform they cut a piece of *Ivory* to its intended length, but ftrong enough to bear working till they bring it to as fmall a *Cilinder* as they can ; which being thus forwarded, they place a *Joint Coller* (as is defcribed in Turning § 17.) made fmall and fit for their purpofe, juft in the middle of their Work: Only that their Work may *Bear* at a fmaller length, and confequently be ftronger for being thus fupported while it is *Turned* yet fmaller. Then they place other *Collers* between the *Pikes,* and the middle *Coller,* and *Turn* the whole *Cilinder* flender yet. And thus by placing *Collers* where ever they find the Work buckle, they (as aforefaid) with *Sharp Tools,* tender touches, fomewhat a loofe and fine *String,* weak Bow, and great care and diligence work the whole *Cilinder* down as fmall as they lift, either with Moldings, or other Work upon it, as beft likes them.

The propereft *Lathe* to *Turn* this flender Work in, is the *Turn-Bench* defcribed § 18. *Plate* 16.

§ XVII. *Of*

§ XVII. *Of the* Brafiers Lathe *and* Turning
Tools ; *and their manner of ufing them.*

BRrafiers that *Turn* Andirons, Pots, Kettles,
&c. have their *Lathe* made different from
the Common *Turners Lathe,* as you may fee in
Plate 16. at A, where the *Cheeks, Puppets* and
Refts, &c. are much ftronger and the *Pikes* ftronger and longer than thofe the common *Turners*
ufe. Their *Edge Tools* which they call *Hooks,*
are alfo of a different fhape, as the Figures of
them defcribed at B 1, B 2, B 3. in the faid
Plate fhew, as being bent backwards and forwards
towards the cutting end, fomewhat like an z.
And as the common *Turners* work with a round
String made of Gut, as hath been defcribed
in Turning § 1. ¶ 14. The *Brafiers* work with a
Flat Leather Thong, which wrapping clofe and
tight about the *Rowler* of their *Mandrel,* com-
mands it the eafier and more forciably about.
Their *Thong* runs between the *Cheeks* of the
Lathe.

The whole *Lathe,* and its parts, are made fo
ftrong, becaufe the Matter they *Turn* being Mettal, is much heavier than Wood, and confequently with forciable coming about, would (if
the *Lathe* were flight) make it tremble, and fo
fpoil the Work ; as hath been faid before.

The reafon why the *Hook* is fo turned backwards, and again forwards, towards the end, is,
that they may the better direct the Edge of it as
much below the Horizontal Plain of the *Pikes* as
they lift, the better (in many cafes) to come at
the Work: For contrary to Soft Wood, Hard
Wood and Ivory *Turners,* they always dip the
end of their *Hook* below the *Reft,* that fo the
Hook refting very fteddy upon the *Reft,* and alfo
againft one of the Iron *Pins* ftanding upright in

P 4   the

the *Reft*, and held very fteddy forwards to the Work, the ftrong coming about of the Work a-gainft the ftrong Edge of the *Hook*, fcrapes off the extuberant Mettle lying in that Sweep.

I need no further defcribe the *Lathe*, and other *Tools* that belong to *Brafiers* Turning; or more of the manner of ufing them; becaufe, by the whole proceeding Difcourfe, thefe Arguments are largely and fufficiently handled; efpecially confidering I have given you the Figures of them in *Plate* 16. as aforefaid.

Only, their way of *Whetting* their *Tools* being different from the *Whetting* of other Turning *Tools*, I fhall fay fomewhat to: For they *Whet* their *Hooks* upon a broad Flat Slate, holding the *Hook* almoft perpendicular, that the *Bafil* of its Edge may comply with the Flat of the *Slate*; with clafping the upper end of the *Handle* in their left hand to fo lean the heavier on it, and clutching the *Shank* of the *Blade* near the *Hook-end* in the right hand, to guide it: And thus with Spittle, or Water, rub forwards and backwards on the Slate, till they have fharpned the Edge of the *Hook*. But if it be a round end *Hook* they whet, they chufe a *Groove* in the *Slate* fit to comply with the round edge of the *Hook* (for they have dif-ferent fized *Grooves* in the Slate for that purpofe) and fo in it rub forwards and backwards as afore-faid.

§ XVIII. *Of* Turning *Small Work of* Brafs, *or other* Mettle.

SMall Work in *Mettal* is *Turned* in an *Iron Lathe* called a *Turn-bench*. The Figure of it is de-fcribed in *Plate* 16. at C. when they ufe it they fcrew it in the *Chaps* of a *Vice*, and having fitted their Work upon a fmall *Iron Axis*, with a *Drill-Barrel* fitted upon a fquare Shank at the end of

the

the *Axis* next the left hand, they with a *Drill-bow* and *Drill-ftring* carry it about, as was fhewn in Smithing *fol. 6.* with this difference, that when a Hole is drill'd in a piece of Mettal, they hold the *Drill-bow* in their Right Hand; but when they *Turn* Small Work, they hold the *Drill-bow* in their Left Hand, and with their Right Hand ufe the *Tool,* which is commonly a *Graver,* or fometimes a *Sculpter,* fit to fuch Moldings as are to be made on the *Mettal.*

They begin to work firft with the fharp point of a *Graver,* laying the Blade of it firm upon the *Reft,* and directing the point to the Work, and lay Circles upon it clofe to one another, till they have wrought it pretty true: Then with one of the broad Edges of the *Graver* they fmoothen down what the Point left, and afterwards with *Sculpters, Round* or *Flat,* or great or fmall, they work their intended Moldings.

The Circumftances and Confiderations in the choice of a *Drill-bow* and *Drill-ftring* for *Turning,* are the fame with what you find in Smithing *fol.* 6, 7. for Drilling.

§ XIX. *Of laying* Moldings *either upon* Mettal, *or* Wood, *without fitting the Work in a* Lathe.

I Had, foon after the Fire of *London,* occafion to lay Moldings upon the Verges of feveral round and weighty flat pieces of *Brafs:* And being at that time, by reafon of the faid Fire, unaccommodated of a *Lathe* of my own, I intended to put them out to be *Turned:* But then *Turners* were all full of Employment, which made them fo unreafonable in their Prizes, that I was forc'd to contrive this following way to lay Moldings on their Verges.

I provided a ftrong Iron *Bar* for the *Beam* of a *Sweep:* (For the whole *Tool* marked in *Plate* 16,

is

is by Mathematical *Inſtrument-makers* called a
Sweep.) To this *Tool* is filed a *Tooth* of Steel
with ſuch *Roundings* and *Hollows* in the bottom
of it, as I intended to have *Hollows* and *Roundings* upon my Work: For an Hollow on the
Tooth, makes a *Round* upon the Work ; and a
Round upon the *Tooth*, makes an *Hollow* on the
Work ; even as they do in the *Molding-plains*
Joyners uſe. Then I placed the *Center-point* of
the *Sweep* in a Center-hole made in a ſquare *Stud*
of *Mettal*, and fixed in the *Center* of the Plain of
the Work ; and removed the *Socket* that rides on
the *Beam* of the *Sweep*, till the *Tooth* ſtood juſt
upon its intended place on the Verge of the
Work, and there ſcrew'd the *Socket* faſt to the
Beam.

To work it out, I employ'd a Labourer, directing him in his Left Hand to hold the Head
of the *Center-pin*, and with his Right Hand to
draw about the *Beam* and *Tooth*, which (according to the ſtrength) he us'd, cut and tore a-
way great Flakes of the *Mettal*, till it receiv'd
the whole and perfect Form the *Tooth* would
make ; which was as compleat a Molding as
any Skillful *Turner* could have laid upon it.

Having ſuch good Succeſs upon *Braſs*, I im-
prov'd the invention ſo, as to make it ſerve for
Wood alſo. And make a *Plain-Stock* with my
intended Molding on the *Sole* of it, and fitted an
Iron to that *Stock* with the ſame Molding the
Sole had.

Through the ſides of this *Stock* I fitted an Iron
Beam, to do the Office of the *Beam* I uſed for the
Sweep, viz. to keep the Plain always at what poſition I lifted from the Center (for thus the Iron
in the Plain wrought about the Center, even as
the Tooth in the *Sweep* (before rehearſed) and
to that purpoſe I made a round Hole of about
half

half an Inch Diameter near the end of the Iron: Then in the Center of the Work I fixed a round Iron *Pin*, exactly to fit the said round Hole, putting the round Hole over the *Pin*, and fitting the *Iron* into the *Stock* commodious to work with. I used this Plain with both Hands, even as *Joyners* do other *Plains* : For the *Iron Pin* in the Hole of the *Beam* kept it to its due distance from the Center; so that neither hand was ingaged to guide it.

But note, The *Stock* of this *Plain* was not straight (as the Stocks of other Plains are) but by Hand cut Circular pretty near the size of the Diameter of the intended Molding: And yet was made to slide upon the *Beam*, farther from or nearer to the Center, as different Diameters of Verges might require.

§ XX. *To Turn several* Globes *or* Balls *of* Ivory *within one another, with a* Solid Ball *in the middle.*

YOu must first Turn your *Ivory Ball* or *Globe* truly round, of your intended Diameter : Then describe a Circle exactly through the middle, or Equinoctial of the *Globe:* Divide that Circle into four equal parts, and pitch one point of a pair of Compasses in one of those Divisions, and extend the other point to either of the next Divisions, and describe with it a Circle round about the *Globe.* Then remove the standing point of the Compasses to either of the next Divisions in the Equinoctial, and in like manner describe another Circle round about the *Globe.*

But Note, That the moving point of your Compasses must be somewhat bended inwards; for else its point will not describe a Circle on the greatest Extuberances of the *Globe,* but will slide off it.

Thus

Thus ſhall the Ball or Globe be divided into eight Spherical Quadrants : Deſcribe as great a Circle as you can in each of theſe Quadrants, and each two Centers of every two oppoſite Circles ſhall have an imaginary *Axix* paſs between them : And if the *Globe* be ſucceſſively pitcht upon all the reſt of the Centers, ſo as the imagined *Axis* paſſing between it and its oppoſite Center, lye in a ſtraight line with the *Pike* and the Center of the *Coller* it is *Turned* in, the working out of all the *Hollows* on the *Ball* will be but common *Turners* Work, as you will find hereafter. This is in brief the Theory : But to the Practice.

You muſt uſe an *Hollow-Mandrel*, made fit ſtiſly to receive the convexity of the *Globe* in its concavity, ſo as it may ſtick firmly in the *Man-drel*, in its poſition : And you muſt take care that in pitching the *Globe* into the *Mandrel*, that the imaginary *Axis* of the *Globe* (which is the Line paſſing between the two Centers of the two op-poſite Circles as aforeſaid) lye in a ſtraight Line with the *Axis* of the *Mandrel*; which you may know by examining whether the Circle deſcribed with your *Compaſſes* (as aforeſaid) on the Center (aforeſaid) wabble not in a whole Revolution of the *Globe*, from the point of a Tool applied ſted-dy to it.

Having thus pitcht the *Globe* true, and fixt it faſt into the *Mandrel*, you muſt begin to work with the *Triangular Grooving Point* (deſcribed in Tur-ning § 5. and *Plate* 15.) placing the point of it pretty near the Center of the Circle, and work into the *Ball* with the *Grooving Point*, and ſo by degrees make a Hollow in the *Ball* ſo deep, and ſo wide, as you think convenient, I mean ſo deep from the Superficies of the *Globe* towards the Cen-ter of the *Globe*, and ſo wide from the Center of the Circle deſcribed on the Superficies of the
Globe

Globe towards that Circle, as it may have a convenient Subſtance between this Hole, and the next intended to be *Turned.*

Thus muſt every one of the eight Circles deſcribed on the *Globe,* be ſucceſſively by the ſame Rule, and after the ſame manner be pitcht outwards, and fixt into the *Mandrel,* and then Hollowed out as the firſt was. Where Note, That every Hollow is to be *Turned* to the ſame depth and width exaƈtly as the firſt was : Which to do, you muſt uſe a *Gage* made of a thin Plate of Iron or Braſs, as is deſcribed in *Plate* 17. *Fig.* D. whoſe two ſides from *a* the Bottom of the *Gage,* to *b* the *Shoulder* are the depth of the *Hollow* from the Superficies of the *Globe* towards the Center : *b b.* is the width of the *Hollow* at the Superficies of the *Globe* ; and *a a* is the bottom width of the *Hollow* ; and the concave Arch between *a a* is an Arch that the Convexity of the little ſolid *Ball* to be *Turned* within all the *Spheres* muſt comply with. So that when each *Hollow* is *Turned,* the *Gage* muſt be put into it to try how the ſides of the *Hollow* complies with the ſides of the *Gage,* and alſo how the Arch in the bottom of the *Gage,* complies with the ſurface of the Solid *Ball* in the middle.

Having thus *Turned* all the *Hallows* in the *Globe,* you muſt provide ſeveral thin and narrow Arching *Grooving Tools,* whoſe convex and concave Arches comply both with the Convexity and Concavity of each *Globe,* or *Sphere,* to be *Turned* within the outermoſt : So that begining at the bottom of the Hollow, you Turn juſt half way of the Solid *Ball* looſe from the Sphere it is contained in, *viz.* as far as the Equinoƈtial of the *Globe* ; and in thus Turning it, you muſt take great care, that the Solid Ball on its Convexity and the Concavity of the Sphere it is contained in, be both at the ſame time Turned exaƈtly Spherical.   Thus

Thus one half of the Solid *Ball* being **Turned** loose, you may in like manner *Turn* the next Sphere it is included in half loose alfo : And fo fucceffively as many Spheres as you lift.

Having thus *Turned* one half of all the *Spheres* loofe, you muft take the whole *Globe* out of the *Hollow-Mandrel*, and pitcht and fix the *Globe* again into the *Mandrel*, fo as the imagined *Axis* of the *Hollow* oppofite to the laft loofned *Hollow* lye in a ftraight line (as before was taught) with the *Pike* and *Center* of the *Coller* the *Mandrel* runs in, and then *Turn* the other half of the Solid *Ball* and *Spheres* alfo loofe, as the firft half was *Turned*.

§ XXI. *To* Turn *a* Globe *with feveral loofe* Spheres *in it, and a* Solid Cube, *or* Dy, *in the middle of it.*

THis is *Turned* after the fame manner the for-mer *Ball* was *Turned*; only inftead of dividing the Equinoɛtial of that *Globe* into four equal parts, the Equinoɛtial of this muft be divided but into three equal parts, and their Semi-Circle draw through the divifions into either Pole of the *Globe :* So fhall the *Globe* be divided into fix equal parts, or Segments; in each of which parts muft be defcribed a Circle, as was defcribed before in the *Globes* of eight equal parts; and in thefe fix Circles muft be made fix Hollows, as before there was eight : But inftead of working the Bottom of each hollow Spherical, now the Bottom muft be wrought Flat: So fhall the *Cube* when thefe fix Hollows are thus made, be formed : And the Hollows being exaɛtly of the fame depth, and flat in the Bottom, the *Cube* or *Dy* will loofen, and each of the fix Flats in the Bottom will become the fix fides or Faces of the *Cube*.

The

The manner of loofning all the other inward *Spheres*, is as the Former : Only, that was loof- ned with twice pitching the *Ball* in the *Mandrel*, becaufe the Centers of the *Hollows* lay oppofite to one another ; but to loofen this *Ball* will re- quire three Pitchings into the *Mandrel*; becaufe the Centers lye not oppofite to one another.

§ XXII. *To* Turn *a* Cube, *or* Dy, *in an Hol- low* Globe, *that fhall have but one Hole on the outfide to work at.*

THe Outfide of this *Globe* muft be Turned Round, *viz.* Spherical, as the former, and fixed in an Hollow *Socket* (as before hath been taught.) Then muft an Hole be Turned in the *Globe* fo deep and fo wide as you pleafe, as in the former *Globes*, and the Bottom of that Hole Turned flat, for one fide, or Face of the *Cube*, or *Dy :* Then with a Semi-circular Tool loofen the whole Core, or middle of the Ball, and pitch the Core with the point oppofite to the Center of the already flatted face of the *Dy*, outwards againft the Hole in the *Globe*, and fo faften it in this pofition, by powring in fome melted hard Wax, or other Cement; and then with a flat Tool Turn the forefide, (*viz.* the fide oppofite to the firft fide) flat alfo: Which done, loofen it out of the Wax, and fucceffive- ly pitch the other fides to be Turned flat care- fully againft the Hole, fo as all the fides have right Angles to each other, and faftning them with Wax, or Cement (as before) Turn them by the fame Rule flat alfo.

Now

Now to make this Thing more admirable to the ignorant Spectator, you may make the *Dy* as big as you can, and the Hole you Turn it at as little as you can; that it may the more puzzle the Wit of the Enquirer to find how so great a *Dy* should have Entrance at a small Hole, unless the hollow Ball were turned in two Halves, *&c.*

MECHA-

MECHANICK EXERCISES:

O R,

The Doctrine of *Handy-Works.*

Applied to the ART of *TURNING.*

§ XXIII. *Of Turning* Oval Work.

THIS Work may be perform'd in the Common *Lathe* that goes either with the *Treddle-Wheel*, or the great Wheel; because the Work muft run always one way, if the *Puppet* be made to it with the Machination defcribed in *Plate* 17. and an Iron *Axis* be made to carry the Work about, and to its end be fitted and faftned a *Brafs Coller*, with a Female Screw in it, to fcrew on the *Mandrel* that the Work you intend to Turn is fixt upon.

To the Forefide of this *Puppet* is faftned at *b*, as on a Center-pin, a ftrong Iron *Coller* marked *b h*, and this Coller is called the *Moving Coller*; becaufe it moves between the Iron *Shackle c c*, and the Forefide of the *Puppet*. Into this *Moving Coller* is fitted the *Hollow Axis* marked *c*, fo as to turn round in it as if it were in any of the other *Collors* formerly defcribed; but the *Moving Coller* moving between the *Shackles*, and the Forefide of the *Puppet*, carries the *Hollow Axis* with it athwart the *Puppet*, even fo far as is the

Q   width

width of the *Hollow* between the *Shackle,* and the Foreside of the *Puppet.* And thus by the moving of the *Hollow Axis* backwards and forwards the Work fcrewed in it, having an *Edg'd,* or a *Pointed-Tool* applied to it, receives that *Oval* Form which is made upon the *Guide.*

But to make it move thus to and from you, there are required feveral Machinal Helps : For there is a ftrong *Steel Bow* as at *a,* faftned about its middle part to the further fide of the *Puppet,* which ftands about an Inch forwarder than the Forefide of the *Puppet* with its hollow fide to the Workman. And to the ends of this *Steel Bow* is faftned a ftrong *String* of Gut, and to the middle of that *String* in a Noos is faftned another ftrong *Gut-ftring,* with a Noos at its end. This laft mentioned *String* is made exactly of that length, that when the neareft fide of the *Guide,* viz. its leaft Diameter is fet into the *Groove* of the *Guide-pulley,* and the *Bow* is ftrained, and this *String* laid in the *Groove* of the *String-pulley,* the Noos at the end of it may be put over the Iron *Button* fixed in the top of the *Moving-Coller.* For then as the *Treddle-Wheel* carries the *Axis* about, the *Guide* being firmly faftned upon the *Axis,* comes alfo about; and having the *Groove* of the *Guide-pulley* fet againft the outer edge of the *Guide,* as the great Diameter of the *Guide* is turned againft the *Guide-pulley,* the *Moving-Coller* being drawn by the ftrength of the *Bow,* draws the *Hollow Axis* along with it, as alfo the Work fcrewed in the *Hollow Axis:* And thus as the fmall Diameter of the *Guide* comes to the *Guide-pulley,* the fmall Diameter of the Work is Formed; and as the great Diameter of the *Guide* comes to the *Guide-pulley,* the great Diameter of the Work is formed.

This is the fum of *Oval Turning.*

But

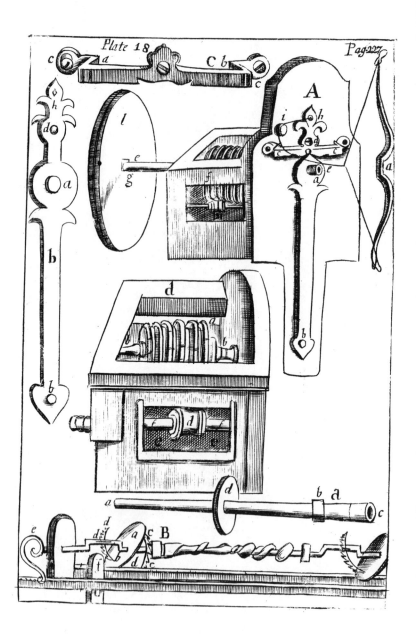

Plate 18

But that the whole Machine may be yet better underſtood, I ſhall more particularly give you the names of all its parts, together with a Deſcription upon its moſt material parts, where the *Fore-puppet* is more largely delineated in *Plate* 18. at A, where alſo ſome of the Members moſt difficult to be deſcribed, are drawn more at large by themſelves.

a The *Bow.*
b The *Moving Coller.*
c c The *Socket* in which the *Coller* is moved.
d The *Stop-ſcrew*, to take out when the *Hollow Axis* moves in the *Moving-Coller.*
e The *Hollow Axis.*
f The *Head*, in which is contained the ſeveral *Guides.*
g The *Center Head.*
h The *Button.*
i The *String-pulley.*
k The *Wheel-pulley.*
l The *Guide-pulley.*

¶ 1. *Of the* Hollow Axis, *and its* Shank, *marked* a *in* Plate 18.

THe *Shank* is a Bar of Iron about an Inch thick, and two Foot long, having in its further end a Center-hole to pitch upon the *Pike* in the further *Puppet* ; but its hither end is made ſquare to fit tight into a ſquare *Socket*, in the Braſs *Hollow Axis*: And when it is thus fitted into the hither end of the Braſs, it is Turned true Cilindrically round, ſo as to fit into the round Hole in the *Moving Coller.* The Diameter of the Round is about two Inches, and the length about two Inches ſtraight ; but then a Shoulder is Turned to the Braſs Cilinder, to ſtop it from ſlipping thro' the *Moving Center.* In the Fore-end

of

of this *Hollow Axis* (*viz.* in the Braſs **Cilinder**) is Turned a wide Hole about an Inch and a quarter Diameter, and an Inch deep : And in this wide Hole is Turned a Female Screw with a courſe Thred, to receive a Male Screw made behind the *Mandrel* that the Work is fixed upon.

About the middle of this Iron *Shank* is placed a *Pulley* made of Wainſcot Board, about eight Inches Diameter, and an Inch thick, with a *Groove* on its outer edge about half an Inch wide, and half an Inch deep, for the *String* of the *Treddle Wheel* that carries the *Axis* about to run in: And between this *Pulley* you may (if you will) have ſeveral lengths of ſuch *Male-ſcrews* as was deſcribed in Turning § 6. ¶ 4. and *Plate* 15. to make Screws with, if you pleaſe.

See the Figure *a d c b*, disjunct from the reſt of the Work.

a The hinder end.

d The Pulley of the *Axis*, or *Wheel-pulley.*

c The Hollow, or Hole in the Fore-end of the *Hollow Axis.*

b The *Shoulder* of the *Hollow Axis.*

¶ 2. *Of the* Moving Coller marked b, in *Plate* 18.

THis whole Member is called the *Moving Coller*, tho' the *Coller* ſtrictly is only the round Hole at *a*, into which the *Hollow Axis* is fitted. It is made of Iron to reach from its top at *b* (the *Button*) down to the bottom of the *Cheeks* of the *Lathe*, as at *b*; upon which Pin (as on a Center) the whole *Moving Coller* moves backwards and forwards; its extream Breadth is about three Inches, and its thickneſs above a quarter of an Inch. Its Neck at *c* is claſped, but not fixed down to the Foreſide of the *Puppet*; for this *Neck* is only gaged in the *Shackle* marcked *c*, ſo as the *Neck*, (and conſequently the whole *Moving Coller*)

ler) may flide from end to end of the *Shackle* forwards and backwards. *d* A fmall *Female Screw*, into which through a Hole in the *Shackle* is fitted a *Male Screw* to hold the *Moving Coller* and the *Shackle* together, that the *Moving Coller* may not move when only round Work is Turned in the *Coller*.

¶ 3. *Of the Forefide of the* Puppet, *and the* Shackle *marked* c.

UNder this *Shackle* (viz. between it and the Forefide of the *Puppet*) moves the *Neck* of the *Sliding-Coller* from *a* to *b*, when the ends at *c c* are fixed down to the Forefide of the *Puppet* with two Iron Screws.

¶ 4. *Of the* Hollow *in the* Puppet *marked* d.

IN the middle of the *Puppet* is hollowed out a Hole about three Inches between the Fore and Back-fide of the *Puppet*, and four Inches athwart the *Cheeks* in the *Puppet*, and four Inches deep : So that about an Inch of Subftance remains on each of the four upright fides. But the Top is quite open, (as at *a*) through the middle of this fquare *Hole* runs the Iron *Axis* marked *b b*, on which is fixed the feveral *Guides* that are to be ufed in this fort of Working.

It is open at the Top, that Light may be let in to fet the *Guide-pulley* to which *Guide* you pleafe, and it is open on the hither fide as at *e e*, about an Inch and an half above and below the *Axis*, that the *Guide-pulley* may be flid on its *Axis* to any of the *Guides*.

The *Guide-pulley* marked *d*, is a brafs Pulley of about an Inch Diameter, and a little above a quarter of an Inch thick, having a *Groove* in the Edge of it to receive the Edge of the *Guide*. It hath in its middle a round Hole about half an

Q 3   Inch

Inch Diameter, which round Hole flips over a round Iron *Pin* of the fame Diameter, marked *f f*, fo as it may flide from one end of the faid Iron *Pin* to the other, according as the *Guides* may be fixed towards either end.

When it is ufed, the Groove in the Edge of this *Guide-pulley* is fet againft the Edge of the *Guide,* and being fitted tight on the round Iron *Pin* aforefaid, and the two ends of the Iron Pin faft fixed into the Wood of the *Puppet,* the *Guide-pulley* may indeed move round on the Iron *Pin*; but the ftrength of the Iron *Pin,* and *Guide-pulley* will refift the extuberick parts of the Edge of the *Guide*; and fo with the affiftance of the ftrength of the *Steel Bow* force the *Guide* and *Hollow Axis* to move backwards; and then an Edge-Tool held to the Work in the *Mandrel* fcrewed in the *Hollow Axis,* will defcribe the fame Figure on the Work, as is on the out Edge of the *Guide.*

Note, that when you are at Work, you muft keep the Hole in the middle of the *Guide-pulley* well oyl'd, as alfo the round Iron *Pin* it flides and turns round upon; becaufe this *Guide-pulley* ought to run round : For then the *Axis* will have and eafier and fwifter motion, tho' it may indeed perform the Work if it run not round upon the Iron Pin.

§ XXIV. *Of* Rofe-work, *&c.*

ROfe-*Work* Turning, or Works of any other Figure, are performed by the fame Rule, and after the fame manner as *Oval Work* is made; only by changing the *Guides,* and ufing one whofe outer Edge is made with the Figure, or feveral Figures you intend to have on your Work.

§ XXV.

§ XXV. *Of Turning* Swaſh-Work.

TO the Turning of *Swaſh-work* you muſt have two ſuch *Puppets*, as the *Fore-puppet* deſcribed in § 22. And alſo a round *Swaſh-board*, about ten Inches Diameter, and an Inch and an half thick, as is *a* in Fig. B. *Plate* 18. Upon both the flat ſides of this *Swaſh-board*, in a dia-metrical Line, is faſtned upright an Arch of a Quadrant made of a Steel Plate, about half a quarter of an Inch thick, and an Inch and a quarter broad, as at *b b*, *c c*. The Convex edges of theſe Quadrants are cut into Notches, like the Teeth of an Hand-ſaw; that according as you may have occaſion to ſet the *Swaſh-board* more or leſs a-ſlope, you may be accommodated with a Notch or Tooth to ſet it at. This *Swaſh-board* hath an Hole made about its Center, to ſlip o-ver the *Iron Axis*, and being thus ſlipt over the *Iron Axis*, you ſet it to that Slope you intend the *Swaſh* on your Work ſhall have. And to fix it faſt in this poſition, you muſt put the Blades of the Quadrants into two *Slits*, made in the *Iron Axis* as at *d d*, and fit the two oppoſite Teeth a-gainſt the two outer Shoulders of the *Slits*.

You muſt moreover make two ſtrong **Steel Springs** as at *c c*, to reach from the bottom of the outer ſides of the *Puppets*, being ſtrong nailed, or rather ſcrewed down there, which muſt reach up ſo high as the *Axis*. And in the inner ſides of theſe *Springs* muſt be made two Center holes for the points of the *Axis* to be fitted in: For the *Oval-Guide* being fitted to one end of the *Axis*, and a Low-Puppet, as at *f*, wedged cloſe to one ſide of the *Swaſh-board*, when the *Swaſh-board* ſtands in its greateſt declirity; then in a Revolution of the *Axis*, as the farther part of the

the circumference of the *Swash-board* comes to the *Low-Puppet*, one *Spring* will be forced backwards, and the other will spring forwards; and an Edg'd-Tool held against the Work fixed on the *Axis*, will make on the Work the Form of a *Swash*, &c.

These *Oval-Engines*, *Swash-Engines*, and all other *Engines*, are excellently well made by Mr. *Thomas Oldfield*, at the sign of the *Flower-de-luce*, near the *Savoy* in the *Strand*, *London*.

AN

―――――――――――――――

*An Explanation of Terms ufed in thefe Ex-
ercifes of* Turning, *Alphabetically digefted.*

A.

AXis. The imagined ftraight Line that paffes through the two Center-points that
Turned Work is Turned upon. Thus the imagined Line that paffes between the two Pikes
through the Work in the Lathe is the Axis.

B.

BOw. The Bow that common Turners ufe is
defcribed § 1. ¶ 11. And the Bow that Oval
Turners ufe is defcribed § 23. and **Plate** 17, 18.
at *a.*

Button. The Button is defcribed § 23. and
Plate 17. at *b.*

C.

CAllippers. Compaffes with bowed fhanks to
meafure the Diameter of any round Body.
See § 11. and **Plate** 14. at O.

Center-head, See § 23. and **Plate** 17. at *g.*

Cheeks. See § 1. ¶ 2. and **Plate** 12. *b b.*

Chock. See § 6. ¶ 5. and **Plate** 13. at F. 5. *a.*

Cleaving-knife. See § 9. and **Plate** 13. at M.

Crank. The end of an Iron Axis turned Square
down, and again turned Square to the firft turning down, fo that on the laft turning down a
Leather Thong is flipt, to Tread the Treddle-
wheel about.

Coller. See § 7. and **Plate** 13. at G H I.

Crook. See *Crank.*

Crofs-Treddle. See § 1. ¶ 8. and **Plate** 12. at *k.*

Drill-

D.

DRill-*Barrel.*   See Smithing Fol. 6. Plate 1.
  and Fig. 8. at C.
Drill-Bench.   See § 12. Plate 14. at *a a a a.*
Drill-Bow.   See Smithing Fol. 6, 7.

F

FEmale *Screw.*   The Screw made in the round
  Hole of a Nut.
  Flat-Chiffel.   See § 3. and Plate 15. at C C.
  Flat-Mandrel.   See § 6. and Plate 13. at F 1.

G

GOuge.   See § 2. ¶ 1. and Plate 15. at B. B.
  Great Wheel.   See § 1. ¶ 12. and Plate
14. at a.
  Grooving Hooks.   See § 5. and Plate 15. at E.
  Grooving Tools.   See *Grooving Hooks.*
  Guide.   See § 23. ¶ 4. and Plate 18.
  Guide-Pulley.   See § 23. ¶ 4. and *Plate* 18. at *d.*

H.

HEad.   See § 23. and Plate 17.
  Hook.   See § 17. and Plate 16. at B. 1.
B 2. B 3.
  Hollow Axis.   See § 17. and Plate 17. at *e.*
  Hollow Mandrels.   See § 6. ¶ 3. and Plate 13.
at F 3.

I.

JOynt *Collar.*   See § 7. and *Plate* 13. at G.

L.

LAthe.   See § 1. and Plate 12.
  Legs.   See § 1. and Plate 12. at *a a a a.*

Man-

M.

MAndrel. See § 6. ¶. 1. and Plate 13. at F 1. F 2. F 3. F 4.

Mawl. See § 8. and Plate 13. at K.

Male-Screw. The Screw made upon a Shank, or Pin.

Moving-Collar. See § 23. ¶ 2. and Plate 18. at *b*.

N.

NUt. A piece of Iron that a Female Screw is made in.

P.

PIke. See § 1. ¶ 5. and Plate 12.

Pin Mandrel See § 6. ¶ 2. and Plate 13. at F 2.

Pole. See § 1. ¶ 9. and Plate 12 at *l*.

Puppet. See § 1. ¶ 3. and Plate 12. at *c c*.

R.

REft. See § 1. ¶ 6. and Plate 12. at *e*.

Rowler. See § 6. and Plate 13. F 1. at *b*.

S.

SCrew-Mandrel. See § 6. ¶ 4. and Plate 13. at F 4.

Seat. See § 1. ¶ 15.

Shackles. See § 23. ¶ 2. and Plate 18. V at *c c*.

Side-Reft. See § 1. ¶ 7. and Plate 13. at *e*.

Socket. See *Chock.*

Steel-bow. See § 23. and Plate 18. at *a*.

Stop-Screw. See § 23. and Plate 17. at *d*.

String. See § 1. and Plate 12. at *m*.

String-Pulley. See § 23. and Plate 17. at *i*.

Swafh. A *Swafh* is a Figure whofe Circumfe-rence is not Round but Oval; and whofe Moldings

lye

lye not at Right Angles, but Oblique to the *Axis*
of the Work.　See § 25. and Plate 18. at Fig. **B.**

Swaſh-Board.　See § 25. and Plate 18. at *a* in
Fig. B.

Sweep.　See § 19. and Plate 16. at D.

T.

T*Read.*　See § 13. Fol. 209.

Treddle.　See § 1. and Plate 12. at *i.*

Treddle Wheel.　See § 1. ¶ 13.

Turn-Bench.　See § 18. and Plate 16. at C.

W.

W*Abble.*　When a piece of Work is not
pitcht true upon its Centers, it will in a
Revolution incline more on one ſide of its Circumference than on its oppoſite ſide.　See § 23.
and Plate 17. at *k.*

There are ſeveral other Terms uſed in theſe
Exerciſes of *Turning,* not explain'd here : But becauſe they are uſed in ſome of the former *Exerciſes,* and there explain'd, I ſhall referr you to
them.

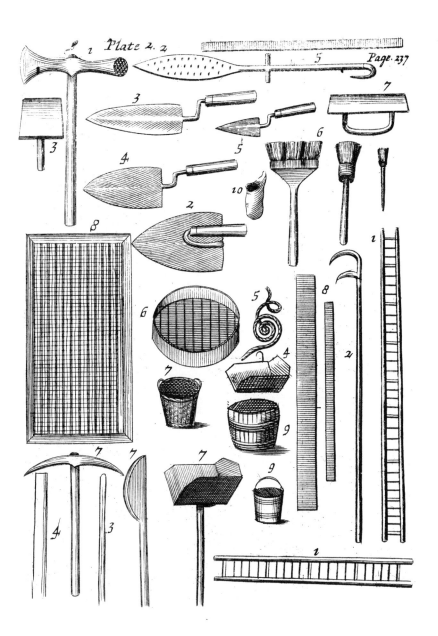

Plate 2. 2.

Page. 237.

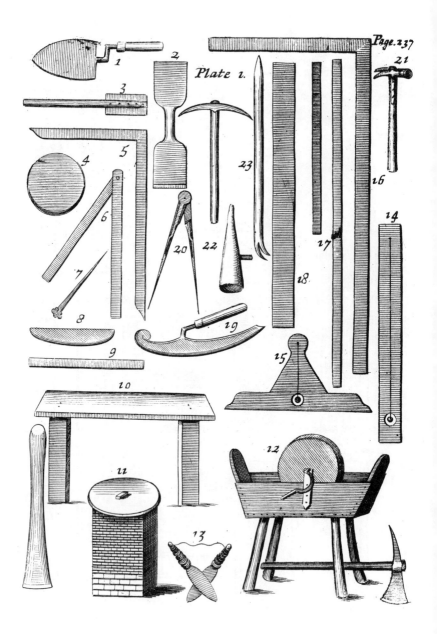

Plate 1.

MECHANICK EXERCISES:

O R,

The Doctrine of *Handy-Works.*

Applied to the A R T of *Bricklayers Work.*

Definition.

Bricklayers-Work is an Art Manual, which Joins *several Bodies so together, that they adhere like one entire Body.*

Whether the *White Mason,* which is the Hewer of Stone, or the *Red Mason,* which is the Hewer of Brick, be the most Ancient, I know not : but in Holy Writ, we read of making of Bricks, before we read of Digging or Hewing of Stones ; therefore we may suppose the *Red Mason* (or *Bricklayer*) to be the most Ancient.

The method that I shall use in Treating of this Art shall be this.

First, I will shew what Materials they use, and their Composition.

Secondly, I will treat of their Tools, and describe their Names and Uses.

Thirdly, I will declare their Method of Working, both in *Bricks, Tiles,* &c.

And

And firſt of Materials.

WHich are compriſed under ſix Heads, *viz.*
1. *Bricks,* 2. *Tiles,* 3. *Morter,* 4. *Laths,*
5. *Nailes,* 6. *Tile-pins.*

Of Bricks.

THey are made of Earth, of which the white-
iſh Chalky ſort of Earth, and the Rediſh
are the beſt.

At *Lunenburg* in *Saxony,* they make them of a
fat Earth full of *Allom.* Alſo there are good
Bricks made at *Pitane* in *Aſia,* of a Pumice ſort
of Earth, which being dryed, will ſwim in Water and not Sink.

Likewiſe the Antients made them of Earth
which was Sandy.

But here in *England* they are made for the
moſt part of a yellowiſh coloured fat Earth ſomewhat Rediſh.

And they are made of ſeveral ſorts and ſizes.

IN *Holland* they make ſmall ones, being about
ſix Inches long, three Inches broad, and one
Inch in thickneſs.

Which ſort of Bricks, is commonly uſed here
in *England,* to pave Yards or Stables withal; and
they make a good Pavement, and are very Durable, and being laid edge-ways looks handſomly,
eſpecially if laid Herring-bone faſhion.

They are alſo uſed in Soap-boilers Fats, and in ma-king of Ciſterns.

THe common Bricks that are made here in *England,* are nine Inches in length, four Inches
and $\frac{1}{4}$ in Breadth, and two and an half in thickneſs; and ſometimes three Inches thick.

Moſt

Moſt Counties in England *afford Earth for the making of* Bricks.

BUt the beſt Earth that we have in *England* for *making* of *Bricks*, is in the County of *Kent*, from whence we have moſt of the *Bricks* which are Rubbed and Hewed for the Ornaments of the chief Fronts in the City of *London:* The Ornamental part of which Fronts, are done with the reddeſt Bricks they can pick from among them; and the Rough or Plain Work, is done with the *Grey Kentiſh Bricks*; alſo thoſe *Gray Kentiſh Bricks* are uſed in making of Ciſterns to hold Water, and Horſe-Ponds, and alſo Fats for Soap-Boilers; and I am of the Opinion, that no time will impair or decay thoſe *Grey Kentiſh Bricks:* But, as *Pliny* ſays, (ſpeaking of *Bricks*,) that they will laſt to Eternity.

There are alſo in moſt Counties of *England*, Bricks made for the Paving of *Floors* of *Rooms, Cellers, Dary-houſes*, &c. which are made of a ſtronger ſort of Earth, than the common *Bricks* for Building, the *Earth* being a kind of *Clay*, and in ſome Countries are called *Clay Bricks*, which are dearer than the *Ordinary Bricks* by about ſix Shillings in a Thouſand.

Likewiſe in ſeveral Counties, but chiefly in *Surrey*, are made Paving *Tiles* of three ſeveral Magnitudes; the largeſt ſort being twelve Inches long, and twelve broad, and one Inch and an half in Thickneſs.

The ſecond ſort are ten Inches long, and ten Inches broad, and one Inch and a quarter thick.

The third ſort are eight Inches long, eight broad, and one Inch thick.

Either of which ſorts being Poliſhed or rubbed with ſharp Sand on the Surface, and the joints made exactly ſquare, and the ſides equal, by

hewing

hewing them with a *Brick Ax*, and rubbing them on a rubbing Stone with sharp Sand, makes an excellent Pavement and pleasing to the Eye, especially when laid *Arris ways*.

Having thus described the several sorts of *Bricks*, and also paving Tiles, we come in the next place to treat of *Tiles*, made and used in the Covering of *Roofs* of *Houses*, both Publick and Particular, of which are four sorts or kinds.

The first sort are called *Plains Tiles*, being made of a strong sort of Earth like *Clay*; and are, or should be ten Inches and an half in length, in breadth six Inches and a Quarter, and in thickness three quarters of an Inch.

The second sort are *Gutter* or *Hip Tiles*, which are used sometimes for *Vallies* and *Hips* of *Rooffs*, altho' here at *London*, the *Vallies* are commonly tiled with *Plain Tiles*, and the *Hips* with *Ridge*, or (as some call them) *Roof Toiles*: These *Gutter Tiles* are in length ten Inches and an half, with convenient breadth and thickness accordingly, and are made Circular or hollow, and wider at one end than at the other.

The third sort are *Ridge* or *Roof Tiles*, being in length thirteen Inches, and made Circular breadthways like an half Cylinder, whose Diameter is about ten Inches, or more, and about half an Inch and half a quarter in thickness: These are laid upon the upper part, or ridge of the Roof, and also on the Hips.

The fourth sort are *Pan-Tiles*, being about thirteen Inches long, with a Nob or Button to hang on the Laths, and are made hollow or circular breadthways, being eight Inches in breadth, and about half an Inch in thickness, or somewhat more. The best sort of these are brought from *Holland* into *England*, and are called *Fleminish Pan-Tiles*, we having such Tiles made here

in

in *England*, but not so good: Which *Flemmish Tiles* are sometimes glazed, and are of a Lead, or Blewish colour, and being glazed they are very durable and handsom.

Having done with the Description of *Tiles*, for the Covering of Roofs, we come in the next place to treat of *Morter*, and first of *Lime*, being the chief Material of which the *Mortar* is made, for the Cementing or joining of *Tiles*, as well as *Bricks* together, we will Treat of it in the first place.

Of Lime.

THere are two forts, one made of Stone, which is the strongest, and the other of Chalk, both forts being burnt in a *Kilne*.

The Lime that is made of soft Stone or Chalk is useful for Plastering of Seelings and Walls within Doors, or on the insides of Houses; and that made of hard Stone, is fit for Structures or Buildings, and Plastering without Doors, or on the out fide of Buildings that lies in the Weather; and that which is made of greasy clammy Stone, is stronger than that made of lean poor Stone; and that which is made of spongy Stone, is lighter than that made of firm and close stone; that is again more Commodious for Plastering, this for Building.

Also very good *Lime* may be made of *Millstone*, not course and Sandy, but fine and Greasy.

Likewise of all kinds of Flints (but they are hard to burn except in a *Reverbratory Kilne*) except those that are roled in the Water, because a great part of its increase goes away by a kind of Glass.

But the shells of Fish, as of Cockles, Oysters, &c. are good to burn for *Lime*.

And

And the Fire in *Lime* burnt, Affwages not, but lies hid, fo that it appears to be cold, but Water excites it again, whereby it Slacks and crumbles into fine Powder.

Lime alfo is ufeful in divers things, for 'tis ufeful in Oyles and Wines, and good to Manure Land with ; fome feafon new Wine with it, mittigating the unpleafantnefs of the Wine therewith.

Moreover *quick Lime* being caft into an arched Vault, and Water thrown upon it, confumes dead Bodies put therein.

Alfo *Diers* and *Tanners,* and likewife *Phyficians* ufe it, but they choofe the neweft, to wit, that which is newly drawn out of the *Kiln,* and not flack'd with Water or Air.

It will burn fo vehemently, that it makes crufts, and will fire Boards or Timber againft which it lies ; but being flackt for fometime, it burns no more, yet it warms and dries, and diffolves Flefh ; and being wafhed three or four times, it Bites or Eats not, but dries quickly.

Lime mixt with Sand is much ufed in Buildings ; and *Vitruvius* fays, That you may put three parts of Sand that is digged (or pit Sand) and one part of *Lime* to make *Morter* ; but if the Sand be taken out of a *River,* or out of the *Sea,* then two parts thereof, and one of *Lime* ; as alfo to *River* to Sea-Sand, if you put a third part of Powder of *Tiles* or *Bricks,* (to wit, *Tile,* or *Brick* duft) it works the better.

But *Vitruvius* his Proportion of Sand feems too much, altho' he fhould mean the *Lime* before it is flacked ; for one Bufhel of *Lime* before it is flack'd, will be five Pecks after 'tis flack'd.

Here at *London,* where for the moft part our *Lime* is made of *Chalk,* we put about thirty fix Bufhels of **Pit-Sand,** to twenty five Bufhels of

Quick-

Quick-Lime, that is about one Bufhel and half of Sand, to one Bufhel of *Lime.*

And *Lime* mixt with *Sand,* and made into *Morter,* if it lye in an heap two or three Years before 'tis ufed, it will be the ftronger and better, and the reafon of fo many infufficient Buildings, is the ufing of the *Morter,* as foon as 'tis made, as *Agricola* faith.

Moreover there is other *Morter* ufed in making of Water-courfes, Cifterns, Fifh-ponds, &*c.* which is very hard and durable, as may be feen at *Rome,* at this day, which is called *Maltha,* from a kind of *Bitumen* Dug there ; for as they build moft firm Walls thereof naturally, fo they ufe it in making of Cifterns to hold Water, and all manner of Water-works ; and alfo in finifhing or Plaftering of Fronts to reprefent Stone.

And I find two kinds of Artifices ufed by the Antients, both of which is compounded of *Lime* and *Hogs-greafe,* but to one is added the Juice of Figs, and to the other *Liquid Pitch* ; and the Lumps of *Lime* are firft wet or flack'd with Wine; then pounded or beat with *Hogs-greafe,* and juice of *Figs,* or with the fame *Pitch* ; that which hath *Pitch* in it, is blacker and eafily diftinguifhed from the other by its Colour, and that which is Plaftered with this *Tarrace,* is done over with *Linfeed* Oil.

Metalifts ufe a kind of *Tarrace* in their Veffels for fining of *Mettals,* that the melted Mettle run not out ; for as the Moderns reftrain *Water,* and contain it, fo the Antients, this liquid Mettal, and 'tis compounded or made of *Quick-Lime* and *Ox Blood,* the *Lime* being beat to Powder and fifted, and then mixt with the *Blood* and beat with a *Beater.*

But their *Cement* differs from both the *Malthas* in Compofition and ufe, for 'tis made of Duft

or

or Powder of *Marble*, and *Glew* made of *Bull* or *Ox* Leather, and with this they glew pieces of Marble or Stones together.

In latter times, two kinds of *Cement* are in use, in both which they use the Powder of *Marble*, or other *Stone*, to one is added the Whites of Eggs, to the other is added *Pitch* ; to these some add other things, as the Gravers of *Gems*, they make it of *Tile Dust* and *Pitch*.

Another Material which *Bricklayers* use are *Laths*, which are made of heart of *Oak*, for out side Work, as *Tiling* and *Plastering* ; and of *Fir* for inside *Plastering* and *Pantile Lathing* ; their usual lengths being 5 Foot, and 4 Foot, and sometimes longer or shorter ; their Breadth sometimes 2 Inches, and one Inch and an half, the thickness about $\frac{1}{4}$ of an Inch or thicker : But for *Pantiling*, the *Laths*, are about ten Foot long, one Inch and half Broad, and half an Inch or more thick.

Another Material is *Nails*, of which they use three sorts, one is called, *Reparatian* or *Lath Nails*, which are used for plain *Tile Lathing*, and outside and inside *Lathing* for Plastring ; another sort are four Penny, and six Penny Nails, used for *Pantile Lathing* ; and a third sort are great Nails for Scaffolding.

Moreover they use *Tile-Pins*, which are sometimes made of *Oak*, and sometimes of *Fir*, which they drive into holes that are made in the *Plain Tiles* to hang them upon their *Lathing*.

They also put *Ox* or *Cow* Hair into the *Mortar* which they use for *Plastering*, being called *Lime* and *Hair*, which Hair keeps the *Mortar* from Cracking or Chaping, and makes it hold or bind together.

And whereas they make use of the sharpest Sand they can get (that being best) for *Morter*,

to

to lay *Bricks* and *Tiles* in ; fo they chofe a fat *Loamy* or Greafy Sand for infide Plafterning, by reafon it fticks together, and is not fo fubject to fall affunder when they lay it on Seelings or Walls.

Having given you an account of the feveral Materials that are ufed in *Bricklayers Work*, we fhall in the next place Treat of their Tools and their ufes, which are as follows.

Tools ufed in Brick Work.

1. **A** *Brick Trowel* to take up the Morter with, and to fpread it on the *Bricks*, with which alfo they cut the *Bricks* to fuch lengths as they have occafion, and alfo ftop the joints.

2. A *Brick Ax*, with which they cut *Bricks* to what fhape they pleafe, as fome for Arches both ftreight and Circular, others for the mouldings of Architecture, as Archytrave Friez and Cornice.

3. A *Saw* made of Tinn, to faw the Bricks which they cut.

4. A *Rub-ftone*, which is round, and is about fourteen Inches Diameter, and fometimes more or lefs at pleafure, on which they rub the Bricks which they cut into feveral fhapes, and alfo others which they cut not, being call'd *Rubbed Returns*, and *Rubbed Headers* and *Stretchers*.

5. A *Square*, to try the bed of the Brick, (*viz.* that fide which lies in the Morter) with the fuperficies or face of the Brick, to make the Brick fquare, or at Rect-angles one fide with the other, which is done by rubing it on the Rub-ftone till it exactly anfwers, or fits to the Square.

6. A *Bevel*, by which they cut the underfides of the Bricks, of Arches ftreight or circular, to fuch oblique Angles as the Arches require, and alfo for other Ufes.

7. *A*

7. *A small Trannel of Iron*, or a large Nail ground'd to a sharp point, with which they mark the Brick, either from a Square or Bevel, or a Mould made of thin Wainscot, or Past-board to direct them in the cutting thereof.

8. Some use a *Float Stone*, with which they rub the moulding of the Brick, after they have cut it with the *Ax*, pretty near to the Pattern described on the Brick, by the *Trannel* from the Wainscot, or Pastboard Mould, that so they may make the Brick exactly to answer to the Pattern or Mould. Others use no Stone at all, but cut the Brick exactly to the Pattern with their Brick-Ax, leaving the Ax stroaks to be seen on the Brick, which, if they be streight and parallel one to another, look very prettily, and is the truest way of Working; but then they must take care, to Ax the Brick off, with an Ax that is exactly streight on the edge, that the moulding in the Brick be neither round nor hollow, from side to side of a Header, or from end to end of a Stretcher.

9. *A Little Ruler*, about 12 Inches in length, and 1 Inch and ½ broad, which they lay on the Brick to draw streight Lines by, with the *Trannel* or *Nail.*

10. A *Banker*, to cut the Bricks upon, which is a piece of Timber about six foot long, or more, according to the number of those who are to work at it, and 9 or 10 Inches square, which must be laid on two Piers of Brick, or fixt on Bearers of Timber about three foot high from the Floor, on which they stand to work.

11. They work up a Pier of Brick-work, about the same height to lay their *Rubbing-Stone* upon, which must be laid in Morter that it may lye fast.

12. A *Grinding-stone*, to sharpen their Axes, Hammers, Trowels, &c. upon.

13. A *Pair of Line Pins of Iron*, with a length of Line on them about sixty feet in length, to lay each Row, or Course of *Bricks*, level on the Bed, and streight on the Surface by, a Line seldom holding to strein, or draw streight in length, above 50 or 60 feet.

14. A *Plumb Rule* about 4 foot long, with a Line and Plummet of Lead, to carry their Work upright, or perpendicular withal.

15. A *Level*, about 10 or 12 foot long, to set out their Foundations level, or parallel to the Horizon, and also to try whether the Walls of the Building, or Jambs of Chimneys, be carried level, as they raise the Work, that so they may bring up all their *Brick-work* to an exact horizontal height, at the laying on of ever floor of Carpentry.

16. A *Large Square*, to set their Walls at rectangles, which may also be done without a *Square*, by setting 6 foot from the angle one way, and 8 foot the other way, then if the Diagonal line, or Hypotenuse, be exactly 10 feet, the angle is a rectangle: If not, you must set the Wall that is to be at rectangles to the other, either this or that way, till the two measures of 6 and 8 feet answer exactly to 10 feet.

17. A *Ten Foot* and a *Five Foot Rod*, as also a *Two Foot Rule*, to take and lay down Lengths, and Breadths, and Heights.

18. A *Jointing Rule*, about 10 foot long, and about 4 Inches broad, whereby to run the long Joints of the *Brick-work*.

19. A *Jointer of Iron*, with which, and the foresaid Rule, they joint the long *Joints*, and also the *Cross Joints*, these being done with the *Jointer* without the *Rule*.

R 4 20. Com-

20. *Compaſſes,* to deſcribe the ſeveral Mouldings on Wainſcot or Paſtboard.

21. A *Hammer,* to cut Holes in *Brick-work,*
and drive Nails for Scarfolding.

22. A *Rammer,* to Ram the Foundations.

23. A *Crow of Iron,* to dig through a Wall,
and alſo a *Pick-Ax.*

The *Manner* and *Shapes* of the aforeſaid *Tools,*
you may ſee in Plate 1. and the Name of each
Tool in the Page next the Plate wherein they are
delineated.

The Names and Uſes of Tools *relating to* Tyling.

1. A *Lathing Hammer,* to nail on the Laths
withal, with two *Gauge Stroaks* (for
Lathing for *Tyling*) cut upon the handle of it,
one at 7 Inches from the head, and the other at
7 Inches and an half; ſome indeed Lath at 8
Inches, but that is too wide, occaſioning Rain-
ings in.

2. A *Lathing Staff of Iron,* in the form of a
Croſs, to ſtay the croſs Laths while they are
nailed to the long Laths, and alſo to clinch the
Nails.

3. A *Tyling Trowel,* to take up the Morter and
lay it on the Tiles, it being longer and narrower
than a *Brick-Trowel,* altho' for a ſhift many times
they uſe a *Brick-Trowel* to Tyle withal, when
they have not a *Tyling-Trowel.*

4. A *Boſſe,* made of Wood, with an Iron Hook,
to hang on the Laths, or on a Ladder, in which
the Labourer puts the Morter which the Tyler
uſes.

5. A *Striker,* which is only a piece of Lath
about 10 Inches long, with which they ſtrike,
or cut off the Morter at the britches of the Tiles.

6. A *Broome,* to ſweep the Tyling after 'tis
ſtrooke,

Of

Of the Names and Uses of Tools relating to Plastering.

1. **A** *Lathing Hammer* being the same as before in Tyling, with which the Laths are nailed on with its head, and with its Edge they cut them to any length, and likewise cut off any part of a Qurter, or Joyst, that sticks further out than the rest.

2. A *Laying Trowel,* to lay the Lime and Hair withall upon the Laths, it being larger than a *Brick Trowel,* and fastned its handle in a different manner from the *Brick Trowel.*

3. A *Hawke,* made of Wood about the bigness of a square Trencher, with a handle to hold it by, whereon the Lime and Hair being put, they take from it more or less as they please.

4. A *Setting Trowel,* being less than the *Laying Trowel,* with which they finish the Plastering when it is almost dry, either by Trowelling and brishing it over with fair Water, or else by laying a thin Coat of fine stuff made of clean Lime, and mixt with Hair without any Sand, and setting it, that is to say, Trowelling and brishing it.

5. A small *Pointing Trowel,* to go into sharp Angles.

6. *Brishes,* of three sorts, *viz.* A *Stock Brish,* a *Round Brish,* and a *Pencil.* With these *Brishes,* they wet old Walls before they mend them, and also brish over their new Plastering when they set, or finish it, and moreover white and size their Plastering with them. The *Pencil,* or *Drawing Tool,* is used in blacking the bottoms, or lower ports of Rooms, *&c.*

7. *Floats,* made of Wood, with handles to them, which they sometimes use to float Seelings or Walls with, when they are minded to make their Plastering very streight and even, these

thefe *Floats* being fome larger, and fome leffer, than the *Laying Trowels:* Likewife they ufe *Floats* made to fit to Mouldings, for the finifhing of feveral forts of Mouldings with finifhing Morter to reprefent Stone, fuch as *Cornices, Facias, Archytraves,* &c.

The finifhing Morter to reprefent Stone, fhould be made of the ftrongeft Lime, and the fharpeft Sand you can get, which Sand muft be wafhed in a large Tub, very well, till no Scum or Filth arife in the Water, when you ftir it about, which fometimes will require to have Water 5 or 6 times, when the Sand is fomewhat foul ; and it requires a greater Proportion of Sand than the ordinary Morter, becaufe it muft be extreamly beaten, which will break all the knots of *Lime,* and by that means it will require more Sand.

8. *Streight Rules* of feveral lengths, to lay Quines ftreight by, and alfo to try whether the Plaftering be laid true and ftreight, by applying the Rules to their Work.

9. A *Pale,* to hold *Water* or *Whitewafh,* or *White* and *Size.*

10. Some ufe a *Budget* or *Pocket* to hang by their fides, to put their *Nails* in when they *Lath,* and others Tuck and tye up their *Aprons,* and put the *Nails* therein.

Having given you a Defcription of the feveral *Tools* and ufes, there are fome things yet remaining, which tho' they cannot be properly called *Tools,* yet they are *Utenfils,* without which they cannot well perform their Work.

And

And they are.

1. **L**adders, of feveral lengths, as *Standard-Ladders*, two Story, and one Story *Ladders*, &c.

2. *Fir Poles*, of feveral lengths for *Standards* and *Ledgers* for *Scaffolding.*

3. *Putlogs*, which are pieces of Timber, or fhort Poles, about 7 Foot long, which lies from the *Leggers* into their *Brickwork*, to bear the boards they ftand on to Work, and to lay *Bricks* and *Morter* upon.

4. *Fir Boards*, about 10 Foot long, and any Breadth, but commonly about a Foot broad, becaufe for the moft part, four of them in breadth, makes the breadth of the Scaffold : Which boards ought to be one Inch and or two Inches in thicknefs, altho' commonly they make ufe of fome, which are not above one Inch thick, which are fometimes fubject to break, efpecially when the *Putlogs* lye far afunder from one another.

5. *Chords*, which fhould be well Pitched to preferve them from the Weather, and rotting, with which they faften the *Ledgers* to the *Standards*, or upright *Poles.*

6. *Sieves*, of feveral forts, fome larger, others leffer, fome finer, others courfer, to fift the *Lime* and *Sand* withal, before they wet it into *Morter* or *Lime* and *Hair.*

7. A *Loame-hook*, *Beater*, *Shovel*, *Pick-Ax*, *Basket* and *Hod*, which commonly belong to *Bricklayers*, *Labourers*, and may be called the *Labourers* Tools.

8. A *Skreen* made of Boards and Wyer, which performs the Office of a *Sieve*, and with which one Man will Skreen as much *Lime*, mixt with *Sand* or *Rubifh*, as two Men can with a *Sieve.*

9. *Boards*

9. *Boards* or *Tubs*, to put the *Morter* in.

And except my memory fails me, thefe are all, or the moft ufual Tools and Utenfils, which they make ufe of.

Having now given you an account of their feveral Materials, together with their neceffary Tools and Utenfils; we fhall proceed in the next place to treat of the Method of working, which is various, fome working after a better Method, and more concifely than others.

And firft of Foundations.

'T Is ufual, and alfo very convenient, for any perfon before he begins to Erect a Building, to have Defigns or Draughts drawn upon Paper or Vellum, and alfo if it be a large Building, to have a Model of it made in Wainfcot; in which Defigns and Model, the Ground Plat or Ichnography of each Floor or Story, is delineated and reprefented: As alfo the fafhion and form of each Front, together with the Windows, Doors, and Ornaments, if they intend any, to wit, *Facias, Ruftick Quines, Architraves, Friezes* and *Cornices*, are to be fhewn in the Draughts or Defigns of the Uprights or *Orthographyes*.

If more Fronts than one be fhewn *Perfpectively* in one Draught, then 'tis called *Scenography*, which is not eafily underftood, except by thofe who underftand the Rules of *Perfpective*.

Therefore it will be more Intelligible to the feveral Workmen, to have a Draught of each Front in a Paper by it felf, and alfo to have a Draught of the Ground-Plat or *Ichnography* of every ftory, in a Paper by it felf; becaufe many times the Conveniences, or Contrivances in one Story, differs from thofe in another, either in bignefs of Chimneys, or divifion of the Rooms, fome being larger in one Story than another, and fome-

fometimes having more Chimnies in one Story than in another, &c.

All which things being well confidered, and drawn on Papers, or a Model made thereof, before the Building is begun, there will be no need of Alterations, or Tearing and pulling the Building to pieces after it is begun; for befides the hindrance of the Procedure of the Work, it makes the Building lame and Deficient, nothing being fo well done, when 'tis put up, and pulled down, and fet up again, as if it were well done at firft.

Befides it makes the Workmen uneafy, to fee their Work, in which they have taken a great deal of pains, and ufed a great deal of Art, to be pull'd to pieces.

The drawing of Draughts is moft commonly the work of a Surveyor, although there be many Mafter Workmen that will contrive a Building, and draw the Defigns thereof, as well, and as curioufly, as moft Surveyors: Yea, fome of them will do it better than fome Surveyors; efpecially thofe Workmen who underftand the Theorick part of Building, as well as the Practick.

MECHA

MECHANICK EXERCISES:

O R,

The Doctrine of *Handy-Works.*

And now concerning the Foundations.

AFter the Cellars are dug, if there are to be any, or if none, after the Trenches are dug, in which the Walls are to ftand; the Mafter-Bricklayer, or elfe his Foreman (which ought to be an ingenious Workman) muft in the firft place try all the Foundations, in feveral places, with an Iron Croe, and Rammer, or, indeed, with a Borer (fuch as Well-Diggers ufe, to try what Ground they have to produce Water) to fee whether the *Foundations* are all found, and fit to bear the Weight which is to be fet upon them. If he find any part of the *Foundations* defective, he ought to dig it deeper till he comes to firm ground; or if it proves to be loofe, or made Ground to a great depth, then he muft take care to make it good and fufficient to carry its Weight by Art, which may be done feveral ways.

Firft, If the *Foundation* be not very lofe, and infufficient, it may be made good, by ramming
in

in great Stones with a heavy Rammer, the Stones being placed clofe together, and about a foot wider on each fide of the Trench than the width of the Wall is to be; becaufe all Walls ought to have a Bafis, or Footing, at leaft 4 Inches on a fide broader than the thicknefs of the Wall; which Stones being well rammed, and the Bafis being 8 Inches more in breadth than the thicknefs of the Wall, and this 8 Inches being fet off, about one Inch, or one Inch and an half at a time on both fides (that fo the middle of the Wall may ftand on the middle of the Bafis) may make the Foundation good, and able to bear its Burden.

But if the *Foundation* be fomewhat worfe than as aforefaid, then he muft get good pieces of Oak, whofe length muft be the breadth of the Trench, or about two foot longer than the breadth of the Wall, which muft be laid crofs the *Foundation* about foot afunder, and being well rammed down, lay long Planks upon them, which planking need not be the length of the crofs pieces, but only 4 Inches of a fide wider than the Bafis, or footing of the Wall is to be, and pin'd or fpiked down to the pieces of Oak on which they lye.

But if the *Foundations* be fo bad that this will not do, then he muft provide good Piles made of Heart of Oak, of fuch a length as will reach ground, whofe Diameter muft be about $\frac{1}{12}$ part of their length, which muft be drove or forced down with a Commander, or an Engin for that purpofe, and then lay long Planks upon them, and fpike or pin the Planks to them, and the clofer together that thefe Piles are drove the better it will be.

More-

Moreover, if the *Foundation* be faulty but in here and there a place, and there be good Ground in the other parts of it, you may turn Arches over thofe infufficient places, which will difcharge and take off the weight from the loofe places.

And when you make thefe Arches to fhun the difficulty of the Earth, and to fave the charge of Expence, they muft be made of Bricks and Morter that are very good, and be well wrought, that they do neither fettle nor give way.

You may obferve for the greater ftrength of thefe Arches, or Difcharges, to make them higher than a Semicircle, or half round, if the Work will admit of it, and to make the fame, of Portions of Arches : As in *Plate* 3. *Fig.* 4. you may fee, they are defcribed from an Equilateral Triangle; that is to fay, fuppofing the breadth of the Arch between the Piers to be *A B*; with this width, and from the points *A* and *B*, make the two Portions of the Arches *A C* and *B C*; this rifing fo high, adds great ftrength to the Arches to refift, or carry the Weight which they are to bear.

The ancient Architect *Leon Baptifta Albert* advifes, when the Earth on which we would make Pillars or Piers is of equal refiftance, that is to fay, not good, to turn Arches inverfed, or upfide down, and fays, by this means one Pillar fhall bear no more weight than another, when the Earth that is underneath is not fo ftrong, or that it bears more than another part; which he doth thus.

Having wrought up the Pillars, or Piers, as high as is neceffary from the *Foundation*, make from thefe Piers inverfe Arches, as *A B C* in *Plate* 3. *Fig.* 5. whofe Joints tend to the Center *D*.

By

Plate 3.

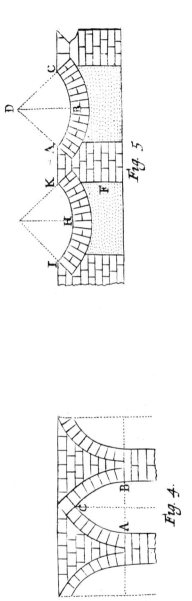

Fig. 5

Fig. 4

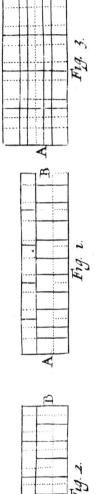

Fig. 3.

Fig. 1.

Fig. 2.

By this conftruction he pretends for Example, that if the Pier *F* hath a worfe *Foundation,* or hath a greater Weight, that is to fay, is more charged than the other Piers, this charge, or weight, will be ftopped, or ftayed by the Inverfe Arches *A B C, I H K,* becaufe the Earth which is under thefe Arches keeps the Piers in the fame height, that is to fay, that they fhall not fink.

But he muft alfo fuppofe that this Earth is as firm as that of the *Foundation* of the Piers, or at leaft it muft be made fo.

The Ingenious Surveyor Mr. *Hook,* made ufe of this Artifice, as I am informed, in building the Lord *Montague*'s brave Houfe in *Bloomsbury,* in the County of *Middlefex,* and where he was then Surveyor.

The *Foundation* being all made firm, and le-velled, the Mafter-Bricklayer, or his Foreman, muft take care to fee all the *Foundations* fet tru-ly out, according to the defign of the Ground-plat, or Cellar-floor, and that all his Walls be made of the fame thicknefs as they are in the Defign; which is very difficult to do, to wit, to take the true thicknefs of the Walls from a Defign that is drawn to a fmall Scale, becaufe the breadth of the Points of the Compaffes will vary fomewhat; therefore 'tis advifable for him that draws the Draught, to fet the Dimenfions in Figures to each Wall, Chimney, Window, *&c.* and then the Workman cannot fo eafily make a Miftake.

And becaufe the well-working and bonding of Brick-walls conduces very much to their ftrength, I will here add fome fome neceffary Rules to be obferved in the laying of Bricks, to make the Walls and ftrong and durable.

S   1. That

First. That the Morter be made of well burnt good Lime, and sharp Sand, and that it have a due proportion of Sand, that is to say, if it be very sharp, a Load of Sand, being about 36 Bushels, is sufficient for an Hundred of Lime, being 25 Bushels, or an hundred Pecks, (for I imagine that the word *Hundred of Lime* is used, because it contains an Hundred Pecks, and that in Old Time they used to sell it by the Peck, but now by the Bushel) to wit, to one Bushel of Quick Lime, a Bushel and half of Sand.

But if the Sand be not very sharp, then you may put a greater quantity of Sand, for Morter which hath its due proportion of Sand, is stronger than that which hath less Sand in it, altho' some think otherwise.

Secondly, When you slack the Lime, take care to wet it every where a little, but do not over-wet it, and cover with Sand every laying, or bed of Lime, being about a Bushel at a time as you slack it up, that so the Stream, or Spirit of the Lime, may be kept in, and not flee away, but mix it self with the Sand, which will make the Morter much stronger, than if you slack all your Lime first, and throw on your Sand altogether at last, as some use to do.

Thirdly, That you beat all your Morter with a Beater three or four times over before you use it, for thereby you break all the Knots of Lime that go through the Sieve, and incorporate the Sand and Lime well together, and the Air which the Beater forces into the Morter at every stroak, conduces very much to the strength thereof.

If

If I might advife any one that is minded to build well, or ufe ftrong Morter for Repairs, I would have them beat the Morter well, and let it lie 2 or 3 Days, and then beat it well again when 'tis to be ufed.

Fourthly, If you lay bricks in hot dry Weather, and be it fome fmall piece of Work that you would have very ftrong, dip every Brick you lay, all over in a Pale of Water, which will make the Wall much ftronger than if the Bricks were laid dry : The reafon why I mention a fmall piece of Work is, becaufe 'tis a great deal of trouble to wet them for much Work, or a whole Building, and befides it makes the Workmen's Fingers fore; to prevent which, they may throw Pales of Water on the Wall after the Bricks are lay'd, as was done at the building of *Phyficians College* in *Warwick-Lane,* by order of the Surveyor, which was the aforefaid Ingenious Mr. *Hook,* if I miftake not.

Fifthly, Cover all your Walls in the Summer-time to keep them from drying too haftily, for the Morter doth not Cement fo ftrongly to the Bricks when it dries haftily, as when flowly.

Sixthly, Be fure to cover them very well in the Winter-time, to preferve them from Rain, Snow and Froft, which laft is a great Enemy to all kinds of Morter, efpecially to that which hath taken wet juft before the Froft.

Seventhly, In working up the Walls of a Building, do not work any Wall above 3 foot high before you work up the next adjoining Wall, that fo you may join them together, and make

S 2

good

good Bond in the Work: For 'tis an ill Cuftom among fome *Bricklayers*, to carry, or work up a whole Story of the Party-walls, before they work up the Fronts, or other Work adjoining, that fhould be bonded or worked up together with them, which occafions Cracks and Setlings in the Walls.

Eightly, Take care that you do not lay Joint on Joint, in the middle of the Walls as feldom as may be, but make bond there as well as on the outfides; for I have feen fome, who in working of a Brick and half Wall, have laid the Header on one fide of the Wall, upright upon the Header on the other fide of the Wall, and fo all along through the whole courfe, which indeed necefarily follows from the inconfiderate fetting up of the Quine at a Toothing; for 'tis common to Tooth in the ftretching courfe two Inches with the Stretcher only, and the Header on the other fide, to be fet upright upon the Header on this fide, which caufes the Headers to lye Joint in Joint in the middle of the Wall, as in *Plate* 3. *Fig.* 1. you may fee.

Whereas if the Header of one fide of the Wall, toothed as much as the Stretcher on the other fide, it would be a ftronger Toothing, and the Joints of the Headers of one fide, would be in the middle of the Headers of the courfe they lye upon of the other fide, as in *Plate* 3. *Fig.* 2.

All that can be faid for this ill Cuftom of working, is this, that the Header will not well hang two Inches over the Bricks underneath it; I grant it will not, but then it may be made, by having a piece of Fir, or any other Wood of the thicknefs of a Courfe of Bricks, and two

Inches

Inches broad, and lay it on the laſt Toothing
Courſe to bear it; or a *Bat,* put upon the laſt
Toothing, will bear it till the next *Quine* is ſet
upon it, and then the *Bat* may be taken away.

Ninthly, The ſame Inconveniency happens at
an upright *Quine* in a *Brick* and half Wall,
where 'tis uſual to lay a Cloſier next the Header
on both ſides of the Wall, and in ſo doing 'tis
Joint in Joint all the length of the Wall, except
by chance a three quartern Bat happen to be laid.

To prevent which Inconveniency, and to make
the Wall much ſtronger, lay a Cloſure on one
ſide, and none on the other; but lay a three
quarter Bat at the Quine in the ſtretching courſe,
and in the Heading courſe adjoin an Header next
to the Header at the Quine, as you may ſee it
done in Plate 3. *Fig.* 1. and 2.

Where A and B in both Figures or Diagrams,
repreſents a Brick and half Wall, having an up-
right Quine at A, and a Toothing at B, and the
Prick Lines repreſents the Courſe of Bricks laid
upon the other courſe; ſo in *Fig.* 1. the black
Lines next you are an heading courſe, and the
Prick-lines next you, ſhew a Stretching courſe:
And on the further ſide from you, the black
Lines ſhew a ſtretching courſe, and the Prick-
Lines an Heading courſe.

In which *Fig.* 1. is ſhewn the uſual way of bad
Working, but in *Fig.* 2. is ſhewn the true way
it ſhould be wrought, to be made firm and ſtrong.

Alſo in working a two Brick Wall, I would
adviſe in the Stretching courſes, wherein you
lay ſtretching on both ſides the Wall next the
Line, ſo alſo to lay ſtretching in the middle of
the Wall, and Cloſiers next to each ſtretching
Courſe that lies next the Line, as in *Fig.* 3. of
Plate 3. you may ſee.

S 3

Where

Where the Diagram or Fig. A B, signifies a two Brick Wall, A being an upright Quine, and B the Toothing, in which, the black lines represent the stretching course, and the Prickt Lines the Heading course, that lies upon the stretching course: In a two Brick Wall if you lay a closier next the upright Quine on both sides of the Wall, it makes good Bond.

Tenthly, In Summer time use your Morter as soft as you can, but in the Winter time pretty stiff or hard.

Eleventhly, If you build in the City of *London*, you must make all your Walls of such thicknesses as the Act of Parliament for rebuilding of the said City enjoyns, but in other places you may use your Discretion.

And because the Act of Parliament may not be in every Builders hands, I will therefore Incert so much of it as relates to *Bricklayers* Work, to wit, the Heights and number of Stories, and the Thickness of Walls of the four several sorts of Buildings, which is as follows.

And be it further Enacted, That the said Houses of the First and least sort of Building Fronting by Streets or Lanes, as aforesaid, shall be of two Stories high, besides Cellars and Garrats; That the Cellars thereof 6 Foot and an half high, if the Springs of Water hinder not; and the First Story be 9 Foot high from the Floor to the Seeling; and the second Story 9 Foot high from the Floor to the Seeling; that all Walls in Front and Reer as high as the first Story, be of the full thickness of the length of two Bricks, and thence upwards to the Garrats of the thickness

nels of one Brick and an half; and that the thick-
nels of the Garrat Walls on the back part, be
left to the Difcretion of the Builder, fo that the
fame be not lefs than the length of one Brick;
and alfo that the thicknefs of the party Walls
between thefe Houfes of the Firft and leffer fort
of Building, be one Brick and $\frac{1}{2}$ as high as the
faid Garrats, and that the thicknefs of the party
Wall in the Garrat, be of the thicknefs of the
length of one Brick at the leaft.

And be further Enacted, That the Houfes of
the fecond fort of Building fronting Streets and
Lanes of Note, and the River of *Thames*, fhall
confift of three Stories high, befides Cellars and
Garrats as aforefaid; that the Cellars thereof be
6 Foot and $\frac{1}{2}$ high, (if the Springs hinder not)
that the firft Story contain full 10 Foot in height
from the Floor to the Seeling: The fecond full
10 Foot, the third 9 Foot; that all the faid
Walls in Front and Reer, as high as the firft
Story, be two Bricks and $\frac{1}{2}$ thick, and from
thence upwards to the Garrat Floor, of one
Brink and $\frac{1}{2}$ thick; and the thicknefs of the
Garrat Walls on the back part be left to the dif-
creation of the Builder, fo that the fame be not
lefs than one Brick thick: And alfo that the
thicknefs of the party-walls between every Houfe
of this fecond, and larger fort of Building, be
two Bricks thick as high as the firft Story, and
thence upwards to the Garrats, of the thicknefs
of one Brick and $\frac{1}{2}$.

Alfo, that the Houfes of the third fort of
Buildings, fronting the high and principle Streets,
fhall confift of 4 Stories high, befides Cellars
and Garrats as aforefaid: That the firft Story
contain full 10 foot in height from the Floor to
the Seeling; the fecond 10 foot and $\frac{1}{2}$; the third

S 4   9 foot;

9 foot; the fourth 8 foot and $\frac{1}{2}$: That all the said Walls in Front and Reer, as high as the firſt Story, be of two Bricks and $\frac{1}{2}$ in thickneſs, and from thence upwards to the Garrat Floor, of the thickneſs of one Brick $\frac{1}{2}$: That the thickneſs of the Garrat Walls on the back part be left to the diſcretion of the Builder, ſo as the ſame be not leſs than one Brick: And alſo that the Party-walls between every Houſe, of this third and larger ſort of Building, be two Bricks thick as high as the firſt Floor, and thence upwards to Garrat Floor, the $1\frac{1}{2}$ Brick in thickneſs.

And, *Be it further Enacted, That all Houſes of the fourth ſort of Building, being Manſion Houſes, and of the greateſt bigneſs, not fronting upon any of the Streets or Lanes as aforeſaid; the number of Stories, and the Height thereof, ſhall be left to the diſcretion of the Builder, ſo as he exceeds not four Stories.*

Alſo, the ſame Act enjoins, That no Timber be laid within 12 Inches of the foreſide of the Chimny Jambs; and that all Joyſts on the back of any Chimny be laid with a Trimmer, at ſix Inches diſtant from the back: Alſo, that no Timber be laid within the Tunnel of any Chimny, upon penalty to the Workman for every Default ten Shillings, and ten Shillings every week it continues unreform'd.

Twelfthly, When you lay any Timber on Brickwork, as Torſels for Mantle-Trees to lye on, or Lintols over Windows, or Templets under Girders, or any other Timbers, lay them in Loam, which is a great preſerver of Timber, for Morter eats and corrodes the Timber: Likewiſe the Joyſt ends, and Girders which lye in the Walls, muſt be Loamed all over, to preſerve them from the

Plate 4.

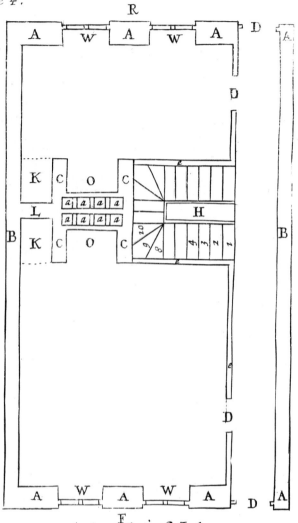

Scale of Feet and Inches 10

| 1 | 2 | 3 | 4 | 5 | 6 | 7 | 8 | 9 | 10 | 11 | 12 |

the corroding of the Morter. Some Workmen pitch the ends of the Timber that lye in the Walls to preferve them from the Morter.

*In the next place you fhall have the **Ground Plat** of a Building, and its Explanation.*

IN Plate 4, you have the Draught of a Ground Plat of a Building, which is 25 Feet, both in the Front and Reer Front; and 40 Feet in the Flank or Depth: The Front and Reer Front Walls, are 2 Bricks and ½ in thicknefs; the Flank Walls are 2 Bricks in thicknefs, as you may prove by the Scale of Feet and Inches annext to the Defign.

You may imagine this Defign to be the Ground Floor, having no Cellar beneath it: And the height of the Story between the Floor and the Seeling to be 10 Foot; and becaufe we do fuppofe this Building to have Houfes adjoining it on each fide, therefore we have drawn the Stair-cafe with an open Nuel to give light to the Stairs; but if the Houfe had ftood by it felf, without other Houfes adjoyning, then we might have had light to the Stairs from the Flank Wall.

Explanation of the Defign.

F. The Front.
R. Reer Front.
B. Flank Walls.
A. Piers of Brick.
W. Windows of Timber.
D. Door-cafes of Timber.
O. Chimneys.
C. Jambs of Chimneys.

H. Open

H. Open Nuel to give light to the Stairs.
K. Cloffets.
L. A Brick and half Wall between the Cloffets.
a. Funnels or Tunnels of Chimneys.
1. 2. 3. 4, *&c.* Steps of Stairs called Fliers.
8. 9. 10, *&c.* Steps of Stairs called Winders.
e. Timber Partitions.

The Scale contains 32 Feet, with a Diagonal
Line to fhew the Inches in a Foot: For Exam-
ple, if you would take of 8 Inches, take the
Interval from 8 in the Horizontal Line to the
Diagonal Line, and that is 8 Inches: From 3 in
the Horizontal Line to the Diagonal Line, is 3
Inches, and fo of the reft.

In the next *Plate* you have the Orthography,
or upright of this Ground Plat, and this the
Explanation thereof, with a Scale of Feet and
Inches annext thereto,

Explanation of Plate 5.

A. The Water-Table.
B. Firft Fafcia.
C. Second Fafcia.
D. Three plain Courfes of Bricks over the
Arches.
E. Cornice.
F. Chimnies.
G. Gable-end.
H. Streight Arches.
W. Shas Frames.
S. Shas lights.
K. Door-cafe.
L. Window-Lighte over the Door.

The

Plate 5

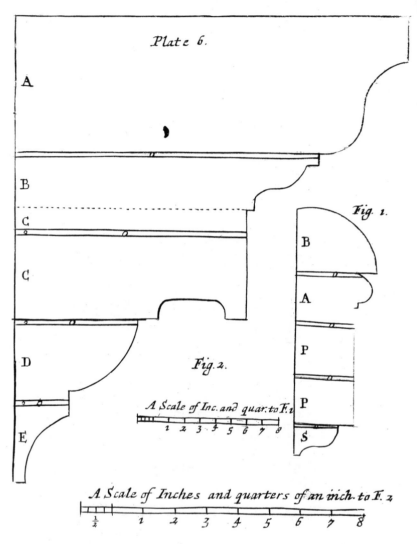

Plate 6.

A

B

C

C

D

E

Fig. 1.

B

A

P

P

S

Fig. 2.

A Scale of Inc. and quar. to F. 1
1 2 3 4 5 6 7 8

A Scale of Inches and quarters of an inch. to F. 2
½   1   2   3   4   5   6   7   8

The Scale of Feet and Inches being the fame, as in the Ground Plat of *Plate* 4. I need not fay any thing concerning it, becaufe I have there fhewn the ufe of it.

And although I have in this Defign, drawn the Fafcias plain without any Mouldings, yet fometimes they are made with Mouldings, which fhew very neat and handfome, I have therefore in *Plate* 6. given you a Defign of a Brick Fafcia, wrought with Mouldings, in which Defign

S. Is Scima reverfa.
O. Joints of Morter.
P. Plain Courfes.
A. Aftragal.
B. Ovolo, or Boltel, reverfed.

In the fame *Plate*, you have the defign of a Brick Cornice, and the Names of the Mouldings, are

A. Scima reɛta, or Ogee.
O Joint of Morter.
B. Scima reverfa, or Scimatium.
C. Corona, or Plancheer.
D. Ovolo, or Boltel.
E. Cavetto, or Cafement.

In which Cornice, the Corona, or Plancheer, ought (according to the Rules of Architeɛture) to Sail over, or projeɛt more ; but the length of a Brick being but about 8 Inches when its head is rubbed for hewing, it will not hang, if it fail over, more than is fhewn in the Draught, which is about 3 Inches and an half. But if you would make it to projeɛt more, then you muft Cement pieces to the ends of your bricks for tailing
ing

ing, or to make them longer: Of which Cement there is two forts, one is called cold Cement, and the other is hot, the making and uſe
whereof, we will ſhew towards the latter end.

*To deſcribe Mouldings on Wainſcot, or Paſtboard,
for Patterns, to cut Bricks by.*

There are two ways to deſcribe the Hollows,
and rounds of Moulding in Faſcias, or Cornices; one from the *oxi*, or *oxigonium*, the other
from the *half round*, or *Semicircle*, that makes
the Moulding flatter, this more circular; I will
ſhew both ways, and then you may make uſe of
which you pleaſe.

Firſt, We will deſcribe a Cavetto, or Caſement, both ways.

In *Plate* 7. the *Fig.* 1. is deſcribed from the
oxi, in this manner, having allowed the projecture of the Moulding at the bottom, and the
Fillet at top, draw the Line *a b*, then with the
Compaſſes taking the interval *a b*, place one
point of the Compaſſes in *a*, and with the other
deſcribe the Arch *d d*; then with one Foot in *b*,
with the other deſcribe the Arch *c c*, and where
theſe two Arches interſect each other, there is
the Center to deſcribe the Cavetto; then fixing
one Foot in the Center, extend the other to *a* or
b, and deſcribe the Arch *a g b*.

You may deſcribe it from a Semicircle thus:
In *Fig.* 2. having allowed the Projecture at bottom, and the Fillet at top, as before, draw the
Line *a b*, biſect, or middle it, as at *c*, then upon *c* as a center, with the Interval *c a*, or *c b*,
deſcribe the Semicircle *a d b*, and biſect it in *d*,
which is the Center to deſcribe the Cavetto, or
Caſement by; then fixing one point of the Compaſſes

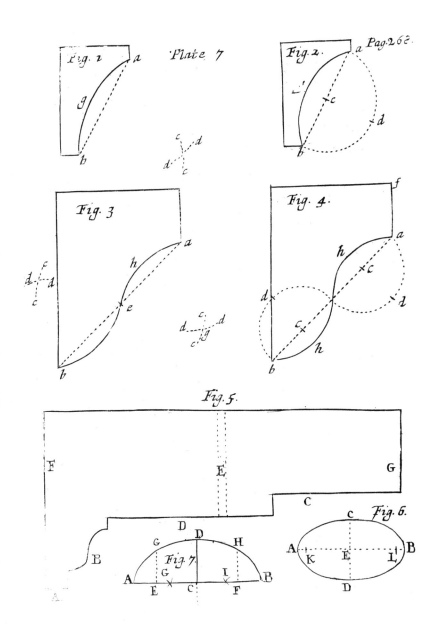

Plate 7

Fig. 1

g

a

b

c d
d c

Pag. 262.

Fig. 2

c

d

b

Fig. 3

a

h

e

b

c
d d
c

Fig. 4

f

a

h

c

d d

c

h

b

Fig. 5

F

E

G

C

D

B

Fig. 6

c

A K E L B

D

Fig. 7

D

G H

A G C I F B

E C F

paſſes in *d*, extend the other to *a* or *b*, and deſcribe the Arch *a g b*.

To deſcribe the Scima Recta, *or* Ogee, both ways.

Fig. 3. is deſcribed by the *Oxi* in this manner ; having allowed the Fillet at top *a f*, draw the Line *a b*, and biſect it, that is, part it in the middle in *e* ; then with your Compaſſes take the Interval *e b*, and fixing one point in *e*, with the other deſcribe the Arch *c c*, then with the ſame Interval, or diſtance, fixing one point in *b*, with the other, deſcribe the Arch *d d*, and where theſe two Arches Interſect, or cut each other, there is the Center to diſcribe the round, or lower part of the *Ogee*, to wit, *e b b* : Then fixing one point of the Compaſſes on the Interſection by *d*, extend the other to *b*, or *e*, and deſcribe the Arch *e b b* : Then to deſcribe the Hollow, or upper part of the *Ogee*, take with your Compaſſes the Diſtance, or Interval *e a*, and fixing one point in *e*, with the other deſcribe the Arch *c c*, then keeping the Compaſſes, at the ſame diſtance, fix one foot in *a*, and with the other deſcribe the Arch *d d*, interſecting the other Arch in *g* : Then fixing one Foot in *g*, extend the other to *e* or *a*, and deſcribe the Arch *e b a*, which compleats the *Scima recta*, or Ogee.

To describe the same Ogee *by a Semicircle.*
Fig. 4.

1. After you have allowed the Fillet *a f,* draw the Line *a b.*
2. Bisect the Line in *s.*
3. Bisect *e b* and *s a,* as at *c c.*
4. On the Center *c.* with the Interval *c a,* describe the Semicircle *s d a.*
5. Middle it, as at *d.*
6. Fixing one point in *d.* extend the other to *e* or *s,* and describe the Arch *a b s.*
7. On the Center *c,* with the distance *c b,* describe the Semicircle *b d s.*
8. Middle it, as at *d.*
9. Fix one Foot in *d,* and extend the other to *b* or *s.*
10. Describe the Arch *b b s,* which compleats the *Scima Recta,* or *Ogee ;* and after either of these ways, which you like best, you may describe any other Moulding.

And because many times *Bricklayers* make Archytrave Jambs and Arches, about Windows and Door-cases in a Front, I will therefore delineat an Archytrave to be cut in the length of a Brick; which is most usual, although you may make your Archytrave larger, and cut it in the length of one Brick and an half.

In *Plate* 7. *Fig.* 5. you have Delineated the Ground Plat of an Archytrave Jamb, to be cut in the length of a Brick, which suppose to be F G, and also Imagine F E G to be a Stretcher, or a Stretching Archytrave : Also you may understand the design to be divided in the middle by the two Prick Lines on each side E, which represents a Joint of Morter, and imagining it

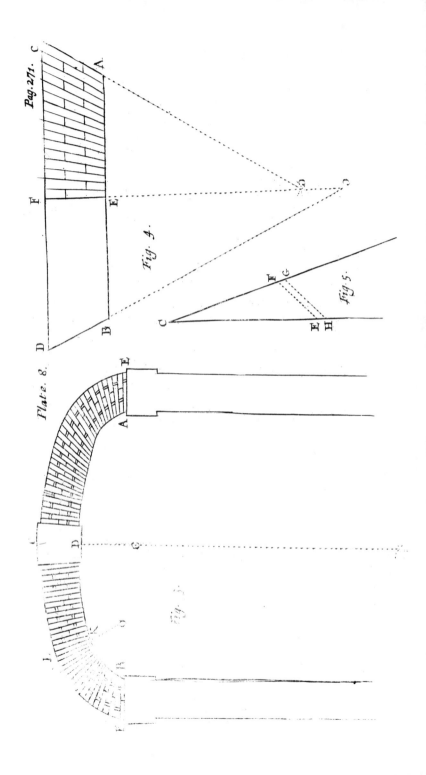

Pag. 271.

Fig. 4.

Fig. 5.

Plate. 8.

to be thus divided; then E F is called a Header; or a heading Archytrave, and E G is called a Jak.

Here follows the Names of the several parts of the Archytrave.

A. Fillet.
B. Scima.
C. Upper Fascia.
D. Lower Fascia.

I did intend here to have added something about the Arching of Vaults, but intending, God willing, to treat largely of the Description of all manner of Arches, and making of Moulds, or Patterns, to cut them by, when I come to exercise in *Masonry*, which will succeed this: I shall therefore omit speaking of Vaults in this Exercise.

I shall now in the next place shew how to describe any Ellipsis Arch in Brick; and make the Moulds, as also to describe streight Arches, and make the Moulds for the same.

To describe an Oval *to any* Length *and* Breadth *given.*

An *Ellipsis Arch* is an half Oval: Therefore in Plate 8. *Fig.* 1. let the length given be A B, and the Breadth C D.

Apply the two given Lines together, so that they may cut each other into two equal parts, and at right angles in the point E, then take half the line A B, between your Compasses, and setting one point of the Compasses in C, extend the other till it touch the line A B, in K and L,

which

which two points are called the *Focasses*, or burning points, in which points drive two Nails, if you describe it on Boards, but upon Paper, as here two Pins will do; the Pins being stuck fast in the points K and L, stick also another Pin in the Point C, then take a Thread, and Encompass these 3 Pins in form of a Triangle, pulling the Thread tight, tye the two ends of the Thread together, by a knot at C, then taking out the Pin at C, take a Pencil of Black-Lead, holding it close to the inside of the Thread, and carrying the Pencil round upon the Paper, about the Pins, with the Thread always streight, the *Ellipsis* or *Oval* A C B D, will be thereby described.

Another way to describe the same.

Here I shall only describe a Semi-Oval, being an Ellipsis Arch.

In *Fig.* 2. let the length given be A B, and the Semidiameter or height of the Arch C D; Divide A B into seven equal parts, then upon one seventh part from A as at E, raise a Perpendicular from the Line A B, (viz. E G.) also at one seventh part from B, as at F, raise another Perpendicular F H; then divide the Semidiameter given C D, into 15 equal Parts, and take Eleven of those Parts, and set upon the Perpendicular from E to G, and likewise from F to H; then taking the space between A and G, setting one point of the Compasses in A, describe the Arch G *i*, keeping the Compasses at the same distance, set one point in G, and describe another Arch, which will cut the former in the point by *i*; from which point, with the Radius A *i*, us A *i*, defcribe the *Hanfe* A G ; this being done, take between your Compaffes the fpace B H, and fetting one point in B, defcribe the arch I *i*, then remove your Compaffes to H, and interfect that Arch in the point by *i*, then fetting your Compaffes on the point *i*, with the fame diftance, defcribe a part of the *Ellipfis* B H, which is called the *Hanfe* : The other part to be defcribed from G to H, is called the *Scheam*, which to defcribe, continue or draw longer the Semidiameter D C, and in that line find a Center, whereon fetting one point of the Compaffes, the other point may touch the three points G D H, as on the Center I; whereby defcribe the *Scheam* G D H, which was to be done.

Thefe *Ellipfis*, or *Semi-Oval* Arches, being neatly wrought in Brick, fhew very pleafant, and are fometimes made over Gate-ways, and alfo over Kitchin-Chimnies, inftead of Mantletrees.

We will fuppofe an Ellipfis Arch to be made over a Chimny, whofe Diameter between the Jambs is eight feet, and the under fide of the Arch at the Key to rife in height 18 Inches from the level of the place, whence you begin to fpring the Arch; the height or depth of the Arch we will fuppofe to be made of the length of two Bricks, which when they are cut to the fweep of the Arch, will not contain above 14 Inches, and perhaps you muft Cement pieces to many of the Courfes in the Hanfe to make them long enough to contain, or hold 14 Inches, efpecially if you intend to make the Courfes of the Hanfe, and the Courfes of the Scheam to feem alike in greatnefs, on the under fide of the Arch: For if you make the Hanfe to come to a true Sommering for the Scheam, by that time that
T   you

you have ended the Hanſe, and are ready to ſet
the firſt Courſes of the Scheam: The Mould,
and ſo likewiſe each Courſe in the Hanſe, will
be much leſs at the lower part, or under ſide
of the Arch, than the Mould, or Courſes of
the Scheam, as you may perceive by the Hanſe
B K, in the 3d. *Fig.* which way of working
theſe kind of Arches is ſtronger, than to make
the Courſes ſeem alike in bigneſs in Hanſe and
Scheam, although it be not ſo pleaſing to the
eye. In the 3d. *Fig.* I will ſhew how to make
one half of the Arch this way, and in the o-
ther half ſhew how to make the Courſes in
Hanſe and Scheam of a bigneſs.

Firſt, Deſcribe the under ſide of the Arch,
(*viz.* the Ellipſis A D B, whoſe Diameter A B
is eight feet, and the height C D 18 Inches)
upon ſome ſmooth Floor, or ſtreight plaiſtered
Wall, or ſuch like; then continue (*viz.* draw
longer) both the lines A B, C D, cutting each
other at right Angles, then from A to E, alſo
from B to F, likewiſe from D to G, ſet 14
Inches, the intended height of your Arch. Then
deſcribe another Ellipſis to that length and height,
after this manner; lay a ſtreight Ruler on the
Centre by I, and on the joining of the Hanſe,
and the Scheam together, as at K, and draw
the line K L, then ſet one point of your Compaſſes in the centre of the Hanſe at M, and open
the other point of the Compaſſes to F, and deſcribe the upper Hanſe F L, likewiſe ſetting one
point of the Compaſſes in the centre by I, with
the other extended to G, deſcribe the Scheam
G L, (although I ſpeak here of Compaſſes,
yet when you deſcribe an Arch to its full bigneſs, you muſt make uſe of centre Lines or
Rues;

Rules; the laft are beft, becaufe Lines are fubject to ftretch) then taking between your Compaffes the thicknefs of a Brick, abating fome
fmall matter which will be rub'd off from both
beds of the Brick; with the Compaffes at this
diftance divide the upper Hanfe from L to F
into equal parts, and if they happen not to divide it into equal parts, then open them, a
fmall matter wider, or fhut them a fmall matter clofer, till it doth divide it into equal parts,
and look how many equal parts you divide
the upper Hanfe into, fo many equal parts you
muft divide the lower Hanfe from K to B into
likewifewife (or you may divide the upper
Hanfe from the centre O, making a right Angle from each fommering Line to the Ellipfis,
as is fhewn in defcribing the ftreight Arches following; and from the centre O, and the Divifions in the upper Hanfe being thus divided,
you may draw the ftreight Lines to the lower
Hanfe, and not divide it with the Compaffes)
through each of which divifions with a Rule,
and Pencil, draw ftreight lines, then get a piece
of thin Wainfcot, and make it to fit between two
of thefe Lines, allowing what thicknefs for
Morter you intend, this will be the Sommering
Mould for the Hanfe; then divide the upper
Scheam likewife, with the Compaffes at the
fame diftance into equal parts, and laying a
Ruler on the centre I, from each Divifion in the
Scheam G L, draw ftreight Lines to the lower
Scheam D K, then make another Sommering
Mould to fit between two of thefe Lines, aba-
ting fo much as you intend the thicknefs of your
Joints of Morter to be, which if you fet very
clofe Morters, the breadth of the Line will be
enough to allow; then laying the inner Edge of

a Be-a Bevil ftreight on the line K L, bring the Tongue to touch the under fide of the firft Courfe of the Scheam, then take up the Bevil, and fet that Bevil line upon the Sommering Mould of the Scheam; which Bevil line ferves for each Courfe in the Scheam; but you muft take the Bevil of each Courfe in the Hanfe, and fet them upon your Sommering Mould by themfelves, and Number them with 1, 2, 3, 4, &c. becaufe each Courfe varies.

Thus having made your Sommering Moulds, in the next place you muft make the Moulds for the length of your Stretchers, and for the breadth of the Headers and the Clofiers; a piece of Wainfcot feven Inches long, and three Inches and an half broad will ferve for the length of the Stretchers, and the breadth of the Headers, the Clofiers will be 1 Inch and ¾ broad. So the Clofier will be half the breadth of the Header, and the Header half the length of the Stretcher, which will look well.

It remains now to fpeak fomething to the other part of the Arch, to wit, A D, whofe Courfes both in *Hanfe* and *Scheam*, run alike upon the *Ellipfis* Lines, and feem of one bignefs, although perhaps there may be fome fmall matter of difference, by reafon I have not divided the Courfes to this Figure, from a right Angle, but every Courfe from the Angle, which it makes with the *Ellipfis*, which I chofe rather to do, that fo the *Bevil* of one Courfe, might not feem to run more upon the *Ellipfis* than the *Bevil* of another, and the difference of the thickneffes being fo inconfiderate, is not difcerned.

Having

Having defcribed both the *Ellipfis* lines **A D**, **E G**, divide each of them into a like number of equal parts, always remembring to make each Divifion on the upper *Ellipfis* line, no greater than the thicknefs of the Brick will contain, when it is wrought; then through each Divifion in both the *Ellipfes* draw ftreight lines; continuing them four or five Inches above the upper *Ellipfis* Line, and as much below the lower *Ellipfis* Line; then having provided fome thin Sheets of fine Paftboard about 20 Inches fquare, cutting one edge ftreight, take one fheet and lay the ftreight edge even upon the line A E, fo that it may cover both the Ellipfis lines, and being cut to advantage, it may cover eight courfes (or nine of the ftreight Lines) having laid it thus upon the figure of the Arch, ftick a Pin, or two, through it, to keep it in its place; then lay a Ruler upon the Paftboard true to the 7, 8, or 9th. ftreight Line of the Arch, according as the Paft-board is in bignefs to cover them, and take a fharp Pen-knife, laying the Ruler upon the Paft-board true to the ftreight Line (whofe ends being continued longer than the Arch is deep, as I directed before, will be feen beyond the Paft-board) and cut the Paft-board true to the Line, then take another fheet, and join to it, and cut it as you did the firft, fo continue till you have covered the Arch from A E, juft to the line D G, fticking Pins in each Sheet to keep them in the places where you lay them: Then defcribe both the Ellipfis Lines upon the Paftboard, from the fame Centres and Radii that you defcribed the Ellipfis's under the Paft-board, and either divide the Ellipfis Lines with the Compaffes on the Paft-board, or elfe draw lines

T 3　　　　　　　upon

upon the Paft-board from or by the ftreight lines underneath them whofe ends you fee; but the furer way is to divide the Ellipfis's on the Paft-board, and draw Lines through thofe Divifions, as you did beneath the Paft-board; then fet feven Inches, being the length of each Stretcher, from A towards E, and from D towards G, and defcribe from the former Centres, the Ellipfis *o o* through each other courfe on the Paft-board, as you may fee in the *Fig.* alfo fet three Inches and an half, being the breadth of the Header, from A towards E, and and likewife from D towards G : Alfo fet the fame three Inches and an half from E towards A, and from G towards D, and defcribe thefe two Ellipfis lines from the fame Centres thro' each Courfe, which the Ellipfis line of the Stretchers mifs'd; likewife draw in the fame Courfes, two other Ellipfis lines, one Inch and $\frac{3}{4}$ from each of thofe two Lines you drew laft, which is the breadth of the Clofiers; thus one Courfe of the Arch will be divided into two Stretchers, and the next to it into three Headers and two Clofiers through the whole Arch; this being done, cut the Paft-board according to the lines into feveral Courfes, and each other Courfe into two Stretchers, and the Heading-courfes into three Headers, and two Clofiers, exactly according to the Sweep of the Black-lead lines, and mark each Courfe with Figures, marking the firft Courfe of the Hanfe with 1, the next with 2, the third with 3, and fo continue till you have marked all the Courfes to the Key, or middle, for every Courfe differs; you were beft to mark the lower Clofier in each courfe with a Cipher on the left hand of its own number, that you may know it readily from the

upper

upper Clofier, and make no miftakes when you come to fet them ; alfo the middle Headers in each Courfe fhould be marked befides its own number ; the thicknefs of the upper Header being eafily difcerned from the lower Header needs no marking befides its own number; the crofs Joints, and likewife the under fide and upper fide of each Courfe muft be cut circular, as the Paft-boards which are your Moulds direct you.

If you will add a Keyftone, and Chaptrels to the Arch, as in the *Figure,* let the breadth of the upper part of the Keyftone be the height of the Arch, *viz.* 14 Inches, and Sommer, from the Centre at I, then make your Chaptrels the fame thicknefs that your lower part of the Keyftone is, and let the Keyftone break without the Arch, fo much as you project or Sale over the Jaums with the Chaptrels.

Other kind of *Circular Arches,* as half Rounds and Scheams, being defcribed from one Centre, are fo plain and eafy, that I need fay nothing concerning them : But fince *Streight Arches* are much ufed, and many Workmen know not the true way of defcribing them, I fhall write fomething briefly concerning them. *Streight Arches* are ufed generally over Windows and Doors, according to the breadth of the Piers between the Windows, fo ought the Skew-back or Sommering of the Arch to be ; for if the Piers be of a good breadth, as three or four Bricks in length, then the *Streight Arch* may be defcribed (as its vulgarly faid) from the *Oxi,* which being but part of a Word, is taken from the word *Oxigonium,* fignifying an Equilateral Triangle,

T 4   with

with three fharp Angles; but if the Piers are
fmall, as fometimes they are but the length of
two Bricks, and fometimes but one Brick and
an half, then the breadth of the Window, or
more, may be fet down upon the middle Line
for the Centre, which will give a lefs Skew-
back, or Sommering, than the centre from an
Oxi. I will fhew how to defcribe them both
ways, and firft from the *Oxi.*

Suppofe a *Streight Arch,* one Brick and an
half in height, to be made over a Window, 4
feet in width. [See *Fig.* 4.] wherein one half
of the Arch is defcribed from the *Oxi,* and the
other half from the width of the Window, let
the width of the Window be A B, taking the
width between the Compaffes, from A and B
as two Centres, defcribe the two Arches, inter-
fecting each other at P, (though I fpeak here
of Compaffes, yet when you defcribe the Arch
to its full bignefs, you muft ufe a Ruler, or a
Line, fcarce any Compaffes being to be got
large enough.) Then draw another Line above
the line A B, as the line C D, being parallel
to it, at fuch a height as you intend your
Arch to be, as in this *Fig.* at 12 Inches; but
moft commonly thefe fort of Arches are but
11 Inches in the height, or thereabouts, which
anfwers to four Courfes of Bricks, but you
may make them more or lefs in height according as occafion requires; then laying a Ruler
on the centre P, and on the end of the line
A, draw the line A C, which is vulgarly called
the *Skew-back* for the Arch.

The next thing to be done, is to divide thofe
two lines A B and C D into fo many Courfes
as

as the Arch will contain; the thicknefs of a
Brick being one of them, which fome do by
dividing the upper line into fo many equal parts,
and from thofe parts, and from the Centre P,
draw the Sommering Lines or Courfes; others
divide both the upper and lower line into fo many equal parts, and make no ufe of a Centre,
but draw the Courfes by a Ruler, being laid
from the Divifions on the upper line, to the
Divifions on the lower line, both which ways
are falfe and erroneous; [but this by way of
caution.]

Having drawn the *Skew-back* A C, take between your Compaffes the thicknefs that a Brick
will contain, which I fuppofe to be two Inches
when it is rub'd, and fetting one point of the
Compaffes on the line C D. So that when you
turn the other Point about, it may juft touch
the line A C in one place, and there make a
Prick in the line C D, but do not draw the
Sommering lines until you have gone over half
the Arch, to fee how you come to the Key, or
middle; and if you happen to come juft to
the middle line, or want an Inch of it, then
you may draw the lines, but if not, then you
muft open, or fhut the Compaffes a little till
you do.

Then keeping one end of the Rule clofe to
the Centre at P. (the fureft way is to ftrike a
fmall Nail in the Centre P. and keep the Rule
clofe to the Nail) lay the other end of the
Rule clofe to the Prick that you made on the
line C D, keeping the Compaffes at the fame
width (*viz.* two Inches) fet one point of the
Compaffes on the line C D, as before, fo that
the

the other Point being turned about, may juft pafs by the Rule; and as it were touch it in one place; (you muft remove the point of the Compaffes upon the line C D, farther or nearer to the Rule, until it juft touch the Rule in one place,) and fo continue with the Rule and Compaffes, until you come to the middle line, and if it happen, that your laft fpace want an Inch of the middle, then the middle of the Key-courfe will be the middle of the Arch, and the number of the Courfes in the whole Arch will be odd, but if the laft fpace happen to fall juft upon the middle line E F, as it doth in the *Fig.* then the Joint is the middle of the Arch, (but if it fhould happen neither to come even to the line, nor want an Inch of it, then you muft open or fhut the Compaffes a fmall matter, and begin again till it doth come right) and the number of the Courfes in the whole Arch, is an even Number.

Note, When the number of all the Courfes in the Arch, is an even Number, then you muft begin the two fides contrary, *viz.* A Header to be the lower Brick of the firft Courfe on one fide (or half) of the Arch, and a Stretcher the lower Brick of the firft Courfe on the other fide (or half) of the Arch: And contrariwife, if it happen that the Number of the Courfes be an odd Number, as 25 or 27, or fuch like, then the firft Courfes of each half of the Arch, muft be alike, that is, either both Headers, or both Stretchers, at the bottom.

Thus having defcribed the Arch, the next thing to be done, is to make the Sommering Mould, which to do, get a piece of thin Wainfcot

ſcot (being ſtreight on one edge, and having one ſide plained ſmooth, to ſet the Bevil ſtrokes upon) about 14 Inches long, and any breadth above two Inches, then laying your Ruler, one end at the Centre P, and the other end even in the Skew-back line, clap the ſtreight edge of the Wainſcot cloſe to the Rule, ſo that the lower end of the Wainſcot may lye a little below the line A B, then take away the Centre Rule, but ſtir not the Wainſcot; and laying a Ruler upon the Wainſcot juſt over the line C D, ſtrike a line upon the Wainſcot, then ſet one Point of the Compaſſes being at the width of a Courſe (*viz.* two Inches) upon that line, ſo that the other Point being turned about, may juſt touch the ſtreight edge of the Wainſcot ; (as you did before in dividing the Courſes) then make a Prick on the line on the Wainſcot, and laying your Centre Rule upon it, and on the Centre P, draw a line upon the Wainſcot by the Ruler, with a Pencil, or the Point of a Compaſs, and cut the Wainſcot to that line, and make it ſtreight by ſhooting it with a Plain, then your Wainſcot will fit exactly between any two lines of the Arch ; you may let it want the thickneſs of one of the lines, or ſome ſmall matter more, which is enough for the thickneſs of a Mortar; the length of your Stretcher in this Arch, may be 8 Inches and $\frac{1}{4}$, and the Header 3 Inches and $\frac{3}{4}$, but if your Arch be but 11 Inches in height, then make your Stretcher 7 Inches and $\frac{1}{2}$ long, and the Header 3 Inches $\frac{1}{2}$; one piece of Wainſcot will ſerve both for the length of the Stretcher, and the length of the Header, making it like a long ſquare or Oblong, whoſe ſides are 8 Inches $\frac{1}{4}$, and 3 Inches and $\frac{3}{4}$. Then take a Bevil, and lay-

ing

ing the inner edge of it ftreight with the line
A B, and the Angle of the Bevil juft over the
Angle at A, take off the Angle that the Skew-back
line A C makes with the line A B, and fet it
upon the fmoothed fide of your Sommering
Mould, for the Bevil ftroke of your firft Courfe;
then drawing your Bevil towards E, ftreight in
the line, until the Angle of the Bevil be juft
over the Angle, that the fecond Sommering line
makes with the line A B; when it is fo, draw
the Tongue of the Bevil to lye even upon the
fecond Sommering line; (in brief, caufe the
Bevil to lye exactly on the line A B, and on
the fecond Sommering line) then take up your
Bevil and lay it on the Mould; and ftrike that
Bevil line on the Mould, with the Point of the
Compaffes, about half a quarter of an Inch
diftant from the firft, and that is the Bevil of
the underfide of the fecond Courfe; proceed
thus until you come to the middle line E F,
but after you have fet three Bevil lines upon
your Sommering Mould, leave about $\frac{1}{4}$ of an
Inch between the third and the fourth, and fo
likewife between the 6th and 7th, and the 9th,
and 10th, which will be a great help to you,
in knowing the Number of each line on the
Mould.

The Moulds for the other half of the Arch,
namely E B, are made after the fame manner,
but but the Arch is defcribed from a Centre
beneath P, as Q which caufeth a lefs Skew-
back (*viz.* B. D.)

The diminifhing of the Sommering Mould
to any Skew-back may be found by the Rule of
Three, by dividing a foot into 10 equal parts,
and

and each of thefe into 10 parts, fo that the
whole foot may contain 100 parts, then proceed thus. The upper line C F, will be 309,
that is three Feet and almoft one Inch, and the
lower line A E will be 252, that is two Feet
and an half an $\frac{2}{100}$, and the upper part of the
Sommering Mould will be 17 almoft, that is,
two Inches of fuch whereof there are 12 in a
foot line meafure; having thefe three Numbers
(viz. 309, 252, 17.) work according to the
Rule of Three, and you will find 13 and $\frac{5}{}$ of
100 parts, that is almoft 14 (fuch parts whereof there are 100 in a Foot line meafure) for
the breadth of the lower part of the Mould.

Tau may likewife find it Geometrically thus.

HAving drawn the upper line and under line
of the Arch, as C F, and A E, and drawn
any Skew-back, as fuppofe A C in [*Fig.* 4.]
make at difcretion the Angle G C H in [*Fig.*5.]
then take the upper line C F, and fet it from
C. to F; alfo take the lower line A E, and fet
it from C to E, and draw the line E F; then
take the thicknefs of your Brick, which fuppofe
to be two Inches, and fet it from F to G, and
draw G H, parallel to F E, I fay F G is the
breadth of the upper part of the Sommering
Mould, and E H the breadth of the lower part:
Then make your Sommering Mould true to thofe
two lines, and beginning in the middle line F E,
defcribe the ftreight lines by the Mould from
the Key F E, until you come to the Skew-
back A C, and then take of the Bevil lines, and
fet them on your Sommering Mould.

I fhall

I shall conclude this Exercise with the Art of making two sorts of Cements, for the Cementing Bricks.

THere are two sorts of Cement, which some Bricklayers use in Cementing of Bricks for some kind of Mouldings, or in Cementing a block of Bricks, as they call it, for the Carving of Scroles or Capitals or such like, &c. One is called cold Cement, the other is called hot Cement, because the former is made and used without Fire, but the latter is both made and used with Fire; the cold Cement being accounted a Secret, is known but to few Bricklayers, but the hot Cement is common.

To make the cold Cement.

TAke ½ a Pound of Old Cheshire-Cheese, pair of the Rine, and throw it away, cut or grate the Cheese very small, and put it into a Pot, put to it about a Pint of Cows-milk, let it stand all Night, the next Morning get the Whites of 12 or 14 Eggs, then take ½ a Pound of the best Unslackt or Quick Lime that you can get, and beat it to Powder in a Morter, then sift it through a fine Hair Sieve into a Tray or Bole of Wood, or into an Earthen Dish, to which put the Cheese and Milk, and stir them well together with a Trowel, or such like thing, breaking the Knots of Cheese, if there be any, then add the Whites of the Eggs, and Temper all well together, and so use it; this Cement will be a White Colour, but if you would have it of the Colour of the Brick, put into it either some very fine Brick-Dust, or Almegram, not too much, but only just to colour it.

To

To make the hot Cement.

TAke one Pound of Rozin, one Quarter of a Pound of Bees-Wax, half an Ounce of fine Brick-Duft, half an Ounce of Chalk-Duft, or Powder of Chalk, fift both the Brick-Duft and Chalk-Duft through a fine Hair Sieve, (you may beat the Brick and the Chalk in a Morter, before you fift it) boil altogether in a Pipkin, or other Veffel, about a quarter of an hour, ftirring it all the while with an Iron or a piece of Lath or fuch like, then take it of, and let it ftand 4 or 5 Minutes, and 'tis fit for ufe.

Note, That the Bricks that are to be Cemented with this kind of Cement, muft be made hot by the Fire before you fpread the Cement on them, and then rub them to and fro on one another, as Joiners do, when they Glew two Boards together.

E I N I S.

Mechanick Dyalling:

TEACHING

Any Man, tho' of an Ordinary Capacity and unlearned in the Mathematicks,

To Draw a True

SUN-DYAL

ON ANY

GIVEN PLANE,

However Scituated :

Only with the help of a ſtraight *Rule* and a pair of *Compaſſes*; and without any Arithmetical Calculation.

𝕿𝖍𝖊 𝕱𝖔𝖚𝖗𝖙𝖍 𝕰𝖉𝖎𝖙𝖎𝖔𝖓.

By JOSEPH MOXON, *Fellow of the Royal Society, and Hydrographer to the late King* Charles.

LONDON:

Printed for *Tho. Leigh* and *Dan. Midwinter*, at the *Roſe and Crown* in St. *Paul's-Church-Yard.* 1703.

Mechanick Dyalling.

Defcription of Dyalling.

DYalling originally is a *Mathematical Science*, attained by the Philofophical contemplation of the Motion of the Sun, the Motion of the Shadow, the Conftitution of the Sphere, the Scituation of Planes, and the Confideration of Lines.

Explanation.

THE Motion of the Sun is reguler, it moving in equal Space in equal Time ; But the Moon of the Shadow irregular, in all parts of the Earth, unlefs under the two Poles, and that more or lefs according to the Conftitution of the *Sphere* and Scituation of the *Plane.* And therefore Scientifick Dyalifts by the Geometrick Confiderations of Lines, have found out Rules, to mark out the irregular Motion of the *Shadow* in all *Latitudes*, and on all *Planes*, to Comply with the regular Motion of the Sun. And thefe Rules of adjufting the Motion of the Shadow to the Motion of the Sun, may be called *Scientifick Dyalling.*

But though we may juftly account *Dyalling* originally a *Science*, yet fuch have been the Generofity of many of its ftudious Contemplators, that they have communicated their acquired Rules ; whereby it is now become to many of the Ingenious no more difficult than an *Art*, and by many late Authors

thors

thors fo Intituled : Nay more, by this fmall Trea-
tife it will fcarce be accounted more than a *Manual
Operation*; for, though (hitherto) all the Authors
I have met with feem to pre-fuppofe their Reader
to underſtand *Geomeſtry*, and the *Projecting of the
Sphere* already, or elfe endeavour in their Works
to make him underſtand them, as if they were ab-
folutely neceſſary to be known by every one that
would make a Dyal, when as in truth, (the Con-
templative pains of others aforefaid of confidered)
they are not; but indeed are only ufeful to thofe
that would know the reafon of *Dyalling.* Thus
they do not only difcourage young beginners, but
alfo difappoint many Gentlemen and others, that
would willingly either make them themfelves, or
fet their Workmen about them, if they knew how
to make them.

This little Piece I have therefore compofed for
the help of thofe who underſtand neither the *Pro-
jection of the Sphere*, or *Geometrical Operations*: Only,
if they know how to draw a ſtraight Line between
two points by the fide of a Ruler, defcribe a Circle with a pair of Compaſſes, erect a Perpendicular and draw one Line parallel to another, they
may know how to draw a *Dyal* for any given *Plane*,
however fcituated in any Latitude.

But perhaps thefe two laſt little Tricks are not
known to all new beginners, therefore I fhall fhew
them. Firſt,

How to erect a Perpendicular. For Example, in Fig. 1.

Upon the Line A B, you would erect a Perpendicular to the Point C: Place one Foot of your Compaſſes upon the point C, and open the other to
what diftance you pleafe : For *Example*, to the
point A, make there a mark; then keeping the
firſt Foot ſtill in C, turn the other Foot towards B,
and make there another mark ; then open your
Com-

Compaffes wider, fuppofe to the length A B, and placing one Foot in the point A, with the other Foot de-fcribe a fmall Arch over the point C, and removing the Foot of your Compaffes to the point B, with the other Foot defcribe another fmall Arch, to cut the firft Arch, as at D. Then lay your ftraight Ruler to the point where the two fmall Arches cut each other, and upon the point C, and by the fide of the Ruler draw the Line C D, which fhall be a Per-pendicular to the Line **A B.**

Another way with once opening the Compaffes, as by Fig. 2.

Draw the Line A B, and place one Foot of your Com-paffes upon the point you would have the Perpendicu-lar erected, as at the Point C, and with the other Foot defcribe the Semi-circle A *a b* B, then placing one foot in B, extend the other foot to *b*, in the Semi-circle ; and keeping that Foot in *b*, extend the other Foot to D, and make there a fmall Arch : Then remove one Foot of your Compaffes to A, and extend the other Foot to *a* in the Semi-circle, and keeping that Foot in *a*, ex-tend the other to D, and make there another fmall Arch, to cut the firft fmall Arch ; and laying a ftraight Ruler to the point where thefe two fmall Arches cut each other, and upon the point C, draw

by

by the fide of the Ruler the Line C D, which fhall be perpendicular to the Line A B.

To erect a Perpendicular upon the end of a Line, as by Fig. 3.

On the point B, at one end of the Line A B, place one Foot of your Compaffes in the point B, and extend the other on the Line towards A, as to *b*, and with it defcribe the Arch *b a* C ; then placing one Foot in *b*, extend the other to *a* in the Arch, and make there a mark ; Divide with your Compaffes the Arch *b a* into two equal parts, and keeping the Feet of your Compaffes at that diftance, meafure in the Arch from *a* to C, then draw a ftraight Line from the point C to the end of the Line B, and that ftraight Line fhall be Perpendicular to the end of the Line A B.

To draw a Line Parallel to another Line, as by Fig. 4.

Example. If you would draw a Line parallel to the Line A B, open your Compaffes to the diftance you intend the Lines fhall ftand off each other, and placing one Foot fucceffively near each end, defcribe with other Foot the fmall Arches C D ; lay a ftraight Ruler to the top of thefe Arches, and draw a Line by the fide of it, and that Line fhall be parallel to the Line A B.

Definitions.

A Dyal Plane is that Flat whereon a *Dyal* is intended to be projected.

Of *Dyal Planes* fome be *Direct*, others *Decliners*, others *Oblique.*

Of *Direct Planes* there are five forts.

1. The *Horizontal* whofe Plane lies flat, and is parallel to the *Horizon*, beholding the *Zenith*.

2. The *South Erect*, whofe Plane ftands upright, and directly beholds the *South*.

3. The

3. The *North Erect*, whose Plane stands up-right, and directly beholds the *North*.

4. The *East Erect*, whose Plane stands up-right, and directly beholds the *East*.

5. The *West Erect*, whose Plane stands upright and directly beholds the *West*.

Of *Decliners* there are infinite ; and yet may be reduced into these two *Kinds*.

1. The *South Erect* Plane, declining more or less towards the *East* or *West*.

2. The *North Erect* Plane, declining more or less towards the *East* or *West*.

Of *Obliqae Planes* some are *Direct* other *Declining*; and are of four sorts.

1. *Direct Inclining* Planes, which lean towards you, and lie directly in the *East*, *West* , *North*, or *South* quarters of Heaven.

2. *Direct Reclinig* Planes, which lean from you, and lie directly in the *East*, *West*, *North* or *South* quarters of Heaven.

3. *Inclining Declining* Planes, which lean to-wards you, but lie not directly in the *East*, *West*, *North*, or *South* quarters of Heaven ; But decline more or less from the *North* or *South*, towards the *East* or *West*.

4. *Reclining Declining* Planes, which lean from you, but lie not directly in the *East*, *West*, *North* or *South* quarters of Heaven ; But Decline more or less from the *North* or *South*, towards the *East* or *West*.

If the Scituation of the *Plane* be not given, you must seek it : For, there are several ways how to know these several kinds of *Planes* used among Artists ; But the readiest and easiest is by an Instu-ment called a *Declinatory*, fitted to the variation of your Place : And if it be truly made, you may as safely rely upon it as any other.

O P E-

OPERARTIONI I.
The Defcription of the Clinatory.

THE Clinatory is made of a fquare Board, A B C D, of a good thicknefs, and the larger the better; between two of the fides is defcribed on the Center A, a *Quadrant* as E F divided into 90 equal parts or degrees, which are figured with 10, 20, 30 to 90; and then back again with the Complements of the fame Numbers to 90 : Between the Limb and the two Semi-diameters is made a round Box, into which a Magnetical Needle is fitted ; and a Card of the Nautical Compafs, divided into four nineties, beginning their Numbers at the *Eaft Weft North* and *South* points of the Compafs, from which points the oppofite fides of the Clinatory receives their Names of *Eaft*, *Weft*, *North* and *South*.

But *Note*, That the North point of the Card muft be placed fo many degrees towards the *Eaft* or *Weft* fides of the Clinatory, as the Needle varies from the true *North* point of the World, in the place where you make your Dyal ; which your Workman that makes your Clinatory will know how to fit.

Upon the Center A, whereon the Quadrant was defcribed, is faftned a Plumb-line, having a Plummet of Lead or Brafs faftned to the end of it, which Plumb-line is of fuch length that the Plummet may fall juft into the Groove G H, below the Quadrant, which is for that purpofe made of fuch a depth, that the Plummet may ride freely within it, without ftopping at the fides of it, *See the Figure annexed.*

With

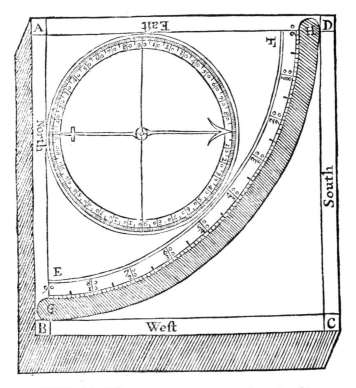

With this Clinatory you may examine the fcituation of Planes. As if your Plane be Horizontal, it is direct: and then for the true fcituating
your Dyal, you have only the true North and
South Line to find: which is done only by fetting
the Clinatory flat down upon the Plane, and turning it towards the right or left hand, till you can
bring the North point of the Needle to hang juft
over the Flower-de-luce; for then if you draw a
Line by either of the fides parallel to the Needle,
that Line fhall be a North and South Line.

If your Plane either Recline or Incline, apply
one of the fides of your Clinatory parallel to one

of

of the Semi-diameters of the Quadrant to the
Plane, in fuch fort that the Plumb-line hanging at
liberty, may fall upon the Circumference of the
Quadrant, for then the number of degrees of the
Quadrant comprehended between the fide of the
Quadrant parallel to the Plane, and the Plumb-line
fhall be the number of degrees for Reclination, if
the Center of the Quadrant points upwards; or
Inclination, if the Center points downwards

If your Reclining or Inclining Plane decline,
draw upon it a Line parallel to the Horizon,
which you may do by applying the Back-fide of
the Clinatory, and raifing or depreffing the Center of the Quadrant, till the Plumb-line hang juft
upon one of the Semi-diameters, for then you may
by the upper-fide of the Clinatory draw an Horizontal Line if the Plane Incline, or by the under-fide, if it Recline. If it neither Incline or
Recline, you may draw a Horizontal Line both by
the upper and under fides of the Clinatory. Having drawn the Horizontal Line, apply the North
fide of the Clinatory to it, and if the North end
of the Needle points directly towards the Plane,
it is then a South Plane. If the North point of
the Needle points directly from the Plane, it is a
North Plane : But if it points towards the *Eaft*,
it is an *Eaft* Plane : If towards the *Weft*, a *Weft*
Plane. If it do not point directly either Eaft,
Weft, North, or South, then fo many degrees as
the Needle declines from any of thefe four points
to any of the other of thefe four points, fo many
degrees is the Declination of the Plane.

You may find a Meridian Line another way ;
thus, If the Sun fhine juft at Noon, hold up a
Plumb-line fo as the fhadow of it may fall upon
your Plane, and that fhadow fhall be a *Meridian
Line.*

O P E-

OPERAT. II.

To defcribe a Dyal upon a Horizontal Plane.

Firſt draw a North and South Line (which is called a *Meridian Line*) through the middle of the Plane ; Thus. Set your *Declinatory* flat upon the Plane, and turn it too and fro till the Needle hang precifely over the *Meridian Line* of the *Declinatory* ; then by the fide of the *Declinatory* parallel to its *Meridian Line*, draw a ſtraight Line on the Plane, and if that ſtraight Line be in the middle of the Plane, it ſhall be the *Meridian Line*, whithout more ado : But if it be not in the middle of the Plane, you muſt draw a Line parallel to it, through the middle of the Plane for the *Meridian Line*, or twelve a Clock Line : And it ſhall be the *Meridian Line*, and alſo be the *Subftilar Line* ; then draw another ſtraight Line through the middle of this Line, to cut it at right Angles for the VI a Clock Lines ; and where thefe two Lines cut one another make your Center, whereon you defcribe a Circle on your *Plane* as large as you can, which by the *Meridian Line*, and the Line drawn at right Angles with it will be divided into four *Quadrants* ; one of the *Quadrants* divide into 90 degrees thus, keeping your Compaffes at the fame width they were at when you defcribed the *Quadrant*, place one Foot in the twelve a Clock Line, and extend the other in the *Quadrant*, and make in the *Quadrant* a mark with it, fo ſhall you have the ſixtieth degree marked out : Then place one Foot of your Compaffes in the fix a Clock Line, and extend the other in the *Quadrant*, and make in the *Quadrant* another mark with it ; fo ſhall that *Quadrant* be divided into three equal parts, each of thefe three equal parts contains 30 Degrees : Then with your Compaffes divide one of thefe three

equal

equal parts into three parts, and transfer that diftance to the other two third parts of the *Quadrant*, fo fhall the whole *Quadrant* be divided into nine equal parts. Then divide one of thefe nine equal parts into two equal parts, and transfer that diftance to the other eight equal parts, fo fhall the *Quadrant* be divided into Eighteen equal parts. Then divide one of thefe Eighteen equal parts into five equal parts, and transfer that diftance to the other Seventeen equal parts, fo fhall the whole *Quadrant* be divided into 90 equal parts, Each of thefe 90 equal parts are called Degrees.

Note, That you may in fmall *Quadrants* divide truer and with lefs trouble with Steel Dividers, (which open or clofe with a Screw for that purpofe,) then you can with Compaffes.

In this *Quadrant* (thus divided) count from the *Subftilar* or *Meridian Line* the Elevation of the *Pole,* that is, the number of Degrees that the *Pole* of the World is elevated above the *Horizon* of your Place, and draw a Line from the Center through that number of Degrees for the *Stilar Line.* Then on the *Subftilar Line* chofe a point (where you pleafe) and through that point draw a Line at right Angles to the *Subftilar Line* as long as you can, for the Line of *Contingence,* and from that point in the *Subftilar Line* meafure the neareft diftance any part of the *Stilar Line* hath to that point ; and keeping one Foot of your Compaffes ftill in that point, fet of that diftance in the *Subftilar Line,* and at that diftance defcribe againft the *Line* of *Contingence* a Semi-circle, which divide from either fide the *Meridian* or *Subftilar Line* into fix equal parts thus; Draw a line through the Center of this Semi-circle parallel to the *Line* of *Contingence,* which fhall be the *Diametral Line,* and fhall devide this Semi-circle into two *Quadrants*; one on one fide the *Subftiler Line,* and the

Q. a-

Quadrant on the other fide the *Subſtiler Line*: then keeping your Compaſſes at the ſame diſtance they were at when you defcribed the Semi-circle, place one Foot firſt on one fide the *Diametral Line* at the Interfe&ion of it and the Semi-circle, and then on the other fide, at the Interfe&ion of it and the Semi-circle, and extend the other in the Semi-circle, and make marks in the Semi-circle on either fide the *Subſtilar Line*; then place one Foot of your Compaſſes at the Interfe&ion of the Semi-circle and the *Subſtilar Line*, and turn the other Foot about on either fide the Semi-circle and make marks in the Semi-circle, fo ſhall the Semi-circle be divided into fix equal parts ; Divide one of thefe equal parts into two equal parts, and transfer that diſtance to the other five equal parts, fo ſhall the whole Semi-circle be divided into twelve equal parts. Thefe twelve Divifions are to defcribe the twelve Hours of the Day, between fix a Clock in the Morning, and fix a Clock at Night.

If you will have half Hours, you may divide each of thefe twelve into two equal parts, as before: If you will have Quarters you may divide each of thefe twenty four into two equal parts more, as before.

For thus proportioning the Divifions in the Semi-circle, you may proportion the Divifions and Sub-divi-fions of Hours upon the *Dyal Plane* ; for a ſtraight Ruler laid upon each of thefe Divifions, and on the Center of this Semi-circle, ſhall fhew on the *Line of Contingence* the feveral Diſtances of all the Hours and parts of Hours on the *Dyal Plane.* And ſtraight Lines drawn from the Center of the *Dyal Plane*, through the feveral Divifions on the *Line of Contingence* ſhall be the feveral Hour Lines and parts on the *Dyal Plane.*

But

But an *Horizontal Dyal* in our Latitude will ad‑admit of four Hours more, *viz.* V, IV, in the Morning, and VII, VIII, in the Evening. There‑fore in the Circle defcribed on the Center of the *Dyal Plane* transfer the diftance between VI and V, and VI and IV, on the other fide the fix a Clock Line ; and transfer the·Diftances between VI and VII, and VI and VIII on the other fide the oppo‑fite fix a Clock Hour Line, and from the Center of the *Dyal Plane* draw Lines through thofe transfer‑red Diftances for the Hour Lines before and after VI.

Then mark your Hour Lines with their refpe‑ctive numbers. The *Subftilar Line* in this Dyal (as aforefaid) is XII, from thence towards the right hand mark every fucceffive Hour Line with I, II, III, *&c.* and from XII towards the left hand with XI, X, IX, *&c.*

The *Stile* muft be erected perpendicularly over the *Subftilar Line,* fo as to make an Angle with the *Dyal Plane* equal to the *Elevation* of the *Pole* of your Place.

Example.

You would draw a Dyal upon a *Horizontal Plane* here at *London* ; Firft draw the *Meridian* (or North and South Line) as XII B, and crofs it in the mid‑dle with another Line at right Angles, as VI, VI, which is an Eaft and Weft Line ; where thefe two Lines cut each other as at A, make the Center, whereon defcribe the·Semi-circle B, VI, VI ; but one of the *Quadrants,* viz. the *Quadrant* from XII to VI, towards the right hand you muft divide in‑to 90 equal parts (as you were taught in *Fol.* 12.) and at 51½ degrees (which is *Londons* Latitude) make a mark, and laying a ftraight Ruler to the Center of the *Plane,* and to this mark draw a Line by the fide of it for the Stilar Line. Then on the
Subftilar

Subftilar Line chufe a point as at C, and thro' that point draw a Line as long as you can perpendicular to the Eaft and Weft Line VI, VI, as E F, (which is called the *Contingent Line*) where this *Contingent Line* cuts the *Subftilar Line* place one Foot of your Compaffes, and from thence meafure the fhorteft Diftance between the point C and the *Stilar Line.* And keeping one Foot of your Compaffes ftill in the point C, fet off the fhorteft diftance between the point C, and the *Stilar Line* on the *Subftilar Line*, as at D; which point D fhall be a Center, whereon with your Compaffes at the fame width you muft defcribe a Semi-circle to reprefent a Semi-circle of the *Equinoctial.* This Semi-circle divide into fix equal parts (as you were taught *Fol.* 13.) to each of which equal parts, and to the Center the *Equinoctial* Semi-circle lay a ftraight Ruler, and where the ftraight Ruler cuts the *Line of Contingence* make marks in the *Line of Contingence.* Then lay the ftraight Ruler to the Semi-circle of the *Dyal Plane*, and to each of the marks in the *Line of Contingence*, and by the fide of it draw twelve ftraight Lines for the twelve Fore and Afternoon Hour Lines, *viz.* from VI in the Morning to VI in the Evening. Then in the *Quadrant* VI B, meafure the diftance between the VI a Clock Hour Line, and the V a Clock Hour Line, and transfer the fame diftances from the VI a Clock Line to VII, and V on both fides the VI a Clock Hour Lines, and through thofe diftances draw from the Center of the Plane the VII and V a Clock Hour Lines, and meafure the diftance between the VI a Clock Hour Line and the IV a Clock Hour Line, and tranfer the fame diftance from the VI a Clock Line to VIII and IV, and through thofe diftftances draw from the Center of the Plane the VIII a Clock and IV a Clock Hour Lines.

If

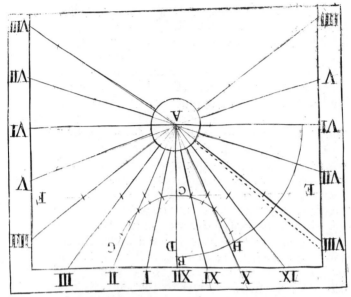

If you will have the half Hours and quarter
Hours, or any other divifion of Hours, you muft
divide each fix Divifions of the *Equinoctial* into fo
many parts as you intend, and by a ftraight Ruler laid to the Center of the *Equinoctial*, and thofe
divifions in the *Equinoctial* Circle make marks in
the *Line of Contingence*, as you did before for the
whole Hour Lines: and Lines drawn from the
Center of the Plane through thofe marks fhall be
the Sub-divifions of the Hours: But you muft remember to make all Sub-divifions fhort Lines, and
near the verge of the *Dyal Plane*, that you may
the eafier diftinguifh between the whole Hours and
the parts of Hours; as you may fee in the Figure.

Having drawn the Hour-Lines, fet the Number
of each Hour-Line under it, as you fee in the Figure. Laft of all fit a Triangular Iron, whofe angular Point being laid to the Centre of the *Dyal*
                                                    Plane

Plane, one fide muft agree with the *Subftilar Line,* and its other fide with the *Stilar Line*; fo is the *Stile* made. And this *Stile* you muft erect Perpendiculary over the *Subftilar Line* on the *Dyal Plane,* and there fix it. Then is your *Dyal* finifhed.

OPERAT. III.

To defcribe an Erect Direct South-Dyal.

YOU may know an *Erect Direct South-Plane,* by applying the North-fide of the *Declinatory* to it; For then, if the North-end of the Needle hang directly over the North-point of the Card in the bottom of the Box, it is a *South-Plane*; but if it hang not directly over the North-point of the Card it is not a *Direct South-Plane,* but *Declines* either Eaft or Weft and that contrary to the Pointing of the Needle Eafterly or Wefterly, from the Northpoint of the Card: For, if the North-point of the Needle points Eafterly, the *Plane Declines* from the South towards the Weft: if it point Wefterly the *Plane Declines* from the South towards the Eaft.

You may know, if the *Plane* be truly *Erect* or upright, by applying one of the fides A D or A B to it; for then by holding the Center A upwards, fo as. the Plumb-line play free in the Groove, if the Line falls upon o, or 90, the Plane is upright; but, if it hang upon any of the intermediate Degrees, it is not upright, but *Inclines* or *Reclines.*

If you find it incline, apply the fide **A B** to it; and fee what number of Degrees the Plumb-line falls on, for that number of Degrees, counted from the faid A B, is the number of Degrees of *Inclination.*

If you find the *Plane Reclines,* apply the fide A D to it, and fee what number of Degrees the Plumbline falls on, for that number of Degrees counted from the fide A D, is the number of Degrees of *Reclination.*

X These

Thefe Rules being well underftood, may ferve you to find the fcituation of all other fort of *Planes.*

But for the making a *Dyal* on this *Plane*, you muft firft draw a *Meridian Line* through the middle of the *Plane*, by applying a Plumb-line to the middle of it, till the Plumbet hang quietly before it: for then, if the Plumb-line be blacked (for a white Ground, or chalked for a dark Ground) and ftrained as Carpenters do their Lines, you may with one ftroke of the ftring on the *Plane*, defcribe the *Meridian Line*, as A XII. This *Meridian* is alfo the *Subftilar line.*

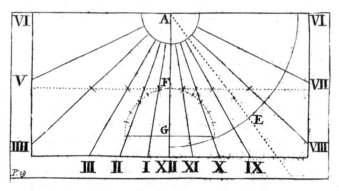

Then on the top of this *Meridian Line*, as at A draw another Line athwart it, to cut it at right Angles, as VI, VI. for an Eaft and Weft Line. At the meeting of thefe two Lines at the top, make your Center, whereon defcribe a Semi-Circle on your *Plane*, as large as you can, which by the *Meridian Line* and the Eaft and Weft Line, will be divided into two *Quadrants*. One of thefe *Quadrants* divide into 90 Degrees (as you were taught *Fol.* 12.) and from the *Subftilar Line* count the Complement of the *Poles Elevation*, which (here at *London* where the *Pole* is elevated 51½ Degrees, its Complement to 90) is 38½ Degrees, and make there

there a mark, as at E. Then on the *Subſtilar line*
chuſe a point (where you pleaſe) as at F, for the *line
of Contingence* to paſs through; which *Line of Contingence* draw as long as you can, ſo as it may cut
the *Subſtilar Line* at right Angles, and from the
point F in the *Subſtilar line,* meaſure the ſhorteſt
diſtance between it and the *Stilar Line,* and keeping
one Foot of your Compaſſes ſtill in the point F,
transfer that diſtance into the *Subſtilar Line* as at
G; then on the point G deſcribe a Semi-Circle of
the *Equinoctial* againſt the *Line of Contingence,* which
Semi-Circle divide into twelve equal parts, (as you
were taught by the *Example* in the *Horizontal Dyal,*
Fol. 13.) and by a ſtraight Ruler laid to each of
theſe Diviſions, and to the Center of the Semi-
Circle make marks in the *Line of Contingence* by the
ſide of the Ruler; For ſtraight Lines drawn from
the Center of the *Dyal plane* through theſe marks
in the *Contingent line* ſhall be the 12 Hour Lines before and after Noon.

Then mark your Hour Lines with their reſpective Numbers; the *Subſtilar* or *Meridian Line* is
XII, from thence towards the right hand with I,
II, III, &c. and from thence towards the left
hand with a XI, X, IX, &c.

The *Stile* muſt be erected perpendicular over the
Subſtilar Line, ſo as to make an Angle with the
Dyal Plane equal to the Complement of the *Poles
Elevation,* viz. 38 ½ Degrees.

OPERAT. IV.

To make an Erect Direct North Dyal.

THE *Erect Direct* North Dyal Stile and all, is
made by the ſame Rules, changing upwards
for downwards, and the left ſide for the right,
the *Erect Direct South Dyal* is made; for if the *Erect
Direct South Dyal* be drawn on any tranſparent

Plane, as on Glafs, Horn, or an oyled Paper, and the *Horizontal Line* VI, VI, turned downwards, and the Line VII mark't with V, the Line VIII with IIII the Line V with VII, and the Line IIII with VIII, then have you of it a *North Erect Direct* **Dyal.**

All the other Hour Lines in this Dyal are ufelefs, becaufe the Sun in our Latitude fhines on a North Face the longeft Day only before VI in the Morning, and after VI at Night.

OPERAT. V.

To defcribe an Erect Direct Eaft Dyal.

HAving a Plumb-line a little above the Place on the Wall where you intend to make your Dyal, and wait till it hang quietly before the wall: Then if the Line be rubbed with Chalk (like a Carpenters Line) you may by holding the Plumbet end clofe to the wall, and ftraining it pretty ftiff, ftrike with it a ftraight Line, as Carpenters do: This Line fhall be a perpendicular, as A B. Then chufe a convenient point in this Perpendicular, as at C, for a Center, whereon defcribe an occult Arch, as D E; This Arch muft contain the number of Degrees of the *Elevation* of the *Equinoctial,* counted between D and E, which in our *Latitude* is 38½, or (which is all one) the Complement of the *Poles Elevation.* Therefore in a *Quadrant* of the fame *Radius,* with the occult Arch meafure 38½ Degrees, and fet them off in the Plane from E to D: Then from D to the Center C in the Perpendicular, draw the prick't Line D C; this prick't Line fhall reprefent the *Axis of the World.* Then crofs this Line at right Angles with the Line C F, and draw it from C to F, fo long as poffibly you can: This Line fhall be the *Contingent Line.* Then chufe a point in this *Contingent Line,* as at VI, draw a Line through that point at right Angles for the *Subfti-*
lar

lar Line, as G VI H for the *Subftilar Line* ; then o-
pen your Compafles to a convenient width, (as to
VI G) and pitching one foot in the point G, with
the other Foot defcribe a Semi-Circle of the *Equinoctial* againft the *Line of Contingence,* which Semi-Circle divide from VI both ways into fix equal
parts, as you were taught by the *Example* in the
Horizontal Dyal; and laying a ftraight Ruler on
the Center of this Semi-Circle of the *Equinoctial,*
and to each of thofe equal parts mark on the *Contingent Line* where the Ruler cuts it, for thofe
marks fhall be the feveral points from whence
Lines drawn parallel to the Line C D fhall be the
refpective Hour Lines.

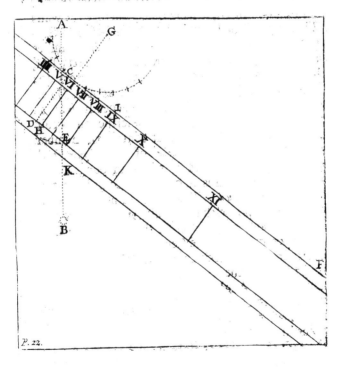

X 3   The

The reason why the *Contingent Line* is drawn from VI to F, so much longer than from VI to C is; because the Hour Lines from VI towards XII are more in Number towards Noon, than they are from VI backwrd towards IIII, for this Dyal will only shew the Hours from a little before IV in the Morning to almost Noon. For just at Noon the Shadow goes off the Plane; as you may see, if you apply a straight Ruler to the Center of the equinoctial Semi-Circle G, and lay it to the point 12 in the Semi-Circle; for the straight Ruler will then never cut the *Line of Contingence,* because the *Line of Contingence* is parallel to the line G XII on the Equinoctial Circle, and Lines parallel, though continued to never so great a length, never meet.

To these *Hour Lines,* set Figures as may be seen in the Scheme.

The *Stile* I K of this Dyal, as well as of all others, must stand parallel to the *Axis of the World;* and also parallel to the Face of the *Plane,* and parallel to all the *Hour lines,* and stand directly over the *Substilar* or VI a Clock *Hour line,* and that so high as is the distance of the Center of the Equinoctial Semi-Circle from the *Contingent Line.*

O P E R A T. VI.

To describe a Dyal *on an* Erect Direct West Plane.

AN Erect Direct *West-Dyal,* is the same in all respects with an Erect Direct East-Dyal; only as the East-Dyal shews the Forenoon Hours, so the West shews the Afternoon Hours.

Thus, if you should draw the *East-Dyal* on any transparent *Plane,* as on Glass, Horn, or oyled Paper, on the one side will appear an *East Dyal,* on the other side a *West*; only the numbers to the *Hour Lines* (as was said before in the *North- Dyal,*) must
be

be changed; for that which in the *Eaſt-Dyal* is XI, in the *Weſt* muſt be I; that which in the *Eaſt-Dyal* is X, in the *Weſt* muſt be II; that which in the *Eaſt Dyal* is IX, in the *Weſt* muſt be III, *&c.* The Stile is the ſame.

OPERAT. VII.

To Deſcribe a Dyal on an Erect North, *or* Erect South Plane Declining *Eaſtwards or Weſtwards.*

THeſe four Dyals, viz. the *Erect North Declining Eaſtwards,* the *Erect North Declining Weſtwards,* the *Erect South Declining Eaſtwards,* and the *Erect South Declining Weſtwards,* are all projected by the ſame Rules; and therefore are in effect but one Dyal differently placed, as you ſhall ſee hereafter.

Firſt draw on your *Plane* a ſtraight Line to repreſent the *Horizon* of your place, and mark one end of it W for *Weſt,* and the other end E for *Eaſt.* Chuſe a point in this *Horizontal* Line for a Center, as at A, whereon you may deſcribe a Circle to comprehend all theſe four Dyals: Draw a Line as MAM perpendicular to the *Horizontal Line* WE, through the Center A for a *Meridian Line* and on that Center deſcribe a Circle, which by the two Lines W A E, and M A M will be divided into four *Quadrants,* which will comprehend the four *Dyals* aforeſaid; for if it be a *North Declining Weſt* you are to draw, the upper *Quadrant* to the left hand ſerves your purpoſe; If a *South declining Weſt,* the ſame Lines continued through the Center A into the lower *Quadrant* to the right Hand ſerves your turn; if a *North Declining Eaſt,* the upper *Quadrant* to the right hand ſerves your turn; or if a *South declining Eaſt,* the ſame Lines continued through the Center A into the lower *Quadrant* to the left hand ſerves your turn; and you muſt draw the *Declination, Com-*

X 4 *plement*

plement of the Poles Altitude ; *Subſtile Stile* and *Hour Lines* in it ; but the *Hour Lines* muſt be differently marked as you ſhall ſee hereafter. I ſhall only give you an Example of one of theſe Dyals, *viz.* A *South Declining Eaſt.*

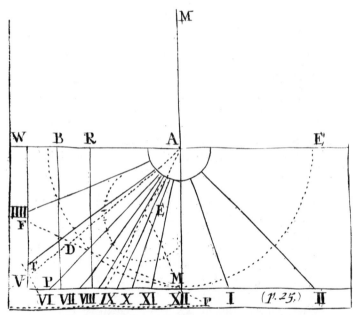

(*F. 25.*)

We will ſuppoſe you are to draw a Dyal that *declines* from the *South* 50 Degrees towards the *Eaſt* ; here being but one *Dyal*, you need deſcribe but one *Quadrant* of a Circle. Set off in the lower *Quadrant* W A M 50 degrees from the *Meridian Line* M towards W, and from the Center A draw a ſtraight Line through that mark in the *Quadrant* as D A, which may be called the *Line of Declination* ; then ſet off from the *Meridian Line* the *Complement* of the *Poles Elevation*, which in our Latitude is 38 ½ degrees, and there draw another Line from the Center as A P, which we will call the *Polar Line.* Then

Then take in the *Horizontal Line* a convenient portion of the *Quadrant*, as A B, and from the point B draw a Line parallel to the *Meridian Line* A M, and continue that Line till it interfect the *Polar Line*, as at P, from which Point P draw a Line parallel to W A, as P C: Then meafure the diftance of A B in the *Horizontal Line*, and fet off that diftance in the Line of *Declination*, as from A to D, and from that point of diftance draw a Line parallel to the *Meridian* A M through the *Horizontal Line* at R. and through the Point D. and continue it through the Line P C, as at S; then laying a ftraight Ruler to the Center A and the Interfection of the line P C, at S draw the Line A S for the *Subftile*: Then upon the point S erect a Line perpendicularly as S T; Then meafure the diftance between R and D, and fet that diftance off from S to T, and from the Center to the point T draw the Line A T for the *Stile* or *Gnomon*; and the *Triangle* S A T made of Iron or Brafs, and erected perpendicularly over the *Subftile* S A, fhall by its upper fide T A, caft a fhadow upon the Hour of the day. But you will fay, the Hour Lines muft be drawn firft: It is true; Therefore to draw them you muft chufe a point in the *Subftile Line* where you think good, and through it draw the Line F F as long as you can for the *Line of Contingence*; then with your Compaffes take the diftance between this point and the *Stile*, and transfer that diftance below the *Line of Contingence* on the *Subftile* as at Æ, and with your Compaffes at that diftance defcribe on the Center Æ a Circle to reprefent the *Equinoctial*; then (as you were taught in the Example of the *Horizontal Dyal*) divide the Semi-Circle of the *Equinoctial* into twelve equal parts, beginning at the point in the *Equinoctial Circle*, where a ftraight Line drawn from the Center of it to the Interfection of the Line of *Contingence* with the Meridian Line cuts the *Equinoctial*

noctial Line, as here at the Point G; then lay a ftraight Ruler to the Center of the *Equinoctial Circle* and to every one of the Divifions in the Semicle, and mark where the ftraight Ruler cuts the *Contingent Line* ; for ftraight Lines drawn from the Center A of the Dyal to thofe feveral marks on the *Contingent Line,* fhall be the *Hour Lines* ; and muft be numbred from the Noon Line or *Meridian* A M backwards, as XII, XI, X, IX, &c. towards the left hand. So is your Dyal finifhed.

This Dyal drawn on any tranfparent matter, as Horn, Glafs, or an oyled Paper, fhall on the other fide the tranfparent matter become a *South Declining Weft* (*Stile* and all) but then the I a Clock Hour Line muft be marked II. the XII, XII, the XI a Clock Hour Line, I, X, II, IX, III, &c.

If you project it a new, you muft defcribe the *Quadrant* M W on the other fide the *Meridian Line,* on the Center A from M to E, and then count, (as before) the *Declination, Altitude* of the *Pole, Subftile,* and *Stile* in the *Quadrant,* beginning at M towards E, and work in all refpects as with the *South Declining Eaft* ; only number this *South Declining Weft* as in the foregoing Paragraph.

If you project a *North Declining Eaft,* you muft defcribe the *Quadrant* above the *Horizontal Line* from M upwards, towards E on your right hand and count (as before) the *Declination, Altitude, Complement* of the *Pole, Subftile* and *Stile* from the *meridian Line,* and work as with the *South Declining Eaft* : It muft be numbred from the *Meridian Line* M towards the right hand with XI, X, IX, VIII, &c.

If this Dyal were drawn on tranfparent matter, the other fide would fhew a *North Declining Weft* : But if you will project it anew, you muft defcribe the *Quadrant* above the *Horizontal Line,* from M upwards towards W, and count from the *Meridian Line* A M the *Declination, Complement, Altitude* of

the

the *Pole, Subſtile and Stile* and work with them (in all reſpects) as with the *S-uth Declining Eaſt* ; but then the XI a Clock Hour Line muſt be marked I, the X, II ; the IX, III, *&c.*

O P E R A T. VIII.

To draw a Dyal on an Eaſt *or* Weſt Plane Reclining *or* Inclining.

DRaw a ſtraight Line parallel to the *Horizon,* to repreſent the *Meridian.* or XII a Clock Line and mark one end N, the other S ; chuſe a point in this Line, as at A for a Center : Then if Your Plane be an *Eaſt,* or a *Weſt Incliner,* let fall a Perpendicular upon this Center (that is, the Perpendicular muſt ſtand above the Meridian Line NS) as A E, and upon the Center A deſcribe a Semi-Circle above the Meridian Line N S ; But if your Plane be an Eaſt Incliner, or a Weſt Recliner, let fall a Perpendicular from the Center A under the Meridian Line, and upon the Center A deſcribe a Semi-Circle under the *Meridian Line.* If your Plane be a *Weſt Incliner* ; work (as ſhall be taught) in the *Quadrant* on the left hand above the *Meridian* Line. If an Eaſt Recliner, in the *Quadrant* on the right hand above the Meridian Line. If it be a Weſt Recliner, work in the *Quadrant* on the left hand under the *Meridian.* If an Eaſt Incliner, in the Quadrant under the Meridian Line the right hand.

For Example, *An Eaſt Dyal Reclining* 45 *Degrees.*

You would draw a *Dyal on an Eaſt Plane Reclining* 45 Degrees : Therefore in the *Quadrant* on the right hand above the *Meridian* Line, ſet off from the Perpendicular A E 45 Degrees on the *Quadrant* for the Reclination of the *Plane* ; and ſet
off

off alfo in the *Quadrant* 38 ½ Degrees from the Perpendicular for the *Complement of the Poles Elevation*,
and at thefe fettings off make marks in the *Quadrant* ; Then lay a ftraight Ruler to the Center A,
and to the marks in the *Quadrant*, and draw ftraight
Lines through them from the Center. Then chufe
in the *Meridian* Line N S a convenient point as at
B, and through that point draw a Line parallel to
the perpendicular A E, which will Interfect the
Line drawn for the Complement of the *Poles Elevation* A P in P; from which point P, draw a Line
parallel to the *Meridian* Line N S, to cut the Perpendicular A E in C. and alfo the Line of Obliquity A O in O. Then meafure the length A O,
and fet off that length in the Perpendicular
A C E from A to E, and draw the Line E G parallel to the *Meridian* Line N S which will cut
the Line B P prolonged in G. Meafure alfo the
length of C O, and fet that length off from
A to Q on the Line of Obliquity A O, and draw
the Line Q R parallel to the Perpendicular A C E.
Then meafure the diftance of A R, and upon the
Line G P B, fet it off from G to S ; and laying a
ftraight Ruler to the point S and the Center A,
draw by the fide of it the Line A S, for the
Subftile Line. Then meafure the length of Q R,
and from S raife a Perpendicular, and in that Perpendicular, fet that length off from S to T ; and
laying a ftraight Ruler to the Center A and the
point T, draw the Line A T for the *Stilar* Line,
which *Stilar* Line being Perpendicular erected over
the *Subftilar* Line A S, will ftand parallel to the
Axis of the World, and caft its fhadow on the Hour
of the Day.

To

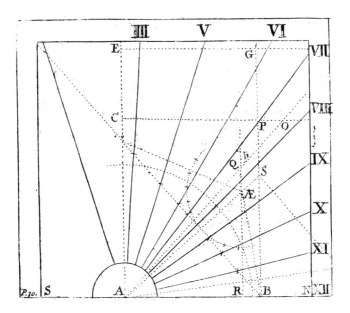

To draw the Hour Lines on this Plane, you must (as you have feveral times before been directed) chufe a point in the *Subſtilar* Line and through that point draw at right Angles with the *Subſtilar* Line, the Line of *Contingence* fo long as you can : Then meafure the ſhorteſt diſtance between that Point and the *Stilar* Line, and transfer that diſtance below the Line of *Contingence* in the *Subſtilar* Line, as at Æ, and with your Compaſſes at that diſtance, defcribe againſt the Line of Contingence the Equinoctial Circle ; then divide the Semicircle of the *Equinoctial* next the Line of *Contingence* into twelve equal parts, as you have formerly been taught, beginning at the Point in the *Equinoctial Circle*, where a ſtraight Line drawn from the Center of it to the Interſection of the Line of *Contingence*

with

with the *Meridian* Line NS cuts the *Equinoctial Circle* as here at the point D; Then lay a ſtraight Ruler to the Center of the *Equinoctial* Circle, and to every one of the Diviſions in the *Equinoctial* Semi-Circle, and mark where the ſtraight Ruler cuts the *Contingent* Line; for ſtraight Lines drawn from the Center A of the Dyal through theſe ſeveral marks in the *Contingent* Line ſhall be the Hour Lines and muſt be numbred from the *Meridian* or Noon-Line N S, which is the XII a Clock Line upwards, with XI, X, IX, VIII, *&c* The Center of this Dyal muſt ſtand downward.

If this Dyal were turned with its Center upwards, it would ſhew a *Weſt Inclining* 45 degrees, only the numbers to the Hour Lines muſt be changed; for to XI you muſt ſet I, to X, II, to IX, III, *&c.* and the *Subſtile* over which the Stile muſt ſtand, muſt be placed in the Semi-circle (at firſt deſcribed) as much to the right hand the perpendicular A E, as it doth on the left hand.

If this Dyal were drawn on Glaſs, or Horn, or an oyled Paper, and you turn the *Meridian* Line N S upwards the back ſide ſhall be an *Eaſt Inclining* 45 degrees, and the Hour Lines muſt be numbred as they are on the *Eaſt Reclining*; But the Subſtile over which the Stile muſt ſtand muſt be placed in the Semi-circle (at firſt deſcribed) as much to the left hand the perpendiculer A E, as it is on the oyled Paper to the right hand.

If you turn the *Meridian* Line N S downwards, the backſide ſhall be a *Weſt Recliner* 45 Degrees, and the Hour Lines muſt be numbred from the XII a Clock line upwads, with I, II, III, *&c.*

You muſt Note that all the Hour-Lines of the Day will nor be deſcribed in this ſingle *Quadrant*, nor does the *Quadrant* at all relate to the Hour Lines; but is deſcribed only for ſetting off the *Complement* of the *Poles Elevation* and *Reclination* of the *Plane*, that

that by working (as hath been ſhewn) you may find the place of the Subſtilar Line, and the Angle the Stile makes with it ; for having the Subſtilar Line, you know how to draw the Line of *Contingence*, and to deſcribe the *Equinoctial* Circle, by which all the Hours are deſcribed on the *Plane.*

To draw a Dyal on a Direct South or North Plane Inclining or Reclining.

Direct Reclining or *Inclining* Dyals are the ſame with Erect Direct Dyals that are made for the Latitude of ſome other Places ; the Latitude of which Places are either more then the Latitude of your place, if the Plane *Recline*, or leſs, if it *Inclines* ; and that in ſuch a proportion as the Arch of *Reclination* or *Inclination* is.

Thus a Direct South Dyal *Reclining* 10 degrees in *London*'s Latitude, (*viz.* 51 ½ degrees) is an Erect Direct South Dyal made for the Latitude of 61 ½ degrees. And a Direct South Dyal *Inclining* 10 in the Latitude of 51 ½ is an *Erect Direct South* Dyal in the Latitude of 41 ½ degrees, and is to be made according to the Direction given in *Operat.* III.

OPERAT. IX.

To draw a Dyal on a South or North Inclining Declining, or Reclining Declining Plane.

THeſe four ſorts of Dyals, *viz.* the South Inclining Declining, and South Reclining Declining, and North Inclining Declining, and South Reclining Declining, are all projected by the ſame Rules ; and therefore are in effect but one Dyal differently placed. as you ſhall ſee hereafter.

Firſt,

First, draw on your Plane a straight Line parallel to the *Horizon*, and mark one end W for *West*, and the other E for *East*. On South Incliners and Recliners, E on the right hand, and W on the left; on North Incliners and Recliners E on the left and W on the right. Chuse a point in this *Horizontal* Line for a Center, as at A; through this point A draw a Line perpendicular to the *Horizon*, and on this point (as on a Center) defcribe a Semi-Circle, one *Quadrant* above, and another below the *Horizontal* Lines, (though for this Example I defcribe but one.) Then if the Plane refpect the South, fet off in the lower *Quadrant* from the perpendicular, the Declination, the Inclination, or the Reclination, and the Complement of the *Altitude* of the Pole; and thro' thefe feveral fettings off in the *Quadrant*, draw ftraight Lines from the Center A, then take in the *Horizontal* line towards the Semicircle, a convenient diftance from the Center A, as B, and through the point B draw a ftraight Line parallel to the Perpendicular, and prolong it thro' the Polar line, as B P; thro' the point P; draw a Line parallel to the *Horizontal* line, as P C; this line will cut the Line of *Obliquity* in the point O, then meafure the diftance of A O, and fet off that diftance on the Perpendicular from A to F, and through the point F draw a ftraight line parallel to the *Horizontal* line, as F G, for the *Horizontal* Interfection. Then meafure the diftance of C O, and fet off that diftance on the Perpendicular from A to L; from the point L draw the line L D parallel to the *Horizontal* line, to cut the line of *Declination* in the point D. Then meafure the diftance of A B, and fet off that diftance in the Line of Declination from A to E; and from the point E, draw a ftraight line parallel to the *Horizontal* line W E, to cut the Perpendicular in the point K. Meafure the diftance of E K, and fet off fet off that diftance on the other fide the Perpendicular in the *Horizontal* Interfection, from F to H, and from the point H draw H N parallel to the Perpendicular to cut the *Horizontal* line in the point N.

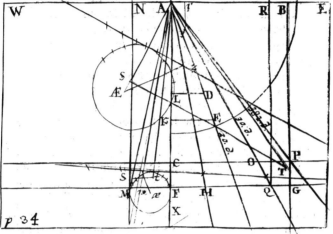

Then to find the *Meridian* line, *Subftile* and *Stile,* do thus. If your *Plane* be a *Southern Incliner,* or a *Norbern Recliner,* meafure the diftance of L D, and and fet off that diftance in the *Horizontal* Interfection from F to M, and through the point M draw the line A M for the *Meridian* line. Then add the diftance of A L to A K, thus.: Meafure the diftance of A L, and place one Foot of your Compaffes in the point K in the Perpendicular line, and extend the other to X, and meafuring the diftance of A X, fet it off in the line of *Obliquity* from A to Q; and from the point Q draw the line QR parallel to the Perpendicular, and cutting the *Horizontal* line in the point R. Then meafure the diftance of A R, and fet off that diftance from H in the *Horizontal* Interſection to S on the line H N, and to the point S draw the line A S for the *Sub-ſtile.* Then meaſure the diſtance of Q R, and ſet off that diſtance perpendicularly from the point S to T ; and laſtly, from the point A draw the ſtraight line A T for the *Stilar* line, which *Stilar* line being perpendicularly erected over the *Subſtilar* line A S, will ſtand parallel to the *Axis of the World,* and caſt its ſhadow on the Hour of the Day.

But if the Plane be a *Southern Recliner,* or *North-ern Incliner,* meaſure (as before) the diſtance of L D, and (as before you were directed) to ſet it off from F in the *Horizontal* Interſection on the right hand the perpendicular line : So now, ſet that diſtance from F to *m* in the Horizontal Interſection on the left hand in the Perpendicular line, and draw the line A *m* for the *Meridian* Line . Then as before you were directed, to add A L to A K ; So now, ſubſtract the diſtance of A L from A K, and the remainder will be L K : Set therefore the diſtance of L K from A to *q* in the ſame line of *Obliquity,* and from the point *q* draw the line *q r* parallel to the perpendicular. Meaſure then the diſtance of A *r,* and ſet of that diſtance in the line H N, from H to *s* for the *Subſtilar* line ; then erect on the point *s* a perpendicular, and on that Perpendicular ſet off from *s* to *t* the diſtance of *qr :* And laſtly, from A draw the Line A *t* for the *Sti-lar Line.*

If K falls upon L the *Plane* is parallel to the *Axis of the World,* and the Dyal drawn upon it will have no Center ; But *s* will fall upon H, and A H (or A *s*) will be the *Subſtile.*

I ſhall give you two Examples of theſe Rules : One of a Dyal with a Center, and the other of a Dyal without a Center. And firſt,

O P E-

OPERAT. X.

How to draw a Dyal *with a Center*, Declining 20 *Degrees, and* Inclining 30 *Degrees.*

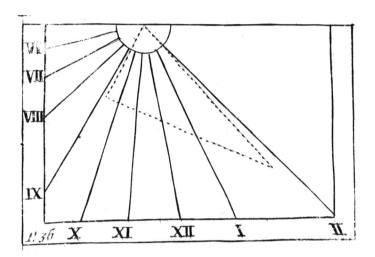

HAving by the foregoing Precepts of the laft *Operat.* found the *Subftile, Stile* and *Meri-dian,* you muft (as you have often been directed) chufe a point in the *Subftilar* line; through which, at right Angles to the *Subftilar* line, draw the line of Contingence as long as you can; then meafure the fhorteft diftance between the point of Inter-fection and the *Stilar line,* and transfer that dift-ance on one fide of the *line* of *Contingence* upon the *Subftilar line,* and fo defcribe the *Equinoctial* Semi-circle againft the *line* of *Contingence* : Then lay a ftraight Ruler to the Center of the *Equinoctial Cir-cle* as at Æ, and to the point where the *line* of *Con-tingence* cuts the *Meridian Line,* as at Z, and mark where the ftraight Ruler cuts the *Equinoctial Circle,*

and

and from that mark begin to divide the *Semi-circle* into twelve equal parts, and by a ftraight Ruler laid to thofe divifions and the Center of the *Equinoctial*, make marks in the *line* of *Contingence*. Then fhall ftraight *lines* drawn from the Center A of the Dyal, through every one of the marks in the *Contingent line* be the Hour lines of the Dyal, and muft be numbred from the XII a Clock line towards the right Hand, with I, II, III, IV, *&c.* And the other way with XI, X, IX, *&c.*

OPERAT. XI.

How to draw a Dyal *without a* Center, *on a* South Plane; Declining Eaft 30 *Degrees,* Recilning 34 *Degrees* 32 Minutes.

HAving by the Precepts of *Operat.* IX. found the *Subftile,* you muft find the *Meridian line* otherwife than you were there taught : For, having drawn the *lines* of *Latitude, Declination* and *Reclination,* and found the *Subftile,* meafure the diftance of B P, and fet it off on the *line* of *Declination* from A to K, and draw from the Perpendicular A F the line K Q parallel to A B : then meafure the length of K Q, and fet it off on the *Polar line* A P, from A to V; then take the neareft diftance between the point V and the *line* A B, and fet it off on the *line* Q K from Q to M; through which point M, draw a *line* from the Center A; then meafure with your Compaffes in the Semi-circle W N E (which in this Dyal may reprefent the Equinoctial) the diftance of the Arch N *m*, and fet off that diftance from the Interfection of the *Subftile* with the Semi-circle at S to T in the Semi-circle, which point T fhall be the point in the *Equinoctial* that you muft begin to divide the Hours at, for the finding their diftances on the *line* of *Contingence.*

Then

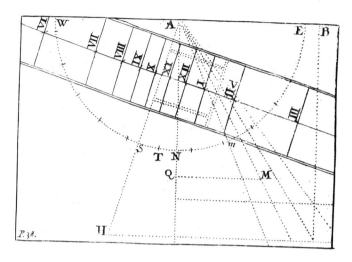

Then confider (according to the bignefs of your
Plane) what height your *Stile* fhall ftand above the
Subftile, and there make a mark in the *Subftile*;
for the diftance between the Center A, and that
mark muft be the height of the *Stile* perpendicularly erected over the *Subftile*, as at I. Draw
through this point I a *line of Contingence*, as long as
you can to cut the *Subftile* at right *Angles*, and then
laying a *Ruler* to the Center A, and fucceffively to
to each Divifion of the *Equinoctial* make marks in
the *line of Contingence*, and through thofe marks
draw ftraight *lines* parallel to the *Subftile*, which
fhall be the *Hour lines*; and muft be numbred from
the left hand towards the right, beginning at the
XII a *Clock line* with I, II, III, &c. and from the
right hand towards the left on the XII a *Clock line*
with XI, X, IX, &c.

The *Stile* to this Dyal may be either a ftraight
Pin of the length of A I, or elfe a fquare of the
fame height, erected Perpendicularly upon the
I, in the *Subftilar-line*.

Y 3   O P E-

OPERAT. XII.

To make a Dyal *on the* Cieling *of a* Room, *where the* Direct Beams *of the* Sun *never come.*

Find fome convenient place in the Tranfum of a Window to place a fmall round piece of Looking-Glafs about the bignefs of a Groat or lefs, fo as it may lie exactly Horizontal. The point in the middle of this Glafs we will mark A, and for diftinction-fake call it *Nodus.* Through this *Nodus* you muft draw a *Meridian line* on the Floor, thus: Hang a plumb-line in the window exactly over *Nodus*, and the fhadow that the plumb-line cafts on the Floor juft at Noon will be a *Meridian line*; or you may find a *Meridian line* otherwife by the Clinatory. Having drawn the *Meridian line* on the Cieling, thus: Hold a *Plumb-line* to the Cieling, over that end of the *Meridian line* next the window; if the *Plumbet* hang not exactly on the *Meridian line* on the Floor, remove your hand on the *Cieling* one way or other, as you fee caufe, till it do hang quietly juft over it, and at the point where the *Plumb line* touches the *Cieling* make a mark, as at B; that mark B fhall be directly over the *Meridian line* on the Floor: Then remove your *Plumb line* on the *Floor,* and find a point on the *Cieling* directly over it, as you did the former point, as at C, and through thefe two points B and C on the *Cieling*, ftrain and ftrike a *line* blackt with *Small-coal* or any other *Colour* (as Carpenters do) and that *line* BC on the *Cieling* fhall be the *Meridan line* as well as that on the Floor: Then faften a ftring juft on the *Nodus*, and remove that ftring, forwards or backwards, in the *Meridian line* on the *Cieling*, till it have the fame Elevation in the *Quadrant* on the *Clinatory* above

above the *Horizon* that the *Equinoctial* hath in your Habitation and through the point where the ftring touches the *Meridian line* in the *Cieling*, fhall a *line* be drawn at right *Angles* with the *Meridian*, to reprefent the *Equinoctial line*.

Thus in our Latitude the *Elevation* of the Equator being 38 ½ degrees ; I remove the ftring faftned to the *Nodu*, forwards or backwards in the *Meridian line* of the *Cieling*, till the *Plumb-line* of the *Quadrant* on the *Clinatory*, when one of the fides are applied to the ftring, falls upon 38½ degrees, and then I find it touch the *Meridian line* at D in the *Cieling* ; therefore at D I make a mark, and through this mark ftrike the *line* D E (as before I did in the *Meridian line*) to cut the *Meridian line* at right Angles : This *line* fhall be the *Equinoctial line*, and ferve to denote the Hour Diftances, as the *Contingent* Lines does on other Dyals, as you have often feen.

Then I place the Center of the *Quadrant* on the *Clinatory* upon *Nodus*, fo as the Arch of the *Quadrant* may be on the *Eaft* fide the *Meridian* Line, and underprop it fo, that the flat fide of the *Quadrant* may lie parallel to the ftring, when it is ftrained between the *Nodus* and the *Equinoctial*, and alfo fo as the ftring may lie on the Semi-diameter of the Quadrant, when it is held up to the Meridian Line on the Cieling. Then removing the ftring the fpace of 15 degrees in the Quadrant, and extending it to the *Equator* on the Cieling, where the ftring touches the *Equator*, there fhall be a point through which the I a Clock Hour-line fhall be drawn : and removing the ftring yet 15 degrees futher to the Eaftwards in the Semi-Circle of Pofition, and extending it alfo to the *Equator*, where it touches the *Equator*, there fhall be a point through which the II a Clock Hour-Line fhall be drawn. Removing the ftring yet 15

Y 4 degrees

further to the Eaftwards in the Semi-circle of Pofition, and extending it alfo to the *Equator*, where it touches the *Equator*, there fhall be a point, through which the II a Clock Hour-line fhall be drawn. Removing the ftring yet 15 degrees further to the Eaftwards in the Semi circle of Pofition, and extending to the *Equator*; there fhall be a point through which the III a Clock Hour-line fhall be drawn : The like for all other Afternoon Hour lines. So oft as the ftring is remov'd through 15 degrees on the Quadrant, fo oft fhall it point out the Afternoon diftances in the Meridian line on the Cieling.

Having thus found out the points in the Equator through which the afternoon Hour-lines are to be drawn, I may find the Forenoon Hour-diftances alfo the fame way, *viz.* by removing the Arch of the Quadrant to the *Weft*-fide the Meridian, as before it was placed on the *Eaft*, and bringing the ftring to the feveral 15 degrees on the *Weft*-fide the Quadrant; or elfe I need only meafure the diftances of each Hours diftance found in the Equator from the Meridian line on the Cieling ; for the fame number of the Hours from XII, have the fame diftance in the Equinoctial line on the other fide the Meridian, both before and after-noon : The XI a Clock Hour diftance is the fame from the Meridian Line, with the I a Clock diftance on the other fide the Meridian ; the X a Clock diftance, the fame with the II a Clock diftance ; the IX with the III, *&c.* And thus the diftances of all the Hour lines are found out on the Equator.

Now

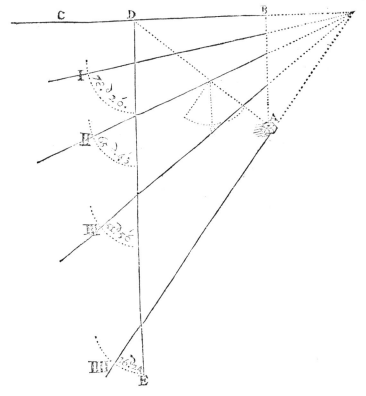

Now if the Center of this Dyal lay within
doors, you might draw lines from the Center
through thefe pricks in the Equator, and thofe
lines fhould be the Hour lines, as in other Dyals :
But the Center of this Dyal lies without doors in
the Air, and therefore not convenient for this purpofe : So that for drawing the Hour lines, you
muft confider what Angle every Hour line in a Horizontal Dyal makes with the Meridian ; that is,
at what diftance in Degrees and Minutes the Hour
lines of an Horizontal Dyal cut the Meridian ;
which you may examine, as by *Overat.* II. For

an

an Angle equal to the Complement of the fame
Angle, muft each refpective Hour line with the
Equator on the Cieling have.

Thus upon the point markt for each Hours diftance in the Equinoctial Line on the Cieling. I defcribe the Arches I II, III, IV, as in the Figure,
and finding the diftance from the *Meridian* of the
Hour Lines of an Horizontal Dyal to be according to *Operat.* II. Thus,

$$\text{Te} \begin{Bmatrix} 1 \\ 2 \\ 3 \\ 4 \end{Bmatrix} \begin{matrix} \text{a Clock} \\ \text{Hour-} \\ \text{Line.} \end{matrix} \begin{Bmatrix} 11.40 \\ 24.15 \\ 38.14 \\ 53\ 36 \end{Bmatrix} \begin{matrix} \text{whofe } Com\text{-} \\ plement \text{ to} \\ 90 \text{ is} \end{matrix} \begin{Bmatrix} 78.20 \\ 65.45 \\ 51.56 \\ 36.24 \end{Bmatrix}$$

I meafure in a Quadrant of the fame Radius
with thofe Arches already drawn from the Equinoctial Line,

$$\text{for the} \begin{Bmatrix} 1 \\ 2 \\ 3 \\ 4 \end{Bmatrix} \text{a Clock Hour} \begin{Bmatrix} 78.30 \\ 65.45 \\ 51.56 \\ 36.24 \end{Bmatrix}$$

and transfer the diftances to the Arches drawn on
the Cieling: For then ftraight lines drawn through
the mark in the Arch, and through the mark in
the Equator, and prolonged both ways to a convenient length, fhall be the feveral Hours lines (a-
forefaid ;) and when the Sun Shines upon the
Glafs at *Nodus*; its Beames fhall reflect upon the
Hour of the Day.

Some Helps to a young Dyalift *for his more orderly and
quick making of* Dyals.

IT may prove fomewhat difficult to thofe that
are unpractifed in Mathimatical projections, to
divide

divide a Circle into 360 Degrees (or which is all one) a Semi-circle into 180, or a Quadrant into 90 Degrees; and though I have taught you in the projectioning the *Horizontal Dyal* the original way of doing this, yet you may do it a fpedier way by a line of Cords, which if you will be curious in your Practife, you may make your felf; or if you ca-count it not worth your while, you may by it already made on Box or Brafs of moft Mathematical Inftrument Makers. This Inftrument is by them call a *Plain Scale* which does not only accommodate you with the divifions of a Quadrant, but alfo ferves for a Ruler to draw ftraight lines with; the manner of making it is as follows.

Defcribe upon a fmooth flat even grain'd Board a quarter of an whole Circle, as B C, whofe Radius A B or A C may be four Inches, if you intend to make large Dyals or two Inches, if fmall; but if you will, you may have feveral lines of Chords on your *Scale* or *Rule.* Divide this Quadrant into 90 equal parts, as you were taught in the making the *Horizontal Dyal*

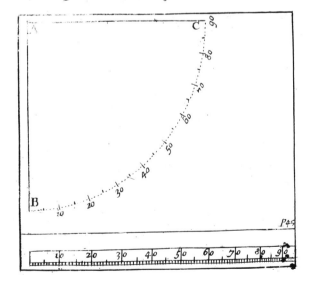

Then draw clofe by the edge of your ftraight Ruler a line parallel to the edge, and at about $\frac{1}{20}$ part of an Inch a fecond line parallel to that, and at about $\frac{1}{8}$ of an Inch a third line parallel to both. Then place one Foot of your Compaffes at the beginning of the firft degree on the Quadrant defcribed on the Board, as at B, and open the other Foot to the end of the firft degree, and transfer that diftance upon your Rule, from B to the firft mark or divifion, between the two firft drawn lines. Then place one Foot of your Compaffes again at the beginning of the firft Degree on the Quadrant defcribed on the Board, as at B, and open the other Foot to the end of the fecond Degree, and transfer that diftance upon your Rule from B to the fecond mark or divifion between the two firft drawn Lines; and thus meafure the diftance of every Degree from the firft Degree defcribe on the Quadrant, and transfer it to the Rule. But for diftinction fake, you may draw every tenth divifion from the firft line parallel to the edge of the third line, and mark them in fucceffion from the beginning with 10, 20, 30, to 90, and the fifth Divifions you may draw half way between the fecond and the third parallel lines; the fingle Divifions only between the two firft parallel lines. So is your lines of Chords made.

The ufe of the Line of Chords.

AS its ufe is very eafie, fo its convenience is very great; for placing one Foot of your Compaffes at the firft Divifion on the *Scale*, and opening the other to the 60th Degree, you may with the points of your Compaffes (fo extended) defcribe a Circle, and the feveral Divifions, on the *Scale* fhall be the Degrees of the four Quadrants of of that Circle, as you may try by working backwards, to what you were juft now taught in the
making

making the *Scale*: For as before you meafured the diftance of the degrees of the Quadrant, and transfer'd them to the *Scale*, fo now you only meafure the Divifions on the *Scale*, and transfer them to the Quadrant, Semi-circle, or whole Circle diferibed on your Paper. For *Example*,

If you would meafure 30 Degrees in your defcribed Circle, place one Foot of your Compaffes at the beginning of Divifions on the *Scale*, as at A, and extend the other Foot to the Divifions marked 30, and that diftance transfer'd to the Circle, fhall be the diftance of 30 Degrees in that Circle. Do the like for any other number of Degrees.

You may draw your Dyal firft on a large fheet of Paper, if your Dyal Plane be fo large; if it be not fo large, draw it on a fmaller piece of Paper; Then rub the back-fide of your Paper Dyal with fmall Coal, till it be well black't; and laying your Paper Dyal on your Dyal Plane, fo that the Eaft Weft, North, or South lines of your Paper agree exactly with the Eaft, Weft, North or South fcituation of your Dyal Plane; then with Wax or Pitch faften the Corners of the Paper on the Plane, and laying a ftraight Ruler on the Hour-lines of your Dyal, draw with the blunted point of a Needle by the fide of the Ruler, and the Small-coal rub'd on the back fide of the Paper will leave a mark of the lines on the Plane.

If you will have the lines drawn Red, you may rub the back fide of your Paper with *Vermillion*; if blew with *Verditer*; if Yellow with *Orpiment*, &c. Then draw upon thefe marked Lines with Oyl Colours, as you pleafe.

If

If your Dyal Decline far towards the Eaſt or Weſt, the Hour Lines (unleſs projeâed to a very great lenght) will run very cloſe to one another; therefore in this caſe you muſt projeât your Dyal

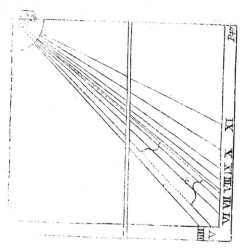

ȯn a large Table, or ſometimes on the Floor of a Room, and cut it off as far as you think good, from the Center; for the further from the Cen‑ ter, the larger the diſtance of the Hour‑lines. *See the Figure.*

An Explanation of ſome Words of Art uſed in this.

A Ngle.   The meeting or joyning of two Lines.
  Arch.   A part of a Circle.

Axis: The ſtraight Line that runs through the Center of a Sphere, and both ways through the Circumference : though in *Dyalling* it is all one with the Diameter of a Circle.

Clinatory.   See Fol. 8, 9, 10.

Chord.   See Fol. 44, 45, 46.

Complement.   The number that is wanting to make up another number 90 Degr. or 180 Degr. or 360 Degrees.   *Con‑*

Contingent. A Line croffing the Subftile at right Angles.

Degree. See Fol. 12.

Diameter. The longeft ftraight Line that can be contained within a Circle, *viz.* the Line that paffes through the Center to the Circumference both ways.

Dyal plane. See *Fol.* 7.

Elevation of the *Pole.* So many degrees as the *Pole* is elevated above the *Horizon.*

Equinoctial. The *Equinoctial* is a great Circle that runs evenly between the two *Poles* of the World. But when we name the *Equinoctial* in this Book, we mean a fmall Circle which reprefents it, and is the Circle or Arch of a Circle which is divided into equal parts, to find thereby the unequal parts on the *Line of Contingence.* In the *Horizontal Dyal* it is that Arch of a Circle marked G C H.

Horizon. Is a great Circle encompaffing the place we ftand upon; but in Dyalling it is reprefented by a ftraight Line, as in *Operat.* III. In the *South Dyal* the Line VI A VI is the *Horizontal Line.*

Latitude. The Latitude of a Place is the number of Degrees contained between the *Equinoctial* and the place inquired after.

Line of Contingence. See *Contingent.*

Magnetick Needle. The Needle touch'd with the *Loadftone,* to make it point to the North.

Meridian. Is a great Circle of Heaven paffing thro' the North and South points of the *Horizon;* but in Dyalling it is reprefented by a ftraight *Line,* as in *Operat.* II. in the *Horizontal Dyal* the Line XII. A is a *Meridian line.*

Nadir. The point directly under our Feet.

Nautical Compafs. Is the Compafs ufed by *Navigators,* whereon is marked out all the 32 Winds or Points of the Compafs.

Oblique

Oblique Plane. See *Fol.* 7.

Parallel. See *Fol.* 6.

Perpendiculer See *Fol.* 5.

Pole. The North or South Points on the Globe of the Earth, are called *North* or *South Pole.*

Quadrant. The fourth Part of a Circle.

Radius. Half the Diameter of a Circle.

Right Angle. A ſtraight *Line* that falls Perpendiculerly upon another ſtraight line, makes at the meeting of thoſe two *Lines* a Right Angle.

Semi-Circle. Half a Circle.

Semi-Diameter. The ſame *Radius* is.

Sphere. The higheſt Heaven with all its imagined Circle, is called the *Sphere.*

Stile. The *Gnomon* or Cock of a Dyal.

Subſtile. The line the Stile ſtands on upon a Dyal Plane.

Triangle. A Figure conſiſting of 3 Sides and 3 Angles.

Zenith. The point Directly over our Head.

F I N I S.

ERRATA.

Page	Line			
148	14	*Joinery*	§	17
	18	*Ibid*	§	19
150	8	*Ibid*	§	31
	9	*Ibid*	§	4
	17	*Ibid*	§	2
153	23	*Ibid*	§	17, 18, 19
154	2	*Smithing Plate* 2 *Fig.* 1.		
	7	*Ibid*	*Fol.* 18	
155	35	*Ibid*	*Fol.* 26, 27	
156	23	*Joinery*		
	25	*Carpentry*		
	29	*Ibid*		
	31	*Joinery*		
159	9	*Carpentry*		
	33	*Ibid*		
161	24	*Joinery*		
162	5	*Ibid*		
	21	*Ibid*		
	35	*Ibid*		
164	30	*Ibid*		
169	1	*Ibid*		
177	9	*Carpentry*		
183	30	*Joinery*		
187	10	*Smithing* *Fol.* 61, 62		
192	19	*Ibid*	31, 32, 33, 34	
195	21	*Joinery*		
	23	*Carpentry*		
196	15	*Joinery*		
199	5	*Carpentry*		
200	25	*Turning*		
206	14	*Ibid*		
207	38	*Ibid*		
208	7	*Ibid.*		

Read

BOOKS *Printed for* D. Midwinter *and* T. Leigh, *at the* Rose and Crown *in St.* Paul's Church-yard.

SHort but yet Plain Elements of Geometry, and Plain Trigonometry: Shewing how by a Brief and easie Method, most of what is necessary and useful in Euclide, Archimides, Apollonius, and other Excellent Geometricians, both Ancient and Modern, may be understood. Written in French by F. Ignat. Gaston, Pardies. The Second Edition: In which are many new Propositions, Additions, and useful Improvements; the Problems being now placed every where in their proper Order, and the whole accomodated to the Capacities of young Beginners.

A New Short Treatise of Algebra; with the Geometrical Construction of Equations, as far as the Fourth Power or Dimension. Together with a Specimen of the Nature and Algorithm of Fluxions. Both by John Harris, M. A. and F. R. S.

Mathesis Enucleata: Or, The Elements of the Mathematicks, By J. Christ. Sturmius, Professor of Philosophy and Mathematicks in the University of Altorf. Made English.

A Mathematical Dictionary: Or, A Compendious Explication of all Mathematical Terms, Abridg'd from Monsieur Ozanam, and Others. With a Translation of his Preface, and an Addition of several easie and useful Abstracts; as Plain Trigonometry, Mechanicks, the first Properties of the Three Conick Sections, &c. To which is added an Appendix, containing the Quantities of all sorts of Weights and Measures, and the Explanation of the Characters used in Algebra. Also the Definition and Use of the Principal Mathematical Instruments, and the Instruments themselves curiously engraven on Copper. Both by J. Raphson, F. R. S.

A New and Most Accurate Theory of the Moon's Motion; whereby all her Irregularities may be solved, and her Place truly calculated to Two Minutes. Written by that Incomparable Mathematician Mr. Isaac Newton, and published in Latin by Mr. David Gregory in his Excellent Astronomy.